A Guide to

nt Ventilation

Martin W Liddament

March, 1996

Contents

1996

A Guide to Energy Efficient Ventilation

Foreword

Ventilation is the mechanism by which clean air is provided to a space. It is essential for meeting the metabolic needs of occupants and for diluting and removing pollutants emitted by indoor sources. On the other hand unnecessarily high rates of air change can present an excessive energy burden on a building's heating (or cooling) needs. It is variously estimated that ventilation accounts for 30% or more of space conditioning energy demand. As a consequence there is often an apparent conflict between a desire to minimise ventilation rate, to reduce energy demand, and to maximise ventilation, to ensure optimum indoor air quality. It is the domain set by the interaction of ventilation with energy and indoor air quality that has motivated much current research and interest in ventilation.

In reviewing the rationale of ventilation, it is important to understand the purpose of ventilation and how it interacts with pollutants and energy performance. This topic is made especially difficult, since it may be almost impossible for the designer to anticipate ventilation needs which vary throughout the life span of a building and on a day to day basis, in response to variations in occupant density, outdoor climate and pollutant load. Good design requires planning for optimum air quality combined with energy efficiency. There is no unique solution and each design must be based on knowledge about building use, climate and the emission characteristics of contaminant sources.

Scope

The purpose of this guide is to review ventilation in the context of both energy efficiency and achieving good indoor air quality. It is concerned primarily with providing an introduction to the topic of ventilation with particular emphasis on the needs of dwellings and commercial buildings. It encapsulates the knowledge and experience derived from experts in all the participating countries of the Air Infiltration and Ventilation Centre. Numerical descriptions have been kept to a minimum, while emphasis is placed on describing ventilation and the decision making involved in selecting and planning for ventilation. By understanding this Guide, it is hoped that the reader will be able to make fundamental judgements about how much ventilation should be provided and how this should be accomplished for optimum cost and energy efficiency.

Target audience

This guide is aimed at the policy maker, architect, building services engineer, designer and building owners and occupiers who require, or are interested in, a background knowledge to ventilation.

Acknowledgements

The completion of this Guide depended on the effort and cooperation of many organisations and individuals. Special assistance was provided by the AIVC Steering Group through workshops and comments to the text:

Mark Bassett, Building Research Association of New Zealand

Jørn Brunsell, Norwegian Building Research Institute, Norway

Viktor Dorer, EMPA, Switzerland

Willem de Gids, TNO Building & Construction Research, Netherlands

Pierre Hérant, ADEME, France

Ole Jensen, Danish Building Research Institute, Denmark

Johnny Kronvall, J&W Consulting Engineers, Sweden

Earle Perera, Building Research Establishment, UK

Jorma Sateri, VTT Building Technology, Finland

John Shaw, National Research Council, Canada

Max Sherman, Lawrence Berkeley Laboratory, USA

Fritz Steimle, University of Essen, Germany

Peter Wouters, Belgian Building Research Institute, Belgium.

Further material was obtained from past and current IEA air flow related and other annexes. These included:

Annex 8, *Inhabitants Behaviour with Regard to Ventilation*

Annex 9, *Minimum Ventilation Rates*

Annex 18, *Demand Controlled Ventilation*

Annex 20, *Air Flow Patterns within Buildings*

Annex 21, *Thermal Modelling*

Annex 23, *Multi-Zone Air Flow Modelling*

Annex 26, *Energy Efficient Ventilation in Large Enclosures*

Annex 27, *Evaluation and Demonstration of Domestic Ventilation Systems*.

Additional assistance was provided by:

Don Colliver of University of Kentucky for information and advice on the energy impact of cooling for inclusion in Chapter 3 *The Energy Impact of Ventilation and Air Infiltration*.

Steve Irving of Oscar Faber Applied Research (UK) for providing material and text for inclusion in Chapter 6 *Ventilation Heat Recovery*,
Chapter 7 *Ventilation and Cooling* and Chapter 10 *Maintenance and Designing for Maintenance*.

Mike Finbow and Sue James of NBA Tectonics Ltd (UK)

Peter Hartmann, Switzerland for guidance on overall structure and valuable help with Chapter 4 *Design Criteria*.

Malcolm Orme of the AIVC, for providing energy data and figures for Chapter 3

The Energy Impact of Ventilation and Air Infiltration, for checking and editing the equations in Chapter 12 *Calculation Methods* and for assistance in desk top publishing.

Mark Limb of the AIVC for finalising the diagrams and for the cover design.

Rhona Vickers of the AIVC for checking and editing the text.

Photographs and Illustrations were provided by:

Jørn Brunsell NBI, Norway, Figures 6.4 and 6.7

Don Dickson EA Technology (UK) Figure 11.9

Viktor Dorer (EMPA) and Peter Hartmann (Switzerland), Figure 6.8

Willem de Gids and Bas Knoll, TNO, Netherlands, Figures 5.3 and 11.11

Doug Lawson, Building Sciences Ltd (UK), Figure 11.12

Paul Linden, University of Cambridge, UK, Figure 11.13

Gunther Mertz, FGK, Germany, Figures 5.12and 6.3

Earle Perera, Building Research Establishment, UK, Figure 11.6

Mike Ratcliffe, CPP Inc., USA, Figure 11.14

Juergen Roeben, Fritz Steimle (University of Essen) Germany, Figure 11.10

Claude-Alain Roulet (Switzerland) and IEA Annex 23, Figure 1.5

Geoff Whittle, Simulation Technology Ltd. (UK), Figures 12.10 and 12.11

David Wilson (University of Alberta), Canada, Figure 12.6

Many other contributions and suggestions were received and gratefully appreciated.

Introduction

Ventilation plays a vital role in securing optimum air quality and thermal comfort in buildings. In fulfilling this need, it touches on a wide range of topics associated with building design and services. For example, the air tightness of the building shell, the pollutant emission characteristics of furnishings and materials, heat gains from solar radiation, lighting and equipment, influence both the need for ventilation and ventilation performance. Added to this, it is estimated that a third of all energy in OECD countries is consumed in buildings and that, for buildings of the next century, one half of this energy will be dissipated through ventilation and air infiltration. Hence it is essential for air related issues to be put in the forefront of energy conservation development.

Early attempts to minimise ventilation energy loss frequently resulted in poor indoor air quality and comfort problems. This was because the provision for ventilation had become dissociated from need. Essentially, the parameters that affect the requirements for ventilation had, themselves, not been addressed. Even, today, ventilation is often emphasised in terms of system technology rather than the factors that influence need and performance. The purpose of this Guide is to try and redress this imbalance. It focuses on ventilation solutions in relation to pollutant problems, building type, air tightness, thermal environment and outdoor climate.

This Guide is largely aimed at the non specialist who needs to acquire a broad background knowledge about the topic. It is therefore presented in a descriptive format in which calculations and equations have been restricted to the final Chapter. In this way, it has been possible to provide both a qualitative review and include sufficient guidance to enable basic calculations to be performed. Each Chapter covers an independent topic and can, in general, be read without particular reference to adjacent Chapters. This approach is aided by cross referencing so that it is possible to jump to specific sections within individual chapters as a particular subject is followed.

The contents of this Guide include:

Chapter 1 provides a basic introduction to the Guide and summarises the role of ventilation in meeting indoor air quality and comfort needs.

Chapter 2 reviews the factors that influence indoor air quality and comfort. It looks at both indoor and outdoor sources of pollutants and reviews the way in which ventilation interacts with the thermal environment.

Chapter 3 is concerned with the energy impact of ventilation. It outlines current work and results associated with identifying the energy impact and reviews the potential for reducing ventilation and air infiltration energy losses.

Chapter 4 assesses the basic design criteria that must be incorporated at the planning stage of a ventilation system. This looks at the building itself in addition to the ventilation system.

Chapter 5 is concerned with the various strategies for ventilation. This examines both natural and mechanical systems and reviews the benefits of demand controlled ventilation.

Chapter 6 looks at techniques for recovering 'waste' heat from the exhaust air. While very effective heat recovery systems are available, performance has to be equated against fan energy and potential air infiltration losses.

Chapter 7 considers the very special needs of cooling. Problems associated with high indoor heat gains can be treated by increasing the rate of ventilation (passive cooling) or by mechanical cooling. Much depends on outdoor temperature, flexibility in acceptable indoor temperature, architectural design to minimise thermal gains and the size of internal heat loads. As a rule, passive cooling requires much less energy than refrigerative systems, thus much design is focused on reducing heat gains.

Chapter 8 focuses on the role of filtration. This can be used to remove specific pollutants (especially particulates) and may provide the only solution when outdoor air quality is poor.

Chapter 9 reviews the topic of ventilation efficiency. This is concerned with describing how ventilation air and pollutants mix and are distributed within a space.

Chapter 10 is concerned with maintenance. In the past, ventilation systems have sometimes been installed without a clear plan for maintenance and replacement. This has resulted in a decline in ventilation performance and high costs associated with repairs and refurbishment. Maintenance schedules and service inspections are now beginning to appear in the Codes of Practice and building Regulations of a number of countries.

Chapter 11 reviews ventilation related measurement methods. This summarises techniques for measuring air change and air flow rates, the pattern of air flow in a space and the air tightness of buildings and components.

Chapter 12 considers the available range of calculation methods. These vary from simplified methods to estimate air change rate, to computational fluid dynamics techniques for predicting air flow patterns and pollutant transport within spaces. Associated techniques covering the calculation of pressure induced by mechanical ventilation, ventilation heat loss and combined thermal transport and air flow simulation methods are also reviewed.

Appendices provide a simple single zone 'network' algorithm to calculate air infiltration and ventilation, combined with some basic air leakage and wind pressure data.

Reference is made throughout the text to sources of more comprehensive information, including the detailed research work being undertaken by related International Energy Agency air flow annexes. All cited references are available from the library and information service of the Air Infiltration and Ventilation Centre.

1 Rationale and Background to Ventilation

What is Ventilation?
Why is Ventilation Needed?
How Does Ventilation Work?
How Much Ventilation is Necessary?
Other Issues (Heat Recovery, Cooling, Design, etc.)

Summary and Introduction

Ventilation is essential for the health and comfort of building occupants. It is specifically needed to dilute and remove pollutants emitted from unavoidable sources such as those derived from metabolism and from the essential activities of occupants. Ventilation represents only one aspect of the total building air quality equation, it should not be used in place of source control to minimise pollutant concentrations in a space. Avoidable pollutants should be eliminated.

Air infiltration can destroy the performance of ventilation systems. Good ventilation design combined with optimum air-tightness is needed to ensure energy efficient ventilation. Ultimately, ventilation needs depend on occupancy pattern and building use. No single economic solution to ventilation exists. A full cost and energy benefit analysis is therefore needed to select an optimum ventilation strategy.

It is important to understand the complexities of ventilation systems and how performance is influenced by the building structure itself. The intention of this Chapter is to review the role of ventilation in contributing to a healthy environment in buildings. It is intended to be purely descriptive and is aimed at providing an introduction to current ventilation philosophy. Examples cover the home, workplace and industry.

What is Ventilation?

Definitions covering ventilation and the flow of air into and out of a space include:

Ventilation is the process by which "clean" air (normally outdoor air) is intentionally provided to a space and stale air is removed.

Purpose provided (intentional) ventilation: Ventilation is the process by which 'clean' air (normally outdoor air) is intentionally provided to a space and stale air is removed. This may be accomplished by either natural or mechanical means.

Air infiltration and exfiltration: In addition to intentional ventilation, air inevitably enters a building by the process of 'air infiltration'. This is the uncontrolled flow of air into a space through adventitious or unintentional gaps and cracks in the building envelope. The corresponding loss of air from an enclosed space is termed 'exfiltration'. The rate of air infiltration is dependent on the porosity of the building shell and the magnitude of the natural driving forces of wind and temperature. Vents and other openings incorporated into a building as part of ventilation design can also become routes for unintentional air flow when the pressures acting across such openings are dominated by weather conditions rather than intentionally (e.g. mechanically) induced driving forces. Air infiltration not only adds to the quantity of air entering the building but may also distort the intended air flow pattern to the detriment of overall indoor air quality and comfort. Although the magnitude of air infiltration can be considerable, it is frequently ignored by the designer. The consequences are inferior performance, excessive energy consumption, an inability to provide adequate heating (or cooling) and drastically impaired performance from heat recovery devices. Some Countries have introduced air-tightness Standards to limit infiltration losses (Limb 1994).

Other air losses, e.g. duct leakage: Air leakage from the seams and joints of ventilation, heating and air conditioning circulation ducts can be substantial. When, as is common, such ducting passes through unconditioned spaces, significant energy loss may occur. Modera (1993), for example, estimates that as much as 20% of the heat from typical North American domestic warm air heating systems can be lost through duct leakage. Pollutants may also be drawn into the building through these openings. As a consequence, considerable research and development into the performance of duct sealing measures is being undertaken.

Air recirculation: Air recirculation is frequently used in commercial buildings to provide for thermal conditioning. Recirculated air is usually filtered for dust removal but, since oxygen is not replenished and metabolic pollutants are not removed, recirculation should not usually be considered as contributing towards ventilation need.

Why Is Ventilation Needed?

Good ventilation is a major contributor to the health and comfort of building occupants.

Ventilation is needed to provide oxygen for metabolism and to dilute metabolic pollutants (carbon dioxide and odour). It is also used to assist in maintaining good indoor air quality by diluting and removing other pollutants emitted within a space but should not be used as a substitute for proper source control of pollutants. Ventilation is additionally used for cooling and (particularly in dwellings) to provide oxygen to combustion appliances. Good ventilation is a major contributor to the health and comfort of building occupants.

How Does Ventilation Work?

Ventilation is accomplished by introducing 'clean' air into a space. This air is either mixed with the air already present in the enclosure to give 'mixing' or 'dilution' ventilation, or is used to 'displace' air in the space to give 'displacement' or 'piston flow' ventilation (see Chapter 5). These techniques give characteristically different pollutant profiles.

Ventilation is accomplished by introducing "clean" air into a space

Mixing ventilation: Mixing is stimulated by natural turbulence in the air and (in the case of mechanical ventilation) by the design of the air supply diffusers. Mixing ventilation is especially important when recirculation is used to provide thermal conditioning. If mixing is perfect, the pollutant concentration is uniform throughout the space. The relationship between ventilation rate and concentration of pollutant (assuming a constant emission rate) is illustrated in Figure 1.1(a).

Displacement ventilation: Displacement ventilation methods are becoming popular in some Countries for offices and other non domestic buildings. In principle they are more effective at meeting ventilation needs than the equivalent mixing approach, however air cooling or heating capacity is limited by nature of the need for careful thermal control of the supply air temperature. Additional conditioning is typically met by radiative ceiling panels (see Chapter 7). Unlike mixing ventilation, the spatial concentration of pollutant within the space is non-uniform, with air upstream of the pollutant source being uncontaminated while the air downstream of source may become heavily contaminated. Good design is aimed at ensuring the separation of occupants from polluted air. A typical pollutant profile is illustrated in Figure 1.1(b). In this example, pollutant build-up (e.g. metabolic carbon dioxide) is kept above the occupant breathing zone. In practice some mixing inevitably occurs. Very careful air flow and temperature control is needed to inhibit mixing, this is covered in further detail in Chapter 5. Contaminants upstream of the occupied space or 'breathing' zone must be avoided. Examples of such pollutants include floor level contaminants and emissions from floor coverings and carpets.

Interzonal ventilation: In dwellings, it is common to extract air from 'wet' rooms such as kitchens and bathrooms. Fresh 'make-up' air is then drawn through air inlets or mechanically supplied to living areas and bedrooms. This induces a flow pattern that inhibits the cross-contamination of air from 'polluted' spaces to 'clean' spaces. Similar examples apply to clean

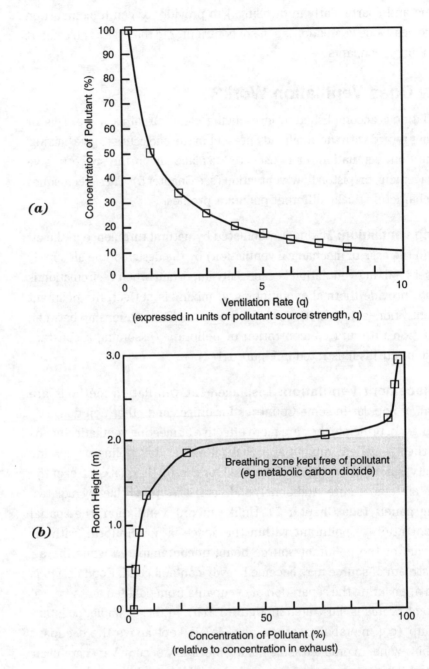

**Figure 1.1 Characteristics of (a) Dilution
Ventilation and (b) Displacement Ventilation**

room and hospital applications.

Short circuiting: If a ventilation system is poorly designed, 'short circuiting' may occur in which fresh ventilation air is extracted from the building before it has mixed with or displaced stale air. This can occur if air diffusers and outlets are positioned too close to each other or, in the case of displacement systems, the supply air temperature is higher than the room air temperature.

How Much Ventilation Is Needed?

The quantity of ventilation needed depends on the amount and nature of pollutant present in a space. In practice an enclosed space will contain many different pollutants. If the emission characteristics of each is known, then it is possible to calculate the rate of ventilation needed to prevent each pollutant from exceeding a pre-defined threshold concentration (see Chapter 12, Section 8). When identical pollutants are emitted from more than one source, then the ventilation rate must be based on the total emission rate from all sources. To determine the overall ventilation need, it is useful to identify the dominant pollutant. This is the pollutant that requires the greatest amount of ventilation for control. Provided sufficient ventilation is achieved to control the dominant pollutant, all the remaining pollutants should remain below their respective threshold concentrations (see Figure 1.2). The minimum acceptable ventilation rate is that which is required to dilute the dominant pollutant to an acceptable concentration. Pollutants from localised sources should be enclosed or extracted at the point of source to avoid contamination of occupied spaces.

> *The quantity of ventilation needed depends on the amount and nature of pollutant present in a space*

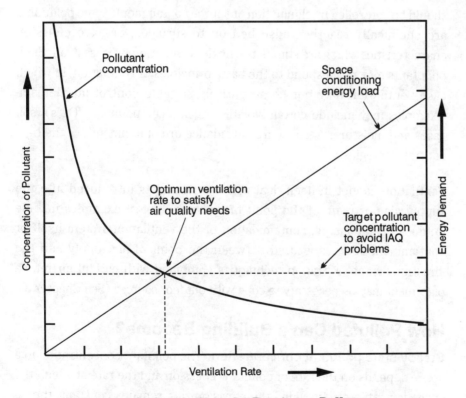

Figure 1.2 Controlling the Dominant Pollutant

It is useful to classify pollutants in terms of unavoidable and avoidable sources. Unavoidable sources are associated with metabolism and the essential activities of occupants. On the other hand, avoidable sources are associated with excessive emissions from materials and poorly designed appliances. If the dominant need for ventilation is from an avoidable source, then the reduction or elimination of the pollutant source will provide the most effective and energy efficient method of air quality control.

Unfortunately, acceptable safety and comfort concentrations of many pollutants are presently unknown. There is, therefore, currently much debate on how to address the ventilation requirements for such pollutants. On the other hand, recommended safe concentrations are available for several of the most common pollutants. Provided these known pollutants represent the dominant need for ventilation and emissions from avoidable sources are minimised, then any risk to health and comfort can be avoided.

When Is Ventilation Not Appropriate?

Too often it falls upon ventilation to accomplish tasks for which it is not appropriate. The prime role of ventilation is to dilute and remove pollutants from unavoidable sources. All other pollutants should be controlled by elimination or source containment.

Too often it falls upon ventilation to accomplish tasks for which it is not appropriate. The prime role of ventilation is to dilute and remove pollutants from unavoidable sources. In essence these are those generated by occupants themselves and by their essential activities. All other pollutants should be controlled by elimination or source containment. Some pollutants are chemically reactive, adsorbed on to surfaces, or have emission characteristics which are stimulated by the ventilation process itself. Such pollutants may not respond to the basic principles of ventilation, in which case ventilation may not be an entirely suitable control mechanism. Examples may include certain volatile organic compounds (VOC's), soil gases and moisture. Again source avoidance or containment are the best control strategies.

Ventilation cannot in itself deal with contaminants introduced into the supply air upstream of the point of delivery. Typical examples include outdoor contaminants, contamination of the ventilation system itself or contaminant sources located between the point of air supply and the 'breathing' zone. Filtration techniques combined with careful air intake placement may be necessary to cope with outdoor sources (See Chapter 8).

How Polluted Can a Building Become?

Steady state pollutant concentration: The pollutant concentration in a space depends on the rate of pollutant emission and the rate at which the space is ventilated. Provided the emission rate remains constant, then a steady state concentration is eventually reached which is independent of the enclosure volume. Under conditions of uniform mixing, the concentration throughout the space will be uniform, whereas if mixing is non uniform (e.g. displacement ventilation), the pollutant concentration will vary throughout the space.

Transient pollutant concentration - the building as a 'fresh air' reservoir: The time it takes for the steady state concentration to be reached depends on the rate of ventilation and the volume of enclosed space. Thus it may sometimes be possible to avoid immediate air quality problems by taking advantage of the fresh air already stored in a room. The capacity of a building to act as a reservoir is useful for absorbing the impact of transient pollution emissions and variations in ventilation rate. It may also be used to advantage if the outdoor air becomes polluted for a short period (e.g.

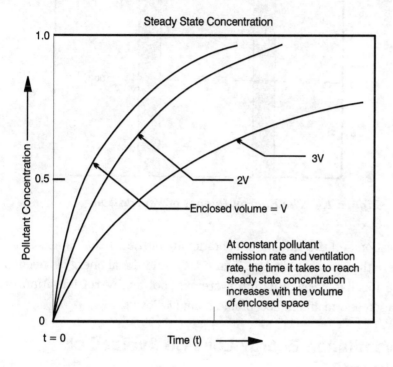

Figure 1.3 The Building as a 'Fresh Air' Reservoir

rush hour traffic) by temporarily restricting the rate of ventilation. Older naturally ventilated buildings are typically constructed with high ceiling heights to provide an air quality reservoir (see Figure 1.3).

What is the Energy Impact of Ventilation?

Approximately 30% of the energy delivered to buildings is dissipated in the departing ventilation and exfiltration air streams. In buildings constructed to very high Standards of thermal insulation, the proportion of airborne energy loss can be much higher. This loss has important implications both at the consumer level, where the cost must be met, and at the strategic level, where it impacts on primary energy need and environmental pollution. These issues are discussed in further detail in Chapter 3. The amount of energy consumed is dependent on the flow rate

Approximately 30% of the energy delivered to buildings is dissipated in the departing ventilation and exfiltration streams.

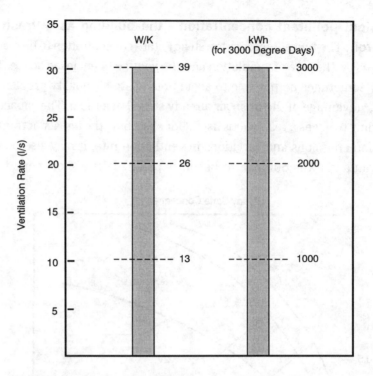

Figure 1.4 The Energy Impact of Ventilation

of ventilation and the amount of conditioning of the air that is necessary to achieve thermal comfort (see Figure 1.4). Additional energy is needed to drive mechanical ventilation systems, cool air by refrigeration or evaporation and maintain acceptable humidity levels.

Can Ventilation Energy Loss Be Avoided or Recovered?

Ventilation energy demand can be reduced considerably by adopting a variety of energy efficient ventilation techniques. These include:

Minimising the need for ventilation: Energy demand may be curtailed by ensuring that the need for ventilation is reduced. This means minimising emissions from avoidable pollutant sources. Any extra ventilation needed to dilute and remove avoidable pollutants can be equated directly against conditioning load.

Poor building air tightness results in excessive air infiltration and resultant uncontrolled energy loss.

Avoid uncontrolled air infiltration losses: Poor building air-tightness results in excessive air infiltration and resultant uncontrolled energy loss. In many Countries building air-tightness can be improved considerably without detriment to indoor air quality. Infiltration driven by stack effect is particularly high when the difference between inside and outside temperature is at its greatest. This often corresponds to periods of maximum thermal conditioning need.

Demand controlled ventilation: If the dominant pollutant can be identified and measured, then the ventilation rate can be automatically adjusted to respond to need by means of demand controlled ventilation (see Chapter 5). This is especially successful at tracking metabolically produced carbon dioxide in densely and transiently occupied buildings (e.g. offices, schools and theatres). In dwellings, moisture sensors are used with varying success to control the rate of ventilation in bathrooms and kitchens.

Heat recovery: As much as 70% of the energy lost through mechanical balanced or extract ventilation can be recovered by the use of ventilation heat recovery systems (Chapter 6). However potential savings must be equated against capital cost, ongoing maintenance needs and electrical (fan and/or heat pump) load. Their performance can also be destroyed by poor building air-tightness. The cost effectiveness of heat recovery systems is largely dependent on the severity of outdoor climate, the quality of the building envelope and the ventilation need. Example calculations are outlined in Chapter 12.

In theory, as much as 70% of the energy lost through mechanical balanced or extract ventilation can be recovered by the use of ventilation heat recovery systems (Chapter 6). However, potential savings must be equated against capital cost, ongoing maintenance needs and electrical (fan and/or heat pump) load.

Ground pre-conditioning of the supply air: Tempering of the supply air is possible by passing the supply air duct underground. Thermal gain must be equated against additional pressure loss introduced into the ventilation system. This approach has been applied to both single family and multi family (apartment) buildings. (See Chapter 6).

What Is the Relationship Between Ventilation Rate and Odour?

Odour can be regarded as a 'pollutant' or as an indicator of the presence of pollutant. Sometimes it may alert the occupant to a potential health risk, although this need not always be reliable since some highly toxic pollutants, such as radon and carbon monoxide, are odourless. More generally, odour causes discomfort, especially in sedentary environments such as the office or home. A difficulty with odour analysis is that many odours cannot be measured by instrumentation. Evaluation, therefore, has to rely on subjective testing by 'panellists', thus making the interpretation of results difficult. A comprehensive study of odour and the control of odour by ventilation has been made by Fanger (1988). These results are summarised in Chapter 2.

Is There a Relationship Between Ventilation and Health?

Poor ventilation can be associated with unhealthy buildings. Miller (1992), for example, highlights the association of increasing bacteriological concentration with decreasing ventilation rates, while Billington (1982) has produced an historical review of the role of ventilation in improving health and reducing the spread of illness. Studies reported by Sundell (1994) and others have shown that symptoms of building sickness can occur at all ventilation ranges. However, any link between the rate of ventilation and the occurrence of symptoms becomes very weak at ventilation rates above approximately 10 litres/s for each occupant (l/s.p). It would be incorrect, therefore, to associate all building health related problems with inadequate ventilation. Health problems in buildings may often have much more to do with the character and source of pollutant present in the space rather than the adequacy of ventilation. This aspect is covered in further detail in Chapter 2.

How is Ventilation Provided?

Natural ventilation is still relied upon to meet the need for fresh air in many types of building throughout the world.

Natural ventilation: Traditionally, ventilation needs have been met by 'natural' ventilation in which the flow process is driven by wind and temperature. In mild climates, design has often relied on no more than the natural porosity of the building, combined with window opening. In colder climates, natural ventilation designs tend to be more specific and incorporate carefully sized air inlets combined with passive ventilation stacks. Other climates might take advantage of a prevailing wind to drive the ventilation process.

The main drawback of natural ventilation is lack of control, in which unreliable driving forces can result in periods of inadequate ventilation, followed by periods of over ventilation and excessive energy waste. Good design can provide some measure of flow control but normally it is necessary for the occupant to adjust ventilation openings to suit demand. Despite the difficulty of control, natural ventilation is still relied upon to meet the need for fresh air in many types of building throughout the world.

Mechanical ventilation: In principle, the shortcomings of natural ventilation can be overcome by mechanical ventilation. These systems are capable of providing a controlled rate of air change and respond to the varying needs of occupants and pollutant loads, irrespective of the vagaries of climate. Some systems enable incoming supply air to be filtered while others have provision for heat recovery from the exhaust air stream. In some countries, especially in parts of Canada and Scandinavia, mechanical systems are being incorporated into virtually all new building construction and included in many building refurbishment programmes. In milder climate, however, the potential advantages of mechanical ventilation, especially for smaller buildings, can often be outweighed by installation and operational cost, maintenance needs and inadequate return from heat recovery. Regardless of climate, mechanical ventilation is often essential in large, deep plan office buildings where fresh air must penetrate to the centre of the building and high heat gains can cause over heating.

Several configurations of mechanical ventilation are possible with each having a specific range of applications. The basic options are:

- supply ventilation,
- extract (or exhaust) ventilation,
- balanced supply extract systems,

A detailed review of ventilation strategies is presented in Chapter 5.

How Do Ventilation Needs and Strategies Differ According to Building Type?

Ventilation needs and strategies differ according to occupancy patterns and building type. These are reviewed in further detail in Chapter 4. Main considerations are:

Ventilation needs and strategies differ according to occupancy patterns and building type.

Dwellings: The 'dominant' pollutant in dwellings is often moisture which is best extracted directly at source from wet zones using mechanical extract ventilation or 'passive' stacks. Fresh supply air is needed in living rooms and bedrooms to meet the needs of metabolism. Additional airing may be necessary if smoking takes place. Further air supply in the form of vent openings is necessary to meet the combustion needs of 'open' flue and 'flueless' combustion appliances. Special care is needed to avoid flue down-draughting resulting from the use of extract systems (Chapter 12, Section 8). In high radon areas, special attention to sealing the foundations is necessary, combined with sub floor venting.

Offices and other non-domestic buildings: Important pollutants in non domestic buildings include metabolic carbon dioxide, volatile organic compounds from furnishings and fittings, and ozone and carbon emissions from printers and photocopiers. In many of these buildings, metabolic carbon dioxide may represent the dominant source of pollutant. High heat gains may affect the choice between minimum ventilation combined with mechanical cooling or maximum ventilation for passive cooling. Industrial processes require special ventilation provision to prevent the discharge of contaminated air both internally to the occupants and externally to the atmosphere. Other special applications include provision for hospital and clean room ventilation design to avoid contamination.

How Is the Choice of Ventilation Influenced By Climate and Local Environment?

The severity of climate influences the degree of heating or cooling that is necessary to condition the incoming air. Greater potential exists for the use of complex ventilation strategies combined with heat recovery when ventilation heating or cooling loads are high. A system that may be cost effective in one climatic zone may not be appropriate in another.

Building location further influences the choice of ventilation strategy. Locations in urban and city areas, for example, can suffer from poor outdoor air quality derived from traffic fumes and industrial pollutants, while outside noise from passing traffic can be excessive, thus restricting the potential for window opening. Adjacent buildings could create conflict in relation to pre-existing air intakes and exhaust points. Rural locations might be subjected to high pollen concentrations and fungal spores resulting in a need for filtration for hypersensitive individuals.

What Regulations and Standards Govern the Choice and Performance of Ventilation Systems?

Numerous Standards relate to the needs and operation of ventilation systems. These vary between countries but Standards are regularly reviewed by the AIVC (Limb 1994). Ventilation related Standards are discussed in greater detail in Chapter 4. Typically they cover the minimum ventilation rate needed for health and safety, requirements for comfort, the operational performance of ventilation systems, requirements for building and component air-tightness, provision for maintenance, component durability and requirements for ventilation heat recovery.

What Other Aspects Must be Considered in the Design Process?

It is necessary to integrate the ventilation system itself into the overall design of the building, especially in relation to air tightness. room partitioning and accessibility.

The designer is faced with many and, sometimes, apparently conflicting requirements in the task of delivering fresh air to occupants. In meeting the design need it is necessary to consider a wide range of criteria, varying from complying with the needs of Building Regulations to planning for maintenance and replacement. It is also necessary to integrate the ventilation system itself into the overall design of the building, especially in relation to air-tightness, room partitioning and accessibility.

Since such a wide range of parameters is involved, there is rarely a unique solution to a particular ventilation design. Instead the designer must base a judgement on the individual needs of each building. Ultimately a robust solution is needed which ensures the health and comfort of occupants. Ventilation needs must be based on criteria that can be established at the design stage of a building. To return afterwards in an attempt to mitigate problems as they arise may lead to considerable expense and failure.

Design criteria are considered in Chapter 4 with special emphasis on the necessity of an integrated approach, design constraints, specifying ventilation needs and design variables.

Can Ventilation be Used for Cooling?

Frequently, the dominant pollutant is 'heat' itself. Particularly in large commercial office buildings, high heat loads are developed through lighting, computing and other electrical sources. Further heat gains are derived from occupants, solar radiation and high outdoor temperatures. These factors make cooling of the indoor air essential. The choice is either to introduce refrigerative cooling or to introduce ventilation cooling. In either case heat gains should be minimised by good building design and reduced power consumption. Refrigerative cooling is energy intensive and contributes to peak power loads. Often, however, climate conditions dictate no other choice especially when the humidity level must be controlled. When refrigerative cooling is needed, ventilation must be minimised to prevent the unnecessary loss of conditioned air. Cooling is sometimes possible by introducing cooler, outdoor air (cooling by ventilation). This may be through window opening or by mechanical means. Ventilation rates for cooling will normally be well in excess of that needed to meet the basic fresh air requirements of occupants but may, nevertheless, accomplish dramatic energy savings over refrigerative cooling. The choice between ventilation cooling and refrigerative cooling is a function of heat gains, humidity loads and outdoor climate. Reducing heat gains by good building design (e.g. minimising solar gains and introducing thermal mass) and by introducing low energy lighting and night cooling can often bring the threshold in favour of cooling by ventilation or reduce the periods in which refrigerative cooling is necessary.

> *Reducing heat gains by good building design and by introducing low energy lighting and night cooling can often bring the threshold in favour of cooling by ventilation or reduce the periods in which refrigerative cooling is necessary.*

Can Outdoor Air be Cleaned?

Outdoor air may be 'cleaned' by filtration. This is a method by which particulates and, sometimes, gaseous pollutants are removed from the air. Pollutants are intercepted by a filter while allowing clean air to pass through. This method of air cleaning is especially necessary when high concentrations of particulates are present or when the source of pollutant is derived from outside the building. Potential benefits can include improved air quality, reduced dependence on ventilation and improved energy efficiency. Filtration is not, however, a substitute for the ventilation needed to meet the metabolic requirements of occupants. Neither can filtration be used in leaky or naturally ventilated buildings.

A review of particulate contamination and filtration methods is presented in Chapter 8.

What is Ventilation Efficiency?

Indices of ventilation efficiency characterise the mixing behaviour of air and the distribution of pollutant within a space. These two aspects may be subdivided into indices of air change efficiency and pollutant removal effectiveness respectively. Ventilation efficiency is based on an evaluation of the 'age' of air and on the concentration distribution of pollutant within the air. Some indices are based on room averaged values, while others refer to specific points or locations. This has important consequences because while room values provide some guidance to the overall performance of a ventilation system, point values indicate regions where localised poor ventilation might occur.

The concepts of ventilation efficiency are described in Chapter 9. These concepts may be applied to entire buildings, single zones or locations within a single zone.

What Provision Should be Made for Maintenance?

Evidence suggest that maintenance is often inadequate and that the need for maintenance may even be ignored in the course of building design.

Maintenance is needed to ensure the reliability of the ventilation system and to secure the economic operation of the ventilation plant. Evidence suggests, however, that maintenance is often inadequate and that the need for maintenance may even be ignored in the course of building design. Typical problems include worn gaskets, dirty fans and grilles, and ill-fitting and clogged filters. This concern has resulted in much more specific guidelines being developed for the maintenance of ventilation systems, some of which are discussed in Chapter 10. Only by correct functioning can a ventilation system be relied upon to meet the indoor air quality needs of a building.

What Measurement Techniques are Available?

Measurements are needed to verify the performance of ventilation systems and to test the air-tightness of the building shell. They are essential for commissioning, diagnostic analysis, design evaluation and research. In addition, measurement results provide the fundamental means for understanding the mechanics of ventilation and air flow in buildings. Measurement data are also needed to provide background information for parametric studies on building air leakage characteristics, indoor air quality and ventilation system performance.

Many measurement techniques have been developed with each having a specific purpose. An analysis of principal methods and applications is presented in Chapter 11.

Techniques include:

- tracer gas testing for ventilation rate and ventilation efficiency evaluation,
- pressurisation measurements to determine building and component air-tightness,
- anemometry techniques to measure air flow velocity and turbulence throughout a space,
- sheet light and laser methods to visualise air flow patterns,
- flume models to design and predict ventilation performance,
- wind tunnel techniques for pressure distribution evaluation.

What Calculation Techniques are Available?

Calculation techniques and numerical models are essential for any design process. They provide the means by which the designer can develop and investigate an idea before being committed to the final product. Typical design aspects cover system sizing, performance evaluation, indoor air quality prediction, energy impact assessment, and cost benefit analysis. A calculation technique or model is used to analyse the interaction of design options with fixed constraints. Such a process is necessarily iterative, with adjustments made to parameters over which control is possible, until an optimum design solution is achieved.

Calculation techniques and numerical models are essential for any design process. They provide the means by which the designer can develop and investigate an idea before being committed to the final product.

A wide range of methods of varying complexity have been developed with no single method being universally appropriate. Selection varies according to the required level of accuracy, the availability of data and the type of building under investigation. As designs have become more complex and performance tolerances more demanding, it is increasingly important for the designer to be able to understand and use calculation techniques. This need has resulted in the development of improved algorithms and wider availability of design data. The current status of calculation methods is outlined in Chapter 12. In addition, sufficient guidance and data are provided to enable basic calculation methods to be performed.

Techniques cover methods to determine:

- air change rates in buildings and rooms,
- the flow rate of air through infiltration and purpose provided flow openings (network methods), see Figure 1.5,
- air flow pattern in a space (computational fluid dynamics).

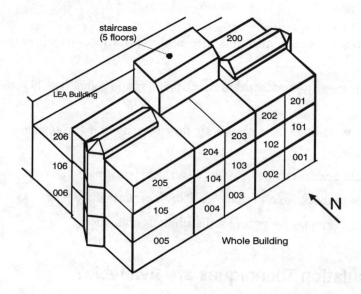

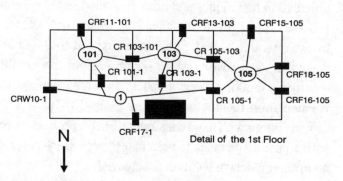

Figure 1.5 Representing the Building as a Flow Network
(Courtesy C-A Roulet, Switzerland)

What Units are Used for Ventilation and Air Infiltration?

Various units are used to describe the rate of ventilation. These include:

Volumetric flow rate: Ventilation and air infiltration is commonly expressed in terms of a volumetric air flow rate e.g. litres/s (l/s) or m³/s.

Per occupant air flow rate: Sometimes the volumetric flow rate is divided by the number of occupants in a space to give a flow rate for each occupant. This is commonly expressed in terms of litres/second for each occupant, i.e. l/s.p.

Unit area flow rate: Alternatively, the air flow rate may be divided by the floor area of an enclosure to give a unit area value, i.e. litres/second.m².

Air change rate: Air flow is also often expressed in terms of hourly 'air change rate' (ach). This is the volume flow rate of air into an enclosure (e.g. a room or the entire building) divided by the room (or building) volume.

Mass flow rate: Sometimes air flow rate is expressed in terms of the mass flow rate of air, e.g. kg/s. Mass flow is needed to determine the thermal energy carried by the air stream. It is also widely used in ventilation and air flow calculation techniques (see Chapter 12).

References

Billington N, *The art of ventilation*, Proc 3rd AIVC Conference 1982

Fanger P O, *Introduction of the olf and the decipol units to quantify air pollution perceived by humans indoors and outdoors*, Energy and Buildings, No 12, 1988.

Limb M J, *Ventilation and building air-tightness: an international comparison of Standards, Codes of Practice and Regulations*, Air Infiltration and Ventilation Centre, Technical Note 43, 1994.

Miller J D, *Microbial contamination of indoor air*, Proc *Indoor air quality, ventilation and energy conservation*, 5th International Jacques Cartier Conference, Montreal, Canada, 1992.

Modera M, *Characterizing the performance of residential air distribution systems*, Energy and Buildings, No 20, 1993.

Sundell J, *On the association between building ventilation characteristics, some indoor environmental exposures, some allergic manifestations and subjective symptom reports*, Indoor Air Supplement No2/94, 1994.

2 Indoor Air Quality and Comfort

Sick Building Syndrome
Pollutants and Pollutant Sources
Reducing indoor Pollutant Concentration
Comfort and Well-being

Summary and Introduction

Ventilation plays an essential role in securing good indoor air quality and thermal comfort. However, to achieve optimum energy efficiency and to avoid unnecessary pollution of occupied zones, ventilation must be considered as just one of the tools needed in the design process. Care of the outdoor environment, the elimination of unnecessary contaminant sources and the enclosing of pollutant producing processes are also essential. Good indoor air quality may be defined as air which is free of pollutants that cause irritation, discomfort or ill health to occupants. Ambient air temperature and relative humidity also affect comfort and health. A poor indoor environment can manifest itself as a 'sick' building in which occupants may experience mild illness symptoms during periods of occupancy. More serious pollutant problems may result in long term or permanent ill-health effects. Since much time is spent inside buildings, considerable effort has focused on methods to achieve an optimum indoor environment, with particular emphasis on health, odour control and thermal comfort.

Good indoor air quality may be defined as air which is free of pollutants that cause irritation, discomfort or ill health to occupants.

An almost limitless number of pollutants may be present in a space, of which many are at virtually immeasurably low concentrations and have largely unknown toxicological effects. The task of identifying and assessing the risk of individual pollutants has become a major research activity. Some pollutants can be tolerated at low concentrations, while irritation and odour often provides an early warning of deteriorating conditions. Health related air quality Standards are typically based on risk assessment and are either specified in terms of a maximum permitted concentration or a maximum permitted dose. Higher concentrations of pollutants are normally permitted for short term exposure than are permitted for long term exposure. Typical examples include 1-hour and 8-hour 'Threshold Limit Values' or TLV's (ACGIH 1990).

Air quality needs for comfort are highly subjective and dependent on circumstances.

Air quality needs for comfort are highly subjective and dependent on circumstances. In the industrial arena, for example, higher levels of odour and heat may be tolerated than would be acceptable in the office or home. As a rule, health related air quality Standards, such as TLV's, set the minimum requirements for safety; these may not necessarily provide for comfort or efficiency at work or in the home. Provisional revisions to ASHRAE Standard 62 (1989) for the recommended maximum concentration of a variety of common indoor pollutants are summarised in Table 2.1.

Table 2.1 Target Concentrations for Selected Contaminants*

Contaminant	Typical indoor sources	Level of interest
Carbon Monoxide (CO) (leaky and unvented). Parking garages	Combustion appliances 9 ppm 8-hour TLV	3 ppm above outdoor level
Formaldehyde (HCHO) Insulation, furnishings	Pressed wood, (fibreboard)	120mg/m³ (0.1 ppm)
Lead (Pb) Fuel additives	Paint dust	1.5mg/m³
Nitrogen Dioxide (NO₂)	Combustion appliances	100mg/m³
Odours Fungi mould VOC Sources	Occupants of occupants or visitors	Acceptable to 80% or more
Ozone Office machines Ozone generators	Electrostatic appliances	100mg/m³ (50 ppb)
Particles Smoke Fragments	Dust	50mg/m³
Radon (Rn)	Soil gas	4 pCi/litre
Sulphur Dioxide (SO₂)	Unvented space heaters	80mg/m³
Total Volatile Organic Compounds (TVOC's) Household products	Building materials Furnishings > 3000mg/m³ (complaints)	<300mg/m³ (good) 300 - 3000mg/m³ (OK)

Information based on proposals for revised ASHRAE Standard 62 (1996/97)

In reality, a perfectly pollutant free environment is unlikely to be attained. Instead, achieving optimum indoor air quality relies on an integrated approach to the removal and control of pollutants based on source control, filtration, enclosing pollutant sources and ventilating the occupied space (see Figure 2.1). It is useful to differentiate between unavoidable pollutants, over which there is little control, and avoidable pollutants, over which control is possible. As a rule, ventilation provides an effective measure to deal with unavoidable pollutants but source control is the most efficient and, sometimes, the only method suitable for minimising the effect of

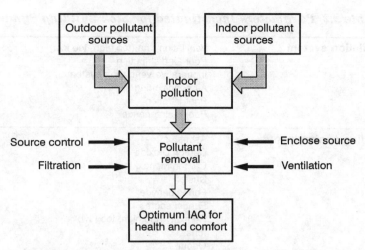

Figure 2.1 Achieving Optimum Indoor Air Quality

avoidable pollutants. Typical unavoidable pollutants are those associated with metabolism (carbon dioxide and odour) and essential occupant activities (e.g. cooking and washing). Avoidable sources include excessive organic emissions from furnishings and fittings, and pollutant emissions from poorly enclosed appliances. A comprehensive guide to the control of indoor air quality by the use of general ventilation has been produced by Vaculik et al (1995).

The purpose of this Chapter is to provide an overview of indoor air quality in relation to pollutant sources, comfort and thermal conditions, and to review needs in the context of ventilation and other control methods.

2.1 Sick Building Syndrome

Poor air quality in buildings sometimes manifests itself in the form of 'Sick Building Syndrome' (SBS). Definitions of SBS vary slightly but generally refer to a range of symptoms that an occupant experiences while present in the building. Typical symptoms include lethargy, headaches, lack of concentration, runny nose, dry throat and eye and skin irritation.

Definitions of SBS vary slightly but generally refer to a range of symptoms that an occupant experiences while present in the building. Typical symptoms include lethargy, headaches, lack of concentration, runny nose, dry throat and eye and skin irritation.

In an effort to understand the causes of sick buildings, many parameters have been investigated. These have tended to focus on ventilation performance, contaminants and various other miscellaneous parameters. Typical parameters investigated are listed in Table 2.2 (Liddament 1990). Various studies have included surveys and medical examinations. No single cause has been identified and much of the evidence concerning the causes of sick buildings is inconclusive. A series of papers by Sundell (1994) includes both an extensive review of the topic and the results of several studies. Among his conclusions is some evidence indicating that low ventilation rates in offices, combined with the presence of various

Table 2.2 Parameters Investigated for Sick Building Syndrome

Ventilation system	Ventilation rate (too high, too low)
	Poor air distribution
	Inoperative ventilation system
	Air conditioning
	Poor filtration
	Poor maintenance
Building contaminants	Asbestos
	Carbon Dioxide
	Carbon Monoxide
	Dust
	Formaldehyde
	Fungal spores
	Humidity (too high, too low)
	Ions
	Odour
	Outdoor pollutants
	Ozone
	Pollen
	Radon
	Smoke
	Volatile Organic Compounds
Occupants	Age
	Gender
	General state of health
	Occupation
Miscellaneous	Building type
	Electromagnetic radiation
	Lack of environmental controls
	Lighting
	Noise
	Psychological factors
	Stress
	Visual display terminals

pollutants, can increase problems although symptoms were found to occur in all ventilation ranges. Intermittent use of office ventilation systems was also found to increase risk. It was further noted that any link with SBS is with the occupant rate of ventilation (i.e. l/s.p) rather than the overall air change rate or unit floor area ventilation rate. Other observations showed weak or no correlation with the use of air recirculation and of rotary heat recovery systems.

Other authors too find only weak correlation or inconclusive results, especially in relation to ventilation. To some extent, conclusions depend on the ventilation range under review. Hanssen (1993), for example, reports on improved air quality in a school when ventilation is increased to 8 l/s.p. while Burge et al (1990) found little association with ventilation rate in offices in the range 4 l/s.p to 23 l/s.p.

Relationship between the type of ventilation system and symptoms is inconclusive.

Relationship between the type of ventilation system and symptoms is also inconclusive. Burge (1993) found fewer symptoms in naturally ventilated rather than air conditioned office buildings. Similar results are reported by other researchers, especially in air conditioned buildings in which humidifiers are used. On the other hand Sundell (1994) found, in Sweden, that SBS was more pronounced in office buildings that were either naturally ventilated or ventilated by mechanical extract only, than in offices incorporating balanced extract-supply systems.

A completely different angle is considered by Miller (1992) who found toxic fungal spores (mycotoxins) in some sick buildings. Other examples of sick buildings have also been associated with the presence of specific pollutants, for example outdoor fumes entering through air intakes.

From on-going research and observations it is clear that ventilation presents only one aspect of a very complex problem. The role played by ventilation appears to be most significant when ventilation rates are very low.

2.2 Pollutants and Pollutant Sources

Indoor pollutants are derived from both outdoor and indoor sources. Each of these sources tend to impose different requirements on the control strategies needed to secure good health and comfort conditions.

Outdoor air pollution: Clean outdoor air is essential for achieving good indoor air quality. Although air cleaning is possible, it is costly and not effective in the many offices and dwellings that are either naturally ventilated, leaky or are ventilated by mechanical extract systems.

Clean outdoor air is essential for achieving good indoor air quality.

Some air quality problems are global and can only be controlled by international effort. Examples include the discharge of ozone depleting chemicals (CFC's) into the upper atmosphere and steadily rising carbon dioxide concentrations resulting from the burning of fossil fuels. Other pollutants are much more regional and may be associated with local industry and traffic. Nature, too, presents its own problems with large volumes of dust and gaseous emissions being associated with volcanic activity, while naturally occurring radon can penetrate buildings from the underlying geological strata. Even rural areas are not immune to pollution, where the presence of pollen and fungi spores can result in allergic reactions.

Typical sources of outdoor pollutant are summarised in Figure 2.2. Examples include:

Industrial contaminants: Industrial emissions tend to create regional and local problems, although contaminated air from highly polluting industry can propagate many hundreds of kilometres. Typical pollutants

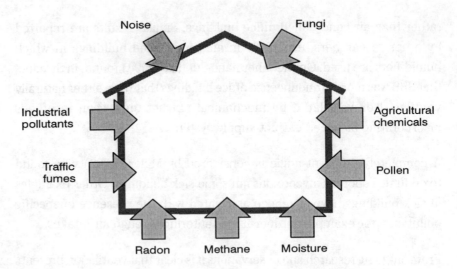

Figure 2.2 Overview of Typical Outdoor Pollutants

include:

- oxides of nitrogen and sulphur,
- ozone,
- lead,
- volatile organic compounds,
- smoke, particulates and fibres.

Industrial pollutant concentrations are exacerbated by stable weather conditions which cause the regional stagnation of polluted air. Some industrial particulates are thought to be carcinogenic or can cause lung irritation. Examples include asbestos, man made fibres, dust and carbon. Increasing concern about emissions from industry have resulted in the introduction of emission controls and 'clean air' Regulations in many Countries. In Europe, for example, clean air requirements are covered by the air framework directive, while, in the United States legislation is covered by the Clean Air Act. Both impose restrictions on pollutant discharges and incorporate requirements to clean exhaust air. The US legislation sets target dates for which outdoor air concentrations of pollutants such as CFC's, oxides of nitrogen, ozone, lead and volatile organic compounds must be reduced. Control measures include emission caps, permits and other restrictions. Emissions from new sources are only permitted if offset by reducing emissions from existing sources by a greater amount. Emission caps prevent a company from increasing the rate of pollution emission as its business expands.

Traffic pollution: Traffic pollution is a particular problem in highly urbanised areas. Major pollutants include:

- carbon monoxide,
- carbon dust,
- lead,
- oxides of nitrogen,
- fuel additives.

Traffic emissions concentrate at street level and may enter through open windows and air intakes to contaminate the indoor air. Fumes from underground and adjacent parking areas (Limb 1994) and at locations adjacent to tunnel entrances are also a problem. In addition, rush hour traffic causes transient problems with large volumes of urban traffic contaminating road side buildings. Measures to restrict traffic pollution include the use of catalytic exhaust emission converters, restrictions on carbon emissions and the elimination of lead in fuel. Despite these controls, increasing growth in traffic is continuing to add to pollution.

Traffic emissions concentrate at street level and may enter through open windows and air intakes to contaminate the indoor air.

Emissions from adjacent exhausts and cooling towers: Air supply can become contaminated by exhaust or combustion emissions from nearby stacks. Contaminate emissions from cooling towers also cause problems, especially in relation to the spread of legionella from poorly maintained systems.

Rural pollution: Intensive farming in rural areas may increase the presence of agriculturally produced pollutants such as pollen and fungi. These are seasonally based pollutants that induce allergic reactions, such as hay fever or asthma. Chemical fertilisers and insecticides may also contaminate the surrounding air.

Soil borne pollutants: Soil borne sources of pollutant can penetrate the building through foundations and sub-floor layers. This can be enhanced by extract ventilation. Important pollutants include:

- radon,
- methane,
- moisture.

Radon is a naturally occurring radioactive gas that has been linked to an increase in risk of contracting lung cancer. Radon is a regional problem related to underlying geological strata. Mitigation is by subfloor sealing combined with extract or natural stack ventilation from beneath the building foundations (Saum et al (1990)).

Methane is an odourless inflammable gas that occurs as a product of organic decay. It may occur naturally underground but is more likely to be generated by the presence of a household landfill (waste) site. Methane has been known to enter buildings in explosive concentrations.

Moisture may enter a building from the sub-soil and contribute total moisture loading. This is particularly a problem in buildings in which no foundation vapour barrier is present.

Indoor Pollutants

Pollutants emitted inside buildings are derived from metabolism, the activities of occupants and emissions from materials used in construction and furnishings.

Pollutants emitted inside buildings are derived from metabolism, the activities of occupants, and emissions from materials used in construction and furnishing. Major pollutants are summarised in Figure 2.3, and include:

Carbon dioxide (see Section 2.4): Carbon dioxide is a product of metabolism. It is also a product of combustion, in which case it can be found in relatively large concentrations in cooking areas and in areas in which unvented heating appliances are used. It is generally regarded as a non toxic gas which, in itself, is unlikely to cause injury, even at relatively high concentrations.

Carbon monoxide: Carbon monoxide is a highly toxic odourless and colourless gas that is a product of incomplete combustion. It can occur from gas, oil, coal or wood burning appliances, especially if oxygen supply or flue venting is restricted. Very sensitive and inexpensive detectors are now available to give warning of the presence of carbon monoxide.

Formaldehyde: Formaldehyde is used in the manufacture of fibre boards and foam insulation. Controls on emissions from such products have been introduced in some Countries. Formaldehyde is an irritant and has been linked to increased risk of cancer.

Moisture: Moisture is principally generated by occupant activities such as cooking washing and clothes drying. It is a major constituent of combustion and hence may be present in large amounts in areas where gas cooking and unvented space heating takes place. Moisture vapour condenses on cold surfaces where it can cause considerable damage through mould growth and fabric decay.

Odour: Odour is generated as part of metabolism and is emitted from furnishings and fabrics. Odour causes discomfort to occupants and can sometimes be the dominant reason for ventilation. (see also Section 2.4)

Ozone: Ozone can present a long term health threat and causes respiratory complaints. It is released from photocopiers, laser printers and other office equipment. Mostly these devices are fitted with active carbon filters to

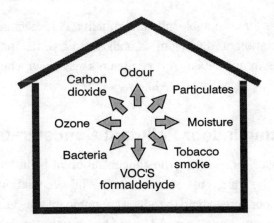

Figure 2.3 Overview of Typical Indoor Pollutants

minimise emissions, but without regular maintenance, ozone levels can become unacceptable. Ozone is also present in the outdoor air. Weschler et al (1989), for example, illustrate examples in which the ozone concentrations in buildings tracked the outside levels at between 20-80%. Cano-Ruiz et al (1992) note that the recombination of outdoor ozone into oxygen as it passes through cracks and gaps in wooden structures is minimal but that recombination can be considerable as it passes through cracks in concrete or brick structures. They also note that recombination is strongly dependent on the lining material of air distribution systems.

Particulates include dust, organic fragments and smoke particles. These have varying levels of toxicity according to type and size.

Particulates: Particulates include dust, organic fragments, fibres, and smoke particles. These have varying levels of toxicity according to type and size. Particulates are reviewed in detail in Chapter 8.

Tobacco smoke: Tobacco smoke is a major source of indoor pollution and can be the dominant source of pollutant in rooms or buildings in which smoking takes place. Tobacco combustion products include carbon monoxide and particulate matter.

Volatile organic compounds (VOC's): VOC's are defined by the World Health Organisation as organic compounds with boiling points in the range 50-260°C (WHO 1989). These have a characteristically strong odour and are emitted from furnishing fabrics and household chemical products. New products, especially, can emit noticeable amounts of VOC's. Countless varieties of VOC's may be present in the indoor air. Some VOC's are known to be toxic while the status of others is, at present, unknown. Analysis is normally restricted to measuring the total VOC content (TVOC) in the air by taking air samples for laboratory (gas chromatograph, see Chapter 11) analysis. Tentative recommendations for TVOC concentrations are given in the proposed 1996-97 revision of ASHRAE Standard 62 on minimum ventilation rates for acceptable indoor air quality. This recommends that a TVOC concentration of <300mg/m^3 is unlikely to give rise to complaints. Between 300mg/m^3 and 3000mg/m^3, complaints may occur while, for values above 3000mg/m^3, complaints are likely.

2.3 Reducing Indoor Pollutant Concentration

Control strategies for reducing the concentration of pollutants in indoor air depend on the source of contamination.

Control strategies for reducing the concentration of pollutants in indoor air depend on the source of contamination. While ventilation or dilution with fresh outdoor air can help to reduce contaminant concentration from emission sources within a space, it cannot eliminate the contamination entirely. Neither is ventilation effective when the incoming air itself is polluted. Optimum control strategies for outside and indoor sources include:

Controlling Outdoor Air Pollutants

In the many buildings ventilated by natural means, little can be achieved to avoid the ingress of contaminated air therefore every effort is needed to ensure the quality of outdoor air. Nevertheless urban pollution, especially from high traffic densities, remains a problem. In these areas, control measures include:

Filtration: Filtration is described in detail in Chapter 8. It is used primarily to remove particulates from the air. Almost all mechanical supply air intakes incorporate filters to prevent dust from entering the ventilation system. Activated carbon filters are able to remove gaseous pollutants while high specification (HEPA) filters enable the minutest of particles to be removed. However, these options are costly and are normally restricted to special applications such as clean rooms and hospital operating theatres. Mechanical supply ventilation systems combined with high efficiency filters may be needed in dwellings occupied by extreme allergy sufferers. Information on building design solutions for hypersensitive occupants is given by Drerup et al (1990).

Siting air intakes: Air intakes must be located away from pollutant sources. Particular problems include street level and car parking locations. Although urban air quality can be much improved at above street level elevations, contamination from adjacent exhaust stacks and cooling towers must be avoided. Determining the optimum position for air intakes may require extensive wind tunnel or fluid dynamics analysis. A simplified technique aimed at estimating the maximum concentration of pollutant in the vicinity of a stack emission source has been developed by Wilson for inclusion in the 1997 ASHRAE Fundamentals (Wilson 1995). Further information on the siting of air intakes is reviewed by Limb 1995.

Air quality controlled fresh air dampers: Traffic pollution in urban areas is often highly transient, with peaks occurring during the morning and evening commuting periods. At these times, it may be possible to improve indoor air quality by temporarily closing fresh air intakes and windows.

Building air-tightness: None of the above control strategies will be effective unless the building is well sealed from the outdoor environment to prevent contaminant ingress through air infiltration. Underground parking garages must also be well sealed from occupied accommodation above. Evidence suggests that sealing is often inadequate.

Controlling Indoor Air Pollutants

The preferred order and methods of pollutant control are summarised in Table 2.3 and include:

Source control: Once a pollutant has entered a space, at best, it can only be diluted. Avoidable pollutants should therefore be eliminated. This means restricting potentially harmful pollutant emissions, such as VOC's and formaldehyde, from furnishings and discouraging tobacco smoking.

> *Once a pollutant has entered a space, at best, it can only be diluted. Avoidable pollutants should therefore be eliminated.*

Table 2.3 Preferred Methods to Control Indoor Pollutant Sources

Method	Pollution source
Source control	Emissions from avoidable sources (VOCs and formaldehyde from furnishings, tobacco smoke etc.)
Enclosure and ventilation at source	Pollutants generated by occupant activities (cooking, clothes washing and drying, use of office equipment etc.)
Dilution and displacement ventilation	Emissions from unavoidable sources (primarily metabolic pollution)

Enclosing and ventilating at source: Pollutants generated as part of the activity of occupants are usually highly localised. In the home, the dominant pollutant is often water vapour generated by washing, clothes drying and cooking. Wherever possible source control should be applied, combined with the use of local extractors and cooker or range hoods to remove these pollutants at source. Similarly localised sources in the workplace should be directly vented to the outside.

General dilution (or displacement) ventilation: General ventilation of a space is needed to dilute and remove residual pollution from unavoidable contaminant sources. Such sources should primarily be odour and CO_2

emissions from building occupants. The necessity to contain metabolic pollution to acceptable levels represents the minimum need for ventilation. A space in which high levels of metabolic products are measured indicates that the ventilation rate is insufficient. Often ventilation is used to dilute avoidable sources of pollutant. Apart from causing unnecessary pollution within such a space, the additional ventilation will result in increased space conditioning load.

The performance of ventilation is dependent on identifying and providing sufficient ventilation for controlling the dominant pollutant. In the home this may be moisture whereas in densely occupied zones it may be the occupant. Provided the dominant pollutant is controlled, all other pollutants should remain below their 'safe' threshold concentration. The equation relating contaminant emission and ventilation rate to the resultant steady state pollutant concentration is described in Chapter 12.

2.4 Comfort and Well-being

Airborne parameters that influence comfort include odour, thermal conditions (see Thermal comfort), relative humidity, air velocity and turbulence.

Comfort is associated with the physical interaction of the individual with the surrounding environment. Airborne parameters that influence comfort include odour, thermal conditions (see Thermal comfort), relative humidity, air velocity and turbulence. Comfort is further dependent on other parameters such as lighting, noise levels, clothing, activity and the overall health and mood of the individual. A discussion on the psychology and mechanics of comfort goes well beyond the scope of this Guide. Instead, this review is restricted to general issues related to the influence of ventilation and air movement on comfort, with particular emphasis on odour, air flow and the thermal environment.

Odour

Objective odour creates discomfort and often provides an indication of poor indoor air quality. It is emitted as part of metabolism and can give warning of high levels of formaldehyde and VOC emissions from furnishings and fabrics. It is also emitted by many other compounds that may be found in buildings. Often occupants become acclimatised to odours that are very noticeable to visitors. In general, good indoor air quality is equated with an absence of odour. If the source of odour is from within the building and cannot be eliminated, then control must be by dilution with fresh air; this can result in an additional ventilation load.

Subjective observations suggest that it is possible to equate the level of dissatisfaction of visitors against odour intensity or 'perceived' air quality. Early studies into odour by Yaglou (1937) considered the impact of occupants on odour. More recently, extensive studies by Fanger (1993) have concentrated on the emission of odour from other sources. This has highlighted the need to consider the building itself as a polluter in addition to pollutants generated by occupants and occupant activities.

There is a need to consider the building itself as a polluter in addition to pollutants generated by occupants and occupant activities.

Since it is not yet possible for odour intensity to be measured with instrumentation, assessment is sometimes based on the judgement of visiting 'panellists' (Fanger 1988). The key units applied to odour analysis are the 'Olf', which is the odour emission rate from a 'standard' person, and the 'decipol', which is the intensity of odour or 'perceived' air quality

Table 2.4 Perceived Indoor Air Quality

	Quality level		
	Perceived air quality		**Required**
Category	**% dissatisfied**	**Decipol**	**Ventilation rate (l/s.Olf)**
A	10	0.6	16
B	20	1.4	7
C	30	2.5	4

derived from a source of one 'Olf' ventilated by 10 l/s of fresh air. Observations have indicated that the percentage of 'visitors' to a space who are dissatisfied with the intensity of odour can be directly correlated with the decipol value (and hence ventilation rate) as indicated in Table 2.4. This approach, therefore, may be used to provide guidance on the amount of ventilation needed to minimise odour discomfort. Implicit in this method is the assumption that odour from different sources can be summed to obtain a total odour value, even though the types of odour may differ (e.g. organic compounds, occupants etc.).

A problem with basing ventilation load on odour intensity is that little information may be available at the design stage of a building about the odour pollutant loading of future furnishings and fittings. Some designs are aimed at anticipating odour load by assuming a basic level of pollutant or categorising pollutant sources in terms of low, medium and high emissions. Proposals for ASHRAE Standard 62 (1989) include a two stage approach in which either prescribed values or an air quality method may be used to estimate ventilation need.

Further studies are attempting to categorise typical odour emission rates from building materials and products so that more specific guidance is available for design.

The rate of emission of metabolic carbon dioxide is well defined and is a function of the level of activity.

Concerted action guidelines have been produced in Europe covering ventilation for health and perceived indoor air quality (CEC 1992). These propose that ventilation rates necessary for health and comfort are calculated separately, with the highest of the two values being used for design purposes. Health values are based on classical dilution calculations (see Chapter 12), while ventilation for comfort is based on the 'decipol' approach.

Metabolic Carbon Dioxide

Carbon dioxide is produced as part of the metabolic process. The rate of

Table 2.5 Energy Production and Emission Rates of Carbon Dioxide for Various Levels of Metabolic Activity *(based on BS 5925 : 1990)*

Activity	Metabolic rate (Watts)	CO_2 production rate (l/s)
Sedentary work	100	0.004
Light work	150-300	0.006-0.012
Moderate work	300-500	0.012-0.020
Heavy work	500-650	0.020-0.026
Very heavy work	650-800	0.026-0.032

emission of metabolic carbon dioxide is well defined and is a function of the level of activity. Typical production rates for various activities are summarised in Table 2.5.

While carbon dioxide, itself, is not harmful, the concentration of metabolically produced CO_2 correlates with metabolic odour intensity. It can thus act as a marker or surrogate to provide an indication of the adequacy of ventilation when occupants themselves represent the dominant source of pollutant.

Following the commencement of occupation in a room or building, the carbon dioxide concentration rises over time to an 'equilibrium' or 'steady state' value. Provided there are no other sources of CO_2 emission, the per occupant rate of ventilation can be estimated from this steady state value (Figure 2.4). In principle, therefore, ventilation rate can be verified against the measured CO_2 value. A steady state CO_2 concentration of 1500 ppm, for example, indicates a ventilation rate of approximately 4 l/s.p, while a value of 800 ppm corresponds to a ventilation rate of approximately 10 l/s.p. This characteristic of metabolic CO_2 forms the basis of carbon dioxide demand controlled ventilation systems. It is especially applicable to transiently and densely occupied buildings such as offices, schools and

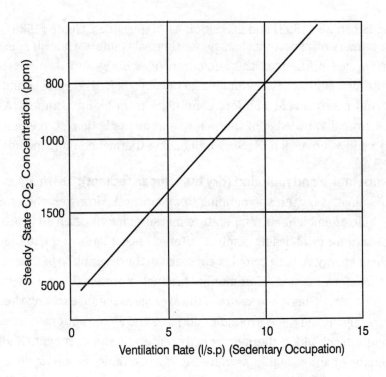

Figure 2.4 Metabolic Carbon Dioxide

theatres. It is not appropriate, however, in buildings in which other sources of pollutant dominate (e.g. tobacco smoke, moisture production, etc.). Neither may it be successful in large or sparsely occupied buildings in which the steady state CO_2 concentration may not be reached. As a rule, if the measured CO_2 concentration is found to be above a given target value, corresponding to the desired ventilation rate, it may be concluded that the rate of ventilation is inadequate. On the other hand, if the CO_2 concentration is found to be at or below the target value, the adequacy of ventilation is not necessarily confirmed, since it is possible that the steady state value has yet to be attained.

Strictly, it is the difference between the indoor and outdoor carbon dioxide concentration that provides a measure of metabolic impact. However, threshold or target CO_2 concentrations are frequently based on an assumption that the ambient outside CO_2 value is approximately 350 to 400 ppm. More detailed information on the application of CO_2 concentration as an indicator of ventilation rate is described by Persily (1994).

Thermal Comfort

Thermal sensation plays a key role in the perception of comfort and, as with other comfort parameters, is highly subjective. A comprehensive review of thermal comfort is published in Chapter 8 of the ASHRAE

Thermal sensation plays a key role in the perception of comfort.

The sensation of thermal comfort is influenced by air speed and the scale of turbulence

Fundamentals (1993) and in Section A1 of the CIBSE Guide (1988). Air is the primary transport mechanism for thermal comfort while air speed and turbulence influences the sensation of cooling and draughts. High infiltration or unnecessary air change rates result in the loss of conditioned air and may prevent comfort conditions from being attained. A good background knowledge of thermal requirements is therefore essential to any ventilation design. Factors influencing thermal comfort include:

Temperature and radiation (dry bulb, mean radiant): Thermal sensation is dominated by the surrounding 'temperature'. However, the standard dry bulb or ambient air temperature measurement is often an insufficient indicator for establishing comfort criteria, since it ignores the influence of radiant energy. A more complex approach to the description of temperature is therefore needed. Commonly this incorporates the 'mean radiant temperature'. This is a measure of the average radiation exchange between the occupant and the surrounding surfaces and is conventionally measured using a black globe thermometer to represent the occupant. Radiation exchange can be highly asymmetric, for example factors such as cold windows may cause local discomfort, by increased radiant cooling.

Relative humidity: In a sedentary environment, about 25% of the body's heat is emitted by transpiration. As ambient air temperature and metabolic activity increases, transpiration losses increase to between 50 and 80% of total body heat emission. Transpiration heat loss is inhibited by high relative humidities, thus creating thermal discomfort. On the other hand dry air at low to normal temperature induces transpiration losses resulting in dehydration Therefore, there is a preferred minimum relative humidity level of typically 30%. In dry cold climates, humidification of the air to acceptable relative humidity levels can be costly.

Air speed and turbulence: The sensation of thermal comfort is influenced by air speed and the scale of turbulence. Where cooling is needed, increased air speed can be used to advantage as, for example, with convective chilled ceilings (see Chapter 7) or with air circulation fans. At other times, draughts cause discomfort by localised cooling. Fanger et al (1985) showed that the number of people dissatisfied with their environment increased substantially as air velocity was increased from 0.1 to 0.5 m/s. In a further study, Fanger et al (1987) demonstrated the impact on thermal comfort of turbulent intensity. Again, discomfort could be caused as turbulent intensity increased.

Clothing: Clothing provides thermal insulation and, as such, has an important influence on acceptable temperature. Choice of clothing can alter comfort preferences by as much as 2 to 3K. The unit used to express

PMV value	Thermal sensation
+3	hot
+2	warm
+1	slightly warm
0	neutral
-1	slightly cool
-2	cool
-3	cold

Table 2.6 Defining Predicted Mean Vote (PMV) (Fanger 1982)

the thermal conductivity of clothing is the 'clo', where 1 clo is equivalent to 0.155 m^2.K/W.

Other parameters: Other parameters such as state of health, level of physical activity, gender, working environment and individual preferences influence perception of thermal comfort.

Perception of thermal comfort: Early test chamber studies conducted in the United States resulted in the development of a thermal sensation scale and the concept of 'predicted mean vote' (PMV). The PMV awarded a numerical value to represent an individual's perceived level of thermal sensation, varying from +3 for hot to -3 for cold. This approach was subsequently used by Fanger (1982) to measure the response of groups of occupants exposed to identical thermal conditions (see Table 2.6). Those not scoring +1, -1 or 0 are deemed to be dissatisfied, from which the predicted percent dissatisfied (PPD) of occupants could be determined. The immediate conclusion of this work was that it was not possible to define a set of thermal conditions that would satisfy everyone. Even when the average of the predicted mean vote was zero, i.e. a neutral thermal environment, 5% of the test occupants were dissatisfied.

The PMV awarded a numerical value to represent an individual's perceived level of thermal sensation, varying from +3 for hot to -3 for cold.

Operative and resultant temperatures: Defining optimum comfort conditions in the home and office has concentrated on combining dry bulb temperature, mean radiant temperature, air speed and relative humidity into an acceptable comfort range. This has been accomplished by means of defining an 'operative' or mean resultant temperature that empirically combines dry bulb and mean radiant temperature with air speed. Equations for operative temperature as defined in ASHRAE Standard 55 (1992) on thermal comfort and the equivalent resultant temperature, as defined in Part A1 of the CIBSE Guide (1988) are summarised in Chapter 12. Essentially the operative and resultant temperatures are derived from the mean of the dry bulb and mean radiant temperature, with an added factor to represent the cooling effect of air speed. The ASHRAE comfort zone

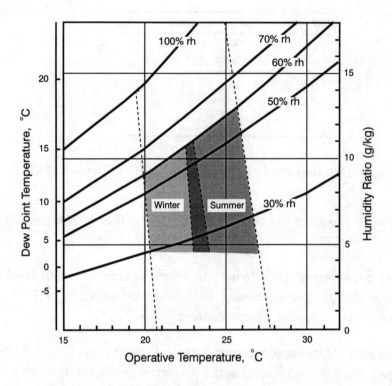

Figure 2.5 Acceptable Thermal Comfort

for 10% PPD, based on the combination of operative temperature with relative humidity is illustrated in Figure 2.5. Operative and resultant temperatures can be approximated by using a pink or grey 50 to 100 mm diameter globe thermometer.

References

ACGIH, *Threshold Limit Values for chemical substances and physical agents and biological exposure indices*, American Conference of Governmental Industrial Hygienists, Cincinnati, 1990.

ASHRAE Fundamentals, American Society of Heating Refrigeration and Air Conditioning Engineers, ISBN 0-910110-97-2, 1993.

ASHRAE Standard 55 *Thermal environmental conditions for human occupancy*, ANSI/ASHRAE Standard 55-92, American Society of Heating Refrigeration and Air Conditioning Engineers, 1992.

ASHRAE Standard 62 *Minimum ventilation for acceptable indoor air quality,* (1989, new revision 1996/7).

Burge P S, Jones P, and Robertson, A S, *Sick building syndrome* Proc Indoor Air, Canada, 1990.

Burge P S, *The sick building syndrome: where are we in 1992?*, Indoor Environment, 1992

Cano-Ruiz J A, Modera M P, Nazaroff W W, *Indoor ozone concentrations: ventilation rate impacts and mechanisms of outdoor concentration attenuation*, Proc. Air Infiltration and Ventilation Centre, 13th AIVC Conference, 1992.

CEC *Guidelines for ventilation requirements in buildings*, European concerted action – indoor air quality and its impact on man – Report No 11, 1992.

CIBSE Guide Volume A, Design Data, Chartered Institution of Building Services Engineers, (UK), ISBN 0 900953 29 2, 1988.

Drerup, O, Mattock, C, Rousseau, D, Salares, V, *Housing for the environmentally hypersensitive (Survey and examples of clean air housing in Canada)*, (CAN) Canada, Mortgage and Housing Corporation, 1990.

Fanger, P.O, *Thermal comfort*, Robert E, Krieger Publishing, USA, 1982.

Fanger P O, and Christensen N K, *Perception of draft in ventilated spaces*, Ergonomics, 1985.

Fanger, P O, Melikov A, Hanzawa H, and Ring J, *Air turbulence and the sensation of draught*, Energy and Buildings, 1987.

Fanger P O, *Introduction of the olf and the decipol units to quantify air pollution perceived by humans indoors and outdoors*, Energy and Buildings, No 12, 1988.

Fanger, P.O., *New principles for a future ventilation standard*, Proc Indoor Air, Finland, 1993.

Hanssen S O, *Increased ventilation reduces general symptoms but not sensory reactions*, proc Indoor Air 1993.

Liddament M W, *Ventilation and building sickness – a brief review*, Air Infiltration Review, 11, No 3, 1990.

Limb M J, *Ventilation and building air-tightness: an international comparison of Standards, Codes of Practice and Regulations*, Air Infiltration and Ventilation Centre, Technical Note 43, 1994.

Limb M J, *Garage ventilation: an annotated bibliography*, Air Infiltration and Ventilation Centre, 1994

Limb M J, *Air intake positioning to avoid contamination of ventilation - an annotated bibliography*, AIVC 1995.

Miller J D, *Microbial contamination of Indoor Air*, Proc 5th Jacques Cartier Conference, 1992.

Persily A K, *Ventilation, carbon dioxide and ASHRAE Std 62*, NIST Report, 1993.

Saum D W, Osborne M C, *Radon mitigation effects of passive stacks in residential new construction,* Proceedings of the 5th International Conference on Indoor Air Quality and climate, Toronto, Volume 3, 1990.

Sundell J, *On the association between building ventilation characteristics, some indoor environmental exposures, some allergic manifestations and subjective symptom reports,* Indoor Air Supplement No2/94, 1994.

Vaculik F, and Shaw C Y, *Managing indoor air quality through the use of HVAC systems*, National Research Council of Canada Report NRCC 38546, 1995.

Weschler C J, Shields H C, Naik D V, *Indoor ozone exposures*, JAPCA, No 39, 1989.

World Heath Organisation, *Air quality guidelines for Europe*, WHO Regional Pubs, European Series No.23, 1989

Wilson D, *Accuracy and realism of ASHRAE handbook estimates of exhaust gas contamination of nearby air intakes,* ASHRAE Winter Meeting, January 1995.

Yaglou, C P, and Witheridge W. N. (1937) *Ventilation requirements*, ASHRAE Trans 1937 pp 423-435.

3 The Energy Impact of Ventilation and Air Infiltration

Definitions Relating to Energy Impact
Estimating Energy Impact
Energy Impact of Ventilation and Air Infiltration
The Potential for Reducing Energy Impact

Summary and Introduction

Ventilation and infiltration energy loss accounts for an important proportion of the total energy transport from a building. Sometimes such losses are intentional, for example when excess heat is vented from a process or activity. At other times, this loss may be directly associated with demands imposed on a building's space heating (or cooling system). When thermal conditioning is needed to compensate for either uncontrollable or unnecessarily excessive air change rate, an energy penalty is imposed. Evidence points to substantial potential for reducing ventilation energy demand. Implementation of energy saving methods relies on an understanding of the air leakage performance of buildings and minimising the need for ventilation. Controlled ventilation, especially during times when conditioning energy is needed to match demand, will further reduce the energy load. In theory, additional energy reduction is possible by using ventilation heat recovery systems (see Chapter 6). However, much depends on the severity of climate, the amount of energy needed to drive the system and the quality of building air tightness.

The energy statistics of OECD countries shows that the percentage of primary energy used in non-industrial buildings (dwellings and commercial buildings etc.) varies from country to country from 30 to 50% (IEA 1994). Ultimately, a significant proportion of this energy is dissipated from the building in the departing air stream. As buildings become more thermally efficient, air change by ventilation and air infiltration is expected to become the dominant heating and cooling loss mechanism in buildings of the next Century (Kohonen 1994). For these reasons it is vital to understand the role that air change plays in contributing to energy loss and to identify methods of improving the energy efficiency of ventilation. Much of the activity in this area is still on-going since this task is complicated by the diverse range of building types, climatic exposure and construction quality.

As buildings become more thermally efficient, air change by ventilation and air infiltration is expected to become the dom,inant heating and cooling loss mechanism in buildings of the next Century

While there are undoubtedly buildings that operate at the extreme efficiency end of ventilation performance, if the building stock is taken as a whole, there is much that can be accomplished to improve energy performance.

Information about energy impact and potential solutions is needed to set the agenda for energy strategies, environmental policies, standards development and legislation.

This potential for improvement has important implications both at the policy or strategic level and at the individual building or consumer level. From the policy aspect, information about energy impact and potential solutions is needed to set the agenda for energy strategies, environmental policies, standards development and legislation. Of particular significance is the impact of air change on primary energy consumption and carbon dioxide emission. Information is also needed about the potential to reduce energy impact without impairing indoor air quality. Other policy issues cover the cost of implementing national or regional schemes. At the consumer level, the cost of implementing energy conservation measures, especially in existing buildings, usually rests with the building owner or occupier. At this level, benefits in relation to payback period and enhanced comfort levels must usually be specified.

Since there is still so much uncertainty about actual air change losses that occur from individual buildings, it is difficult to make a direct estimate of the energy impact of ventilation and air infiltration. As a result, a suitable datum from which strategic planning for improving the energy efficiency of ventilation has proved difficult to establish. Efforts to overcome these difficulties are progressing. In Sweden, for example, an analysis has focused on identifying ventilation rates in a representative cross section (Norlen et al 1993) while, in the United States, the energy impact of air change in domestic and non domestic buildings is currently being determined (Sherman et al, 1993, VanBronkhorst 1995). A general review of energy loss through ventilation and air infiltration is also being co-ordinated through the AIVC (Orme 1995). The purpose of this Chapter is to outline current estimates of the energy impact of ventilation and to review the potential for future reduction.

3.1 Definitions Relating to Energy Impact

Several important definitions relate to the energy impact of air change; these are referred to in Figure 3.1 and include:

'Conditioned' energy: Conditioned energy represents the amount of energy which is actually absorbed by (taken out of) the air stream and building fabric as a consequence of the space heating or cooling process.

Incidental gains: Some heating arises as a result of incidental gains. This

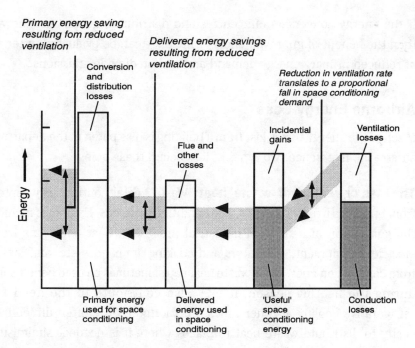

Figure 3.1 Impact of Ventilation Control Delivered and Primary Energy Consumption

comes from solar radiation and internal sources, including electrical equipment and occupants. In the heating season, these gains can reduce the need for space heating and are therefore beneficial. In Summer months, these gains may be undesirable, resulting in the need for refrigerative cooling. Incidental gains are essentially fixed according to ambient conditions (i.e. they are beyond the control of the occupant).

Delivered energy: This is the amount of metered energy, used in meeting conditioning demand. For a given conditioning load, the amount of delivered energy consumed depends on the conversion efficiency of the heating or cooling system. Electrical conversion efficiency is typically very high, amounting to over 90% for storage systems and up to 100% for convective and radiant heaters. Oil systems have efficiencies of 60-70% or more while, depending on type, gas appliances have efficiencies between 60-90%. Solid fuel efficiencies can be much lower and may vary between 35-70%.

Primary energy: This is the energy expended at the power utility to meet downstream demand. Losses arise from conversion and distribution. In the case of fossil fuel to electrical energy conversion, 70% of the primary energy is typically discharged as heat (and CO_2 emission) by the generating process. Losses associated with nuclear and hydro power are largely confined to distribution losses. Gas and oil 'losses' are associated with energy needed for refining and distribution.

If the energy conversion efficiencies and distribution losses are known, then the benefit of improved energy efficiency can be evaluated in terms of reduced primary energy demand and carbon dioxide emissions.

Airborne Energy Loss

Much of the energy that is lost from a building is dissipated in the departing air stream. In essence two types of loss occur, these being:

The loss or venting of 'waste' heat: 'Waste' heat is continuously vented from buildings irrespective of space conditioning needs. Examples include the generation of heat from industrial processes, heat emissions from electrical equipment, computers and cooking appliances etc. and losses from combustion flues. While waste heat can sometimes be used beneficially during the heating season, it may also contribute to the need for refrigerative cooling at other times. Furthermore, it is often difficult or costly to distribute waste heat to places where it is needed. Minimising waste heat losses is dependent on improving the energy efficiencies of appliances and processes. Commercially, much activity is taking place in this area, especially in relation to office equipment and computers.

The loss of thermally conditioned energy: This type of loss is associated with the escape of intentionally conditioned (heated or cooled) air from a space by ventilation and air infiltration; this accounts for as much as 30 to 50% of thermal conditioning demand. It is an assessment of this particular aspect of airborne energy loss that forms the basis of this Chapter. Measures to contain this loss directly produce energy savings.

Thermal Balance

Referring to Figure 3.1, the total thermal input to the building is derived from the combined value of incidental gains and space conditioning energy. This inflow of heat is balanced by ventilation and building transmission losses (conduction, convection and radiation). The 'balance' point is ultimately reflected by the thermal conditions (mean and radiant temperature) within the Building. If insufficient heat is applied to the space, then the balance temperature can become too low for thermal comfort. On the other hand, if the heat gain is too high, then the inside environment can become too hot. Since incidental gains are essentially fixed according to outside solar conditions and indoor thermal sources, any reduction in ventilation (or transmission) loss that does not exceed the space conditioning load, transfers, in direct proportion, to a reduced space conditioning need. This results in a corresponding reduction in delivered and primary energy demand. Such a benefit only ceases to apply if any reduction in building heat loss (i.e. through reduced ventilation or improved thermal insulation) reduces the space conditioning need to zero. At this point, thermal needs will be met by incidental gains only. Minimising the need for space conditioning energy by utilising "free" gains or "free" cooling is one of the challenges of passive 'solar' design.

3.2 Estimating Energy Impact

While, in theory, the calculation of energy impact is straightforward, in practice it is a difficult exercise to undertake. This is because, although the outdoor climate (temperature and wind) is normally fairly well defined and information about the building stock is largely available, there is much uncertainty about the actual level of air change that takes place in buildings and the indoor air temperature that is maintained during periods of space heating or cooling. Because of these uncertainties, it is necessary to base estimates of energy impact on indirect assumptions about ventilation rates and indoor climate. Confidence is improved by applying a variety of essentially independent methods and analysing areas of overlap or agreement.

It is necessary to base estimated of energy impact on inidrect assumptions about ventilation rates and indoor climate. Confidence is improved by applying a variety of essentially independent methods and analysing areas of overlap or agreement.

To estimate energy impact, it is necessary to know:

- the mass flow rate of air into and out of the building,
- the difference in 'enthalpy' between the incoming and outgoing air streams.

Alternatively, energy impact may be evaluated by means of an energy balance approach in which transmission losses are subtracted from total building thermal gain. Enthalpy change (see Chapter 12) may be analysed in terms of 'sensible' (dry bulb) temperature difference (i.e. as in the case of conventional space heating) and 'latent' heat which takes into account the energy associated with changing the moisture content of the air (e.g. refrigerative cooling and humidification systems). Cooling energy calculations are made more complex by the need to consider latent energy loads in addition to thermal (sensible) loads. Also, unlike heating, incidental gains add to the need for cooling. As a consequence, the energy impact of air change in air conditioned commercial type buildings can be extremely difficult to evaluate, especially since, buildings are so diverse and very little is understood about the factors that influence cooling load in buildings in general. Methods to evaluate cooling loads are described by Colliver (1995).

In addition to conditioning load, electrical energy is expended by mechanical ventilation fans. Typically, good designs require 1 Watt or less

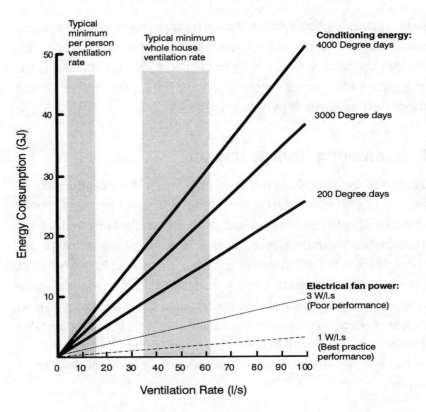

Figure 3.2 Examples of Energy Impact

of power to provide each l/s of air to a space. Inefficient systems may require 3 Watts or more to provide the same air flow rate (see Chapter 5, Section 2). Examples of energy impact, comparing consumption with climate and – when applicable – fan energy, are illustrated in Figure 3.2. The two shaded bands represent the typical minimum ventilation range for individual occupants in an office environment and the typical minimum range for individual dwellings.

Estimating Mass Flow Rate

A generalised approach to the estimation of energy impact, especially at the macro-level, must usually be based on very broad assumptions about climate and mass flow rate.

A generalised approach to the estimation of energy impact, especially at the macro-level (i.e. representing the building stock as a whole), must usually be based on very broad assumptions about climate and mass flow rate. Various methods are used to infer the mass flow or air change rate in buildings; these include:

Direct measurement: Tracer gas techniques may be used to measure ventilation and air infiltration rates in individual buildings (see Chapter 11). This approach is satisfactory at the 'micro' scale to determine airborne losses in specific buildings.

Estimated average air change rate: In the absence of wide scale ventilation measurements, air change data for 'macro' scale regional or national building stock studies must be estimated by other means. One such approach is to base assumptions on typical data available for each building type. Measured air change rates, for example, in many types of offices and dwellings vary between 0.5-1.0 air changes/ hour (ach). Similar air change rates may be inferred from air leakage testing of buildings.

Estimated ventilation rate per occupant: Typical per occupant rates of ventilation in dwellings have been measured in Sweden at 12-18 l/s.p (Norlen et al 1993) By multiplying the per occupant rate by the population, a total mass flow rate for a particular building sector may be approximated and a ventilation energy 'band' determined.

Estimating Enthalpy and Dry Bulb Temperature Difference

Enthalpy difference represents the change in energy content of the air between the incoming and outgoing air streams. In the heating mode, in which no change is made to the moisture content of the air, enthalpy difference translates into dry bulb temperature difference. Under conditions of latent (refrigerative) cooling, in which moisture is extracted from the air, or during humidification in which moisture is added, the latent heat change of the air must also be incorporated into the enthalpy calculation (see Chapter 12). Again, very broad assumptions about typical indoor thermal climate must normally be made, inevitably resulting in a spread of results. Methods include:

Direct measurement: The measurement of indoor and outdoor thermal parameters, on an individual building basis, should present few problems. When combined with the direct measurement of air change, the airborne energy loss from a specific building can be determined directly.

Degree day analysis: The degree day concept provides one method for tracking the variation in temperature difference between the inside and outside of the building throughout a time period. In essence, for heating climates, it is the number of degrees of temperature difference, averaged over a one day period, that the mean outdoor temperature is below a given base temperature. In climates in which cooling and dehumidification of the incoming air is necessary, a similar concept is used to quantify the enthalpy of the air above a given base temperature and moisture loading. On an annual basis, the energy impact of ventilation can be calculated by estimating the total mass flow of air and combining it with local degree day data. Countries such as the United States of America and Canada are subjected to a wide climatic variation and hence must be divided into

The degree day concept provides one method for tracking the variation in temperature difference between the inside and outside of the building throughout a time period.

separate degree day zones. For many other Countries a single average value is often adequate for a macro-scale study, although much more regional data should be applied to studies on individual or small groups of buildings.

The degree day approach is easy to apply, since degree day data are widely available. It provides a useful method for characterising local climate and is extensively used for general thermal analysis. However, there is little international agreement on base temperature for degree day evaluation methods although it is normally regarded as the air temperature below which space heating would be necessary (or base enthalpy above which refrigerative cooling becomes necessary). In terms of heating need, the base temperature is usually set below comfort temperature to make allowances for the benefit of incidental heat gains which are capable of providing several degrees of temperature rise. In theory, buildings designed to benefit from incidental gains and having good thermal insulation should be represented by a lower base temperature than those with poor insulation. Thus, to achieve further accuracy, buildings should be banded according to their thermal insulation properties (e.g. by reducing the base temperature by one or two degrees for thermally efficient structures). Degree day tables usually provide a simple algorithm to enable the effect of a change of base temperature to be calculated.

Average temperature difference: An alternative to the degree day approach is based on estimating inside/outside temperature difference by making assumptions about indoor air temperature and subtracting the average seasonal (daily or monthly) outdoor air temperature. Energy impact is then calculated using estimates of mass air flow rate multiplied by this temperature difference. Again, some allowance must be made for internal gains.

Hourly weather data may be used to provide more detailed information about the energy impact of ventilation and about the rate of ventilation itself.

Hourly 'bin' analysis: Hourly weather data may be used to provide more detailed information about the energy impact of ventilation and about the rate of ventilation itself. Such data may represent 'design', 'average' or 'extreme' weather years. The data are sorted into a matrix or 'bins' representing the number of hours that specific thermal (or other climate) conditions occur. This approach is extremely useful for design analysis. It is also useful when a building is subjected to both Winter heating and Summer cooling since these two needs can be separated and the requirements for each identified. A further advantage is that 'risk' studies may be undertaken to determine the periods over which thermal climate might deviate from design conditions. In addition, 'bin' analysis may be used to determine the effect of flexible design conditions on overall thermal and energy performance. As an example, Colliver (1995) has applied this

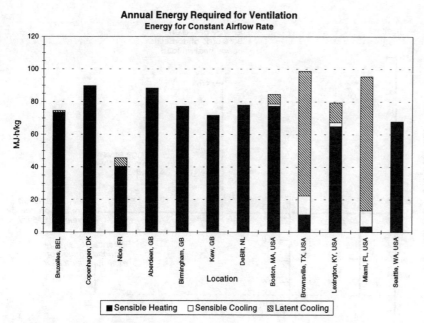

Figure 3.3 Annual Resultant Energy Demand for Various Locations (Colliver 1995)

approach to estimate the energy needed to condition each kg/h of incoming air, to a heating set point of 18°C and a cooling set point of 25.6°C at 40% relative humidity for 43 sites throughout Europe and the United States.

Examples of the annual resultant energy demand are illustrated for a selection of these sites in Figure 3.3. The energy impact of varying the set-point values was also evaluated, to enable allowances to be made for internal heat gains or adjustments to comfort criteria. By multiplying the energy needed to condition each kilogram of air by the actual ventilation rate, the total ventilation energy impact of a building or group of buildings may be determined. Disadvantages include the need to use localised data that might not be as widely available as degree day information. Hourly data requires more computational effort, thus increasing the complexity of energy analysis.

Energy balance methods: Energy balance methods rely on good knowledge about the energy supplied to a building and the amount of incidental thermal gains and losses. Any deficit between the inflow and outflow of energy is attributed to airborne loss. Only very approximate estimates are possible. A common assumption, for example, is that ventilation energy loss amounts to between 30 and 50% of space heating energy. Applying this approximation is a useful independent check against which the results of other methods can be compared.

Energy balance methods rely on good knowledge about the energy supplied to a building and the amount of incidental thermal gains and losses. Any deficit between the inflow and outflow of energy is attributed to airborne loss.

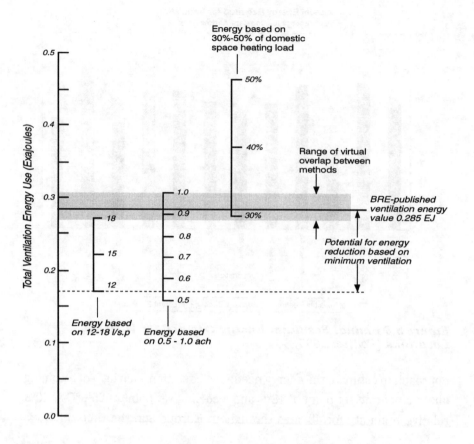

Figure 3.4 Comparison of Evaluation Techniques (UK dwellings)

3.3 Energy Impact of Ventilation and Air Infiltration

The strategic research plan of the IEA Executive Committee on Energy Conservation in Buildings and Community Systems (Kohonen 1994) concludes that a quarter of all energy is consumed in dwellings. This compares with a value of 1/12 th for the remaining types of non industrial buildings. Ventilation energy loss from dwellings has been evaluated as part of an AIVC study (Orme 1995) by applying the various methods of estimating mass air flow, temperature and enthalpy difference. As an example, the results for UK dwellings are illustrated in Figure 3.4. These are based on the calculation of 'bands' of possible energy which allow for the range in uncertainty, especially of air change rate. The methods applied include:

(i) The estimation of mass flow rate assuming:

• an average air change rate per dwelling of 0.5-1.0 ach ,

• an average ventilation rate equivalent to 12-18 l/s.p,

(ii)   climate based on 2500 degree days,

(iii)   a ventilation energy use equivalent to between 30-50% of space heating energy,

(iv)   an independent evaluation based knowledge about average indoor and outdoor temperatures combined with information about typical ventilation rates (Shorrock et al 1992).

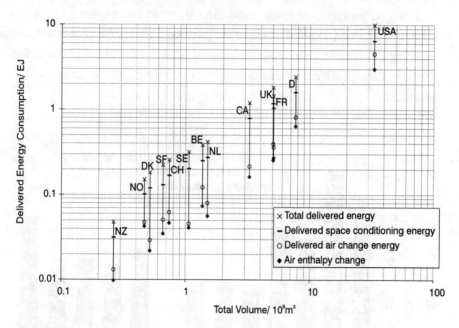

(a) Energy Consumption

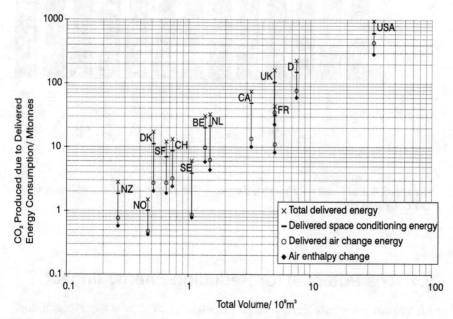

(b) CO₂ Production

Figure 3.5 Estimated Energy Impact of Ventilation and Infiltration in Individual Dwellings in AIVC Countries

A fairly narrow band of near overlap, consistent with the independent result and best available information about the housing stock was obtained. Results using similar techniques for the housing stock of all AIVC countries are consumed in each country is related to climate and size of housing stock. The corresponding energy impact of individual dwellings is illustrated in Figure 3.6.

The calculation of energy impact of ventilation and air infiltration in commercial buildings is made especially difficult by diversity of types, thermal gains and general occupation patterns.

The calculation of energy impact of ventilation and air infiltration in commercial buildings is made especially difficult by diversity of types, thermal gains and general occupation patterns. Research in this area is on-going but initial results indicate proportionately similar potential as for dwellings in relation to ventilation energy consumption and savings potential.

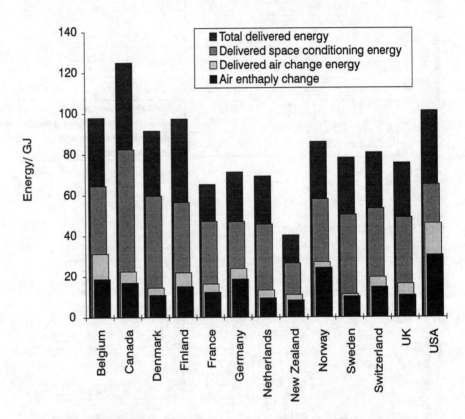

Figure 3.6 Estimated Energy Impact for Individual Dwellings in AIVC Countries

3.4 The Potential for Reducing Energy Impact

An important strategic question is: what, if any, is the potential for reducing the energy impact of air change without detriment to health and indoor comfort? One way to answer this question would be to compare the ventilation energy performance of 'best practice' buildings with that of current buildings. Such studies are currently on-going. A further method is to compare the energy estimates of existing buildings with the theoretical limit of energy improvement that is possible while still retaining a good indoor climate. For example, ASHRAE Standard 62 (1989) prescribes a minimum ventilation rate of 0.35 ach or 7.5 l/s.p, whichever is the greater. Referring back to the UK results (Figure 3.4) and allowing for a considerable safety margin of 12 l/s.p or approximately 0.5 ach, a 40% ventilation energy reduction is theoretically achievable. Theoretically, in dwellings, a further 70% heat recovery from the exhaust air could reduce energy demand to approximately 20% of the current value illustrated in Figures 3.5 (a) and (b). These indicate the best available estimates for:

What, if any, is the potential for reducing the energy impact of air change without detriment to health and indoor comfort?

- the conditioning energy (for ventilation and air infiltration),
- the corresponding delivered energy,
- the total delivered energy,
- the resultant primary energy (for ventilation and air infiltration),
- the resultant CO_2 emission.

(see also Chapter 5).

References

ASHRAE Standard 62 *Minimum ventilation for acceptable indoor air quality*, (1989, new revision 1996/7).

Colliver D, *Energy requirements for conditioning ventilation air*, AIVC Technical Note 47, Air Infiltration and Ventilation Centre 1995.

IEA, *Energy balances of OECD countries 1991-1992*, Organisation for Economic Co-operation and Development/International Energy Agency, Paris, France 1994.

Kohonen R, *Energy conservation in building and community systems - strategy plan 1994-97*, International Energy Agency BCS Implementing Agreement, 1994.

Norlen U, Andersson K, *The indoor climate in the Swedish housing stock*, Swedish Council for Building Research Document D10 : 1993.

Orme M S, *Estimating the energy impact of ventilation and infiltration in AIVC member countries*, 16th AIVC Conference Proc. Supplement, USA, 1995

Sherman M, Matson N, *Ventilation-energy liabilities in US dwellings*, Proc AIVC, 14th AIVC Conference, *Energy Impact of Ventilation and Air Infiltration*, 1993.

Shorrock L D, Henderson G, Bown J H F, *Domestic energy fact file*, UK Building Research Establishment, 1992.

VanBronkhorst D, Persily A K, Emmerich S J, *Energy impacts of air leakage in US office buildings*, Proc AIVC 16th Conference *Implementing the results of ventilation research*, 1995.

4 Design Criteria

> **Design Parameters**
> **Ventilation Need**
> **Design Constraints**
> **Design Variables**

Summary and Introduction

Designing for energy efficient and reliable ventilation extends beyond system sizing. System performance is influenced by a vast range of other parameters covering climate, building type, construction, air-tightness and ventilation strategy. Acceptability by occupants, ease of use, reliability and noise performance are also important aspects of the design process. Many Codes of Practice and Standards are available which, when followed, should assist in securing reliable ventilation design and performance.

Good ventilation design is essential to ensure the reliable provision of fresh air to building occupants.

Good ventilation design is essential to ensure the reliable provision of fresh air to building occupants. In particular, ventilation design should satisfy the following basic requirements:

- comply with relevant Building Regulations and associated Standards and Codes of Practice,
- satisfy minimum ventilation rates for optimum health and comfort,
- be capable of removing pollutants at source before they disperse into occupied areas,
- be compatible with the building in which the system is installed,
- provide high rates of ventilation for cooling purposes or for rapidly purging polluted air from a building,
- incorporate occupant or automatic controls to ensure that the ventilation rate can be adjusted to meet changing demand,
- be reliable,
- be capable of being cleaned and maintained,
- comply with smoke and fire control requirements,
- be cost and energy efficient.

Since such a wide range of parameters is involved, there is rarely a unique solution to a particular ventilation design. Instead judgement must be based on the specific needs of each building. The purpose of this Chapter is to review the key parameters that should be considered as part of the design process.

4.1 Design Parameters

Essential design parameters are summarised in Figure 4.1. These are reviewed in terms of need, constraints, and design variables.

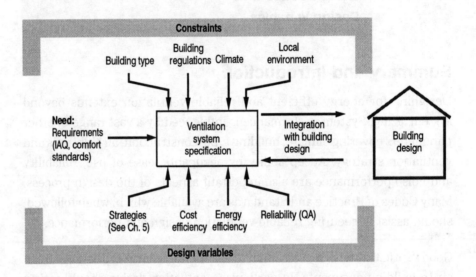

Figure 4.1 Essential Design Parameters

4.2 Ventilation Need

Ultimately the design ventilation rate must reflect the requirements of indoor air quality and comfort conditions.

An essential aspect of the design process is to identify how much fresh air is to be provided to a space. Too little will result in poor indoor air quality, while too much could place an unacceptable burden on the building's space heating or cooling plant. Ultimately the design ventilation rate must reflect the requirements of indoor air quality and comfort conditions. Invariably needs will change according to occupancy pattern, pollution emission rates and seasonal changes in climate, therefore provision to control the rate of ventilation to meet prevailing demand is usually necessary. Typically, design may be based on a minimum need, as set by the relevant Regulations or Code of Practice, with additional amounts being based on specific pollutant problems and any requirement for ventilation cooling. Individual pollutant sources should be identified and vented at source, to minimise the requirement for general ventilation of a space. Guidelines for calculating the rate of ventilation needed to control pollutant concentration by dilution are summarised in Chapter 12, Section 8.

4.3 Design Constraints

The approach to ventilation design is influenced by many design constraints. These set the type of ventilation system that will be acceptable, system cost and energy performance. Important constraints include:

Compliance with Regulations and Standards

Many countries have introduced ventilation related Regulations, Standards and Codes of Practice (Limb 1995). To fulfil the needs of best practice, it is important that these requirements and recommendations are followed. Comprehensive ventilation, health and indoor air quality guidance is regularly produced and updated as part of ASHRAE Standard 62(1989) in the United States. Within the European Union, ventilation related Standards are being developed by Task Group 156, while, in Scandinavia, the Nordic Committee on Building Regulations (NYB 1991) has published comprehensive ventilation guidelines.

To fulfil the needs of best practice, it is important that these requirements and recommendations are followed.

Requirements are often 'prescriptive' in the sense that the minimum rate of ventilation or the minimum size of ventilation openings is specified. Air flow rates are typically indicated for different types of room, occupant density or activity. Additional 'air quality' requirements relate the amount of extra ventilation needed to deal with individual contaminant sources that may be present. Sometimes a choice may be given to select either a 'prescriptive' or an 'air quality' approach to estimating ventilation need.

In general there is a strong linkage between Standards covering the requirements for ventilation and those associated with other aspects of energy efficiency and comfort within buildings (see Figure 4.2). Adherence to this linkage is vital for securing reliable ventilation. Linked topics include:

Health: Requirements cover the minimum ventilation needed to avoid injury to health. Values are largely prescribed according to building type, nature of pollutants, emission rates and acceptable exposure levels (see Chapter 2).

Energy efficiency: Standards cover the avoidance of excessive energy waste. In some cases there may be a requirement for ventilation heat recovery (e.g. BFS 1988, Sweden).

Comfort: Requirements or recommendations may cover thermal comfort (e.g. ASHRAE Standard 55) and odour intensity (Fanger 1988) and the presence of draughts (see also Chapter 2).

Ventilation Strategies: Standards often cover the type of ventilation appropriate to specific applications (e.g. enclosing polluting processes,

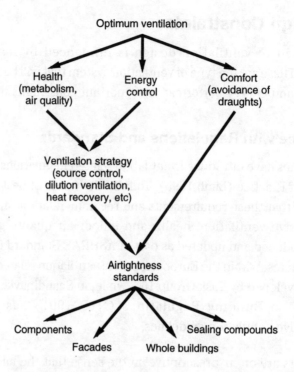

Figure 4.2 Linkage Between Standards Needed to Secure Optimum Indoor Air Quality and Energy Efficiency

extracting from kitchens and bathrooms, provision of fresh air supply to occupied spaces and the sizing of ventilation systems).

Air-tightness: Energy efficient ventilation performance can be destroyed if the air-tightness of the structure is not compatible with ventilation strategy. Several countries have now introduced standards or recommendations covering the air-tightness performance of buildings (see Figure 4.3). Similarly, various Standards cover the air-tightness, durability and performance of the various components used in building construction (e.g. the performance windows, doors, sealants and sealing components).

Building Type

Ventilation need varies according to building type. Typical requirements for the main building sectors include:

Dwellings: Dwellings represent a major proportion of buildings throughout the world. While having generally smaller floor areas than commercial or industrial premises, dwellings are occupied for considerably longer periods and account for much space conditioning demand. The main pollutant is often moisture which is generated from cooking, washing and clothes drying. Other pollutants include combustion products from gas cookers and flueless heaters, tobacco smoke and organic emissions from furnishings

> *Energy efficient ventilation performance can be destroyed if the air-tightness of the structure is not compatible with ventilation strategy.*

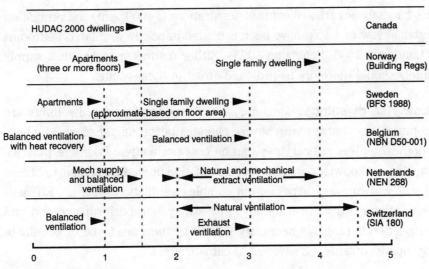

Figure 4.3 Comparison of Air-tightness Standards and Recommendations

and fabrics. Ventilation air may also be needed to provide oxygen to combustion appliances.

Good design in the home is normally based on interzonal ventilation in which either extract fans or passive natural ventilation stacks are located in the 'wet' areas. The resultant suction pressure induces air flow from other parts of the building to the extract zones. In rooms in which combustion flues are installed and/or in which combustion air is drawn from the room itself, air vents or supply fans must be incorporated to relieve excess suction pressures. (see Chapter 12 for vent sizing). Can/CGSB (1995), for example sets a maximum allowable under pressure of 5 Pa. Ideally combustion appliances should be 'room sealed' i.e. the supply of combustion air and removal of flue gases should be isolated from the room itself. As with many other types of buildings, high rates of ventilation may be needed for rapid purging of pollutants or for Summer cooling. This is typically achieved by window opening.

Extract systems can increase radon concentration because the induced suction pressure draws more of the radon through the foundations. Control is normally best accomplished by combining air-tight foundation construction with a sub-floor vent (passive or active) to outside (e.g. Saum et al 1990). country specific design guidelines are normally available. Although mechanical supply ventilation can impede the flow of radon gas into a dwelling, it is not usually a recommended method for dwellings in cold climates since it can force humid air, generated by household activities, into the building fabric where condensation may occur. Notwithstanding problems associated with flues and soil gases, a slight under-pressure is generally preferred in dwellings to prevent moisture from penetrating into the building fabric.

Ideally combustion appliances should be "room sealed" i.e. the supply of combustion air and removal of flue gases should be isolated from the room itself.

High metabolic carbon dioxide concentrations (>4000 ppm) and ventilation rates as low as 1 l/s.p have been recorded in poorly ventilated bedrooms (Lundqvist 1985, Fehlmann 1993). Either natural or mechanical supply inlets should therefore be provided direct to these rooms.

Poor site practice and lack of knowledge concerning installation procedure and air-tightness needs can ruin any benefit from complex ventilation systems.

Low rise dwellings: Mechanical systems for low rise dwellings are common in countries with severe climates but in milder climates where the need is less critical, they can be cost prohibitive. Poor site practice and lack of knowledge concerning installation procedure and air-tightness needs can ruin any benefit from complex ventilation systems. Efficient legislative control covering air-tightness, system performance and site inspection is probably necessary if such systems are to be of benefit to occupants outside the severest of climatic areas.

High rise dwellings (apartment buildings): If each dwelling unit incorporates a self contained ventilation system, care must be taken to ensure that inlets to dwellings (windows, air vents or mechanical air intakes) are not contaminated by ventilation outlets or combustion flue gases from adjacent dwellings. For this reason, centrally ducted ventilation and heating systems may be necessary, especially in gas or oil heated properties.

Commercial (office) buildings: Office buildings tend to be much more densely occupied than dwellings, with typical densities of one or more occupants to each 10m^2 of floor space. Ventilation needs tend to differ from those to be found in the home. Pollutants come from occupancy, electrical equipment (ozone), excessive heat generation and outside traffic fumes. Moisture production tends to be minimal and open flue combustion appliances are uncommon. Occupant pollutants typically include metabolic carbon dioxide emission, odour and tobacco smoke. Increasingly, smoking is being prohibited from office spaces and hence environmental tobacco smoke is becoming less of a problem. Smoking lounges (Straub et al 1992) have, in some instances, fulfilled the need of smokers.

Some ventilation designs track CO2 concentrations as a means to optimise the rate of fresh air supply.

When heat generation is not a problem and tobacco smoking is restricted, occupant generated carbon dioxide and related metabolic odour is often the dominant pollutant. Some ventilation designs track CO_2 concentrations as a means to optimise the rate of fresh air supply (see Chapter 5). Unlike dwellings, mechanically ventilated commercial buildings may operate at a slight over-pressure. This restricts the inflow of air to supply openings,thus enabling the effective use of filtration (see Chapter 8).

Large offices: Considerable heat is generated in large office complexes, often resulting in a need for refrigerative cooling, even in mild and cold climates (see Chapter 7). Heating and cooling systems may have to be zoned to accommodate the differing conditioning needs of perimeter and central zones. In some climates, natural ventilation based on atrium or chimney design may be possible to meet cooling needs (see Chapter 5, Section 1).

Small to medium size offices: Small to medium sized offices often represent the typical working environment outside major city centres. These include buildings up to approximately four storeys in height with the floor area at each level in the range of 1000m². In mild to moderate climates, natural ventilation combined with passive cooling measures (see Chapter 7) may often be possible. Ultimately, much depends on the sources of internal heat gain and on the quality of building design used to avoid excessive Summer solar gains.

Other buildings: Special requirements apply to other types of buildings; these include:

Schools
Schools are dominated by high occupant loads, very transient occupation and high levels of metabolic activity. In the absence of high heat loads, the dominant pollutant is derived from metabolism. In some countries, CO_2 demand control systems and passive infra-red detectors have been used to regulate the rate of ventilation (Norrel 1991).

Atria buildings and shopping malls
These types of buildings often enclose relatively large open spaces. The heat generated in this space by solar gains can sometimes be used to advantage to drive natural ventilation (see Chapter 5, Section 1). Design difficulties can include over heating and contaminant ingress from traffic fumes. Poor air-tightness, especially at roof level, may cause high suction pressures to be generated, resulting in high velocity draughts through entrances. Careful analysis of design using thermal modelling and computational fluid dynamic techniques may prove necessary to avoid expensive design errors (see Chapter 12, Section 9).

Hospitals
Ventilation design in hospitals must aim to provide fresh air to patient areas, combined with clean room design for operating theatres. The need to avoid cross contamination is important by establishing a well defined interzonal air flow pattern. Air-tightness across contamination barriers is needed to ensure that pressure differentials are sustained.

Industrial buildings
Ventilation in industry poses many special problems which usually need to be assessed on an individual basis. Contaminant sources are varied but

normally well defined. Threshold Limit Values are set for typical industrial pollutants. These govern the maximum pollutant concentration and exposure time to which an individual may be exposed. TLV's are set primarily for health and do not necessarily consider annoyance problems such as discomfort caused by odour. High heat loads in process areas are common and may need to be controlled by high rates of ventilation or refrigerative cooling. Specialist applications include clean room ventilation, the avoidance of cross contamination between clean and polluted spaces and protecting of the outdoor environment from process pollution.

Climate

For ventilation purposes, climate can be classified in terms of mild, moderate and severe (both heating and cooling).

The amount of energy needed to heat or cool air to comfort levels is dependent on the severity of climate. Thus climate has a significant impact on the choice of strategy, especially in relation to cost and complexity (see Figure 4.4). For ventilation purposes, climate can be classified in terms of mild, moderate and severe (both heating and cooling).

Mild climate: This type of climate may be typified by a minimum heating or cooling season, perhaps with an annual degree day value of less than 2000. Ventilation heat loss is largely insignificant and therefore the need to restrict ventilation flow is marginal. In this type of climate it may be difficult to justify complex ventilation systems on the basis of energy conservation alone. Air-tightness requirements are not necessarily essential and air infiltration may not be a significant concern for many building types. Ventilation by window opening may be satisfactory, except when the outside environment is noisy or polluted, or when high heat loads are generated within the building.

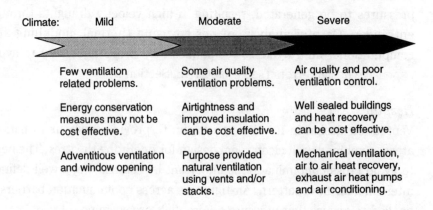

Climate:	Mild	Moderate	Severe
	Few ventilation related problems.	Some air quality ventilation problems.	Air quality and poor ventilation control.
	Energy conservation measures may not be cost effective.	Airtightness and improved insulation can be cost effective.	Well sealed buildings and heat recovery can be cost effective.
	Adventitious ventilation and window opening	Purpose provided natural ventilation using vents and/or stacks.	Mechanical ventilation, air to air heat recovery, exhaust air heat pumps and air conditioning.

Figure 4.4 Influence of Climate on Selection of Ventilation Strategy

Moderate climate: This type of climate may be represented by an annual degree day range of between approximately 2000 and 3000. The energy needed to heat or cool air may be seasonally significant but energy saving measures (such as ventilation heat recovery) could have a lengthy pay-back period. Space heating or cooling (especially for small to medium sized buildings) is unnecessary for large parts of the year. Provided there is no security risk or outside noise, high rates of air exchange should be possible by window opening during these periods. Good building design and control of internal heat loads should minimise the need for refrigerative cooling in all but large buildings or those exposed to poor outside environments. A hybrid approach to ventilation may be considered in which natural ventilation combined with passive cooling is applied whenever possible.

Severe climate (heating and cooling): Severe climates apply to locations with annual heating and cooling degree days of over 3000. This would include extended cold Winters and/or excessively hot Summers. Conditioning loads are significant, resulting in seasonal peaks in energy demand. Refrigerative cooling often cannot be avoided when outside temperatures are high. Building structures should be air-tight and ventilation should be minimised to conserve conditioned air. Internal polluting sources must be eliminated to reduce the need for excessive ventilation. Sensible and latent heat recovery are more likely to be energy and cost efficient than in milder climate zones.

Local Environment

The local outdoor environment further influences ventilation planning. Important categories include:

Heavily industrialised and inner city locations: These locations can suffer from poor outdoor air quality derived from traffic fumes and industrial pollutants. Ventilation systems might, therefore, need to incorporate some form of filtration, especially to remove particulates. Outside noise from passing traffic can be excessive thus restricting the potential for window opening. Finally, 'heat island' effects may increase the need for air conditioning.

Adjacent buildings: Adjacent buildings could create conflict in relation to pre-existing air intakes and exhaust points. Surrounding buildings may also influence the local wind regime thus affecting natural ventilation and air infiltration. Guidelines on air intake positioning are regularly updated in the ASHRAE Fundamentals (1993).

Suburban areas: These are principally residential areas located away from city or town centres. This type of location should not materially add any constraint to ventilation strategy.

Rural areas: These areas are sparsely populated and do not suffer from urban pollution. Local pollutants, however, might include high pollen concentrations and fungal spores. Filtration may be necessary for individuals who are hypersensitive to these pollutants. Wind speeds in exposed areas are much greater than elsewhere thus discomfort from cold draughts in leaky buildings could occur.

Building Integrity – Air-tightness

Building air-tightness must be matched to meet the performance of the ventilation system.

Building air-tightness must be matched to meet the performance of the ventilation system. Efficient ventilation systems need an air-tight building envelope, in which the only sources of openings are intentionally provided. It is necessary to be aware of the detrimental effect of excessive air leakage and of the potential sources of poor air-tightness performance. Good site practice is essential and some countries now impose air-tightness requirements to ensure the quality of construction.

Building air-tightness varies considerably depending on the method of construction and the quality of site practice. Sometimes apparently identical buildings can exhibit completely different air-tightness performance. The air-tightness performance of a building is often specified in terms of an air leakage at an artificially induced pressure (e.g. 50 Pa) or in terms of an equivalent leakage area (see Chapters 11 and 12). Examples of typically acceptable air-tightness ranges for specific ventilation strategies are summarised in Figure 4.5.

Sources of Air Leakage

Air penetrates through porous building materials and through joints in the building structure, therefore, air-tight construction techniques must focus on these aspects.

Air penetrates through porous building materials and through joints in the building structure, therefore, air-tight construction techniques must focus on these aspects. Different construction materials exhibit different leakage characteristics. Irrespective of construction material, a modern building is normally of double skin construction in which the inner and outer leaves are separated by a layer of insulation. Air-tightness is dependent on good sealing of the inner leaf. The building outer shell, especially of dwellings, may be intentionally less air-tight than the inner leaf so that any air that enters the building shell from inside can escape to the outside. This reduces the risk of moist warm indoor air from cooling and condensing in the building fabric.

The method of sealing for good air-tightness is dependent on the material

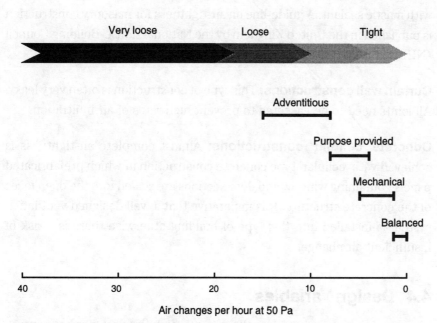

Figure 4.5 Preferred Air-tightness Range According to Strategy (dwellings)

used for construction. Examples described by Elmroth and Levin (1983) include:

Timber construction (typically dwellings): Structural timber construction is essentially non air-tight with the potential for substantial air leakage at building joints. To accomplish air-tight construction, a continuous internal air/vapour barrier, normally of polyethylene construction is necessary. This barrier must be planned at the design stage since it is not possible to fit once the building has been constructed. Examples of design and installation are described by Levin (1991).

Masonry (brick) construction (all building types): Masonry construction is also inherently leaky. Air tends to infiltrate through gaps left by missing mortar and various other cracks and gaps in the brickwork. Further leakage sources include floor/ceiling to wall interfaces, window and door frame joints and service penetrations. Masonry buildings can, nevertheless, be constructed to a high degree of air-tightness. Brickwork is best sealed by rendering with plaster and coating with paint. This approach has become less common with modern construction, which tends to use plaster board panels fixed to the brickwork with spots of adhesive. Although continuous beading of adhesive is now recommended, this may not be put into practice on site. Floor joists are sometimes left to rest on openings in the inner leaf of the structure leaving large penetrations into the cavity. Instead, joist hangers should be used which are embedded into the mortar. Window and door frames should be sealed into the structure with mastic sealant. A guide-line on air-tightness for masonry construction is published in the United Kingdom by the National House-Building Council (NHBC, 1991).

Curtain wall constructions: This type of construction is often very leaky. All joints need to be gasketed to prevent high rates of air infiltration.

Concrete 'cellular' constructions: Almost complete air-tightness is achieved with 'cellular' type concrete construction in which prefabricated panels containing window and door sections are sealed into the open faces of the concrete structure. It is imperative that a well designed ventilation system is installed into this type of building otherwise there is a risk of insufficient air change.

4.4 Design Variables

It is important to ensure that these variables are selected for compatibility, both in relation to the design constraints and system performance.

The remaining parameters are those over which the designer has control. These are the ventilation system itself and the construction characteristics of the building. Again, it is important to ensure that these variables are selected for compatibility, both in relation to the design constraints and system performance.

Strategy

The main design variable is that of the ventilation strategy itself (see Chapter 5). In specifying a strategy, it is important to review the constraints imposed by building type, climate and location, the level of air-tightness to be accomplished, as well as cost performance, energy performance, reliability and ease of maintenance.

Cost Performance

System costs ultimately fall on the building owner or occupier. Therefore, to be widely accepted, the cost performance of the system must be competitive.

System costs ultimately fall on the building owner or occupier. Therefore, to be widely accepted, the cost performance of the system must be competitive. Where alternative strategies are feasible, a comparative payback period may be defined such that, over a given period of time, a system which perhaps incurred a greater initial cost will prove to be less expensive than a much cheaper system incurring a higher operational cost or shorter operating life. Each pay back analysis is specific to the particular building and its location. Heat recovery, for example, despite its high capital cost, becomes more attractive as the outdoor climate becomes more severe (see Chapter 6) or as the payback period is extended.

Energy Performance

Energy is consumed by the conditioning of ventilation (and infiltrating) air and by mechanical air handling systems. Optimum design must ensure that any unnecessary loss of conditioned air is minimised. This is achieved by good building air-tightness and the elimination of avoidable pollutants to reduce the need for ventilation. Distribution energy is controlled by careful fan selection and good design and routing of ductwork. Although no distribution cost is associated with natural ventilation, any benefit must be equated against a reduced capability to control the loss of conditioned air. Design should satisfy ventilation need with minimum use of energy. An analysis of system performance is therefore required. This should consider all main strategies and quantify the energy advantages and disadvantages of each. With mechanical systems, the supply cost should be identified, whereas with natural systems, the heating or cooling losses associated with poor control and risk of over supply should be included.

Reliability and Ease of Maintenance

The system should provide the desired air flow rate with comfort, be free of noise and be acceptable to occupants (e.g. easy to use and difficult to misuse). Good reliability, ease of maintenance (see Chapter 10) and extended operational life are also important.

Life Cycle Planning

Often design has been concerned with providing the least expensive (capital) solution to meet the initial needs, without considering long term problems associated with interaction with other building components, operational costs, reliability and maintenance. Much of the requirements of good design are incorporated in the concepts of 'life cycle' planning. This considers the product from the inception phase, through to installation operation, maintenance and eventual dismantling and replacement. The quality and performance of the design solution in relation to life cycle planning should form part of the design process.

Much of the requirements of good design are incorporated in the concepts of "life cycle" planning. This considers the product from the inception phase, through to installation operation, maintenance and eventual dismantling and replacement.

Design and Analysis Tools

Design tools are needed to develop and improve ventilation design. The tools available for design analysis and evaluation are outlined in Chapters 11 and 12. The roles of measurement and calculation techniques are summarised in Figure 4.6.

Measurements are needed to verify design and for diagnostic analysis.

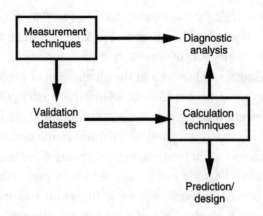

Figure 4.6 Application of Measurements and Calculation in Design

They also provide validation data to evaluate the performance of calculation methods.

Calculation techniques are used for prediction and design. They may also be used for diagnostic analysis.

References

ASHRAE Fundamentals *Air flow around buildings*, Chapter 14, American Society of Heating Refrigeration and Air Conditioning Engineers, ISBN 0-910110-97-2, 1993.

ASHRAE Standard 55 *Thermal environmental conditions for human occupancy*, ANSI/ASHRAE Standard 55-92, American Society of Heating Refrigeration and Air Conditioning Engineers, 1992.

ASHRAE Standard 62 *Minimum ventilation for acceptable indoor air quality*, (1989, new revision 1996/7). ASHRAE Fundamentals.

BFS 1988, *Heat recovery*, Chapter 3, National Board of Housing and Planning, Sweden.

CAN/CGSB-51.71-95, *The spillage test*, National Standards of Canada, 1995.

Elmroth A, Levin P, *Air infiltration control in housing: a guide to international practice*, Swedish Council for Building Research, D2:1983.

Fanger P O, *Introduction of the olf and the decipol units to quantify air pollution perceived by humans indoors and outdoors*, Energy and Buildings, No 12, 1988.

Fehlmann J, Wanner H U, *Indoor climate and indoor air quality in residential buildings*, Proc Indoor Air, Vol 3, 1993.

Levin P, *Building technology and air flow control in housing*, Swedish Council for Building Research, Document D16:1991.

Lundqvist G R, *Indoor air quality and air exchange in bedrooms*, Proc 6th AIC Conference *Ventilation Strategies and Measurement Techniques*, 1985.

NHBC, *Thermal insulation and ventilation - good practice guide*, 1991

NKB, *Indoor Climate – Air Quality*, Nordic Committee on Building Regulations, NKB Publication No 61E, 1991.

Norell L, *Demand controlled ventilation in a school*, Proc. AIVC 12th Conference, *Air Movement and Ventilation Control within Buildings*, 1991.

Saum D W, Osborne M C, *Radon mitigation effects of passive stacks in residential new construction*, Proc. Indoor Air '90, Vol 3, 1990.

Straub H E, Toft H R, Nelson P R, *Evaluation of smoking lounge air distribution*, Proc *Indoor air quality, ventilation and energy conservation*, 5th International Jacques Cartier, 1992.

5 Ventilation Strategies

Mechanisms
Driving Forces
Cross Flow and Single Sided Ventilation
Air Inlets
Passive Stacks and Atria Design
Extract, Supply and Balanced Ventilation
Demand Controlled Systems

Summary and Introduction

A wide range of systems and techniques is available to meet the needs of ventilation with each having its own set of advantages, disadvantages and applications. Sometimes choice is dictated by local climate conditions or building type. Frequently, price competitiveness and an unwillingness to deviate from the minimum specifications of relevant Building Regulations or Codes of Practice can further restrict choice and also limit the opportunity for innovation. To justify a complex strategy, it is usually necessary to demonstrate advantages in terms of improved indoor climate, reduced energy demand and acceptable 'payback' periods. Choice ultimately rests with such factors as indoor air quality requirements, heating and cooling loads, outdoor climate, cost, and design preference. Above all, the selected system must satisfy the needs of design criteria (see Chapter 4).

The purpose of this chapter is to overview ventilation strategies in relation to these needs. Techniques are reviewed in terms of natural and mechanical ventilation systems, methods to achieve 'displacement' air flow and approaches to 'demand control' ventilation.

5.1 Natural Ventilation

Background and Applications

Many buildings throughout the world are 'naturally' ventilated. In the past, this has sometimes meant little more than satisfying needs by relying on an arbitrary combination of uncontrolled air infiltration and window opening. Nowadays, ventilation requirements can be very demanding, with modern systems having to provide much improved reliability and control. By careful design, it is possible for natural ventilation to provide a

Many buildings throughout the world are "naturally" ventilated. In the past, this has sometimes meant little more than satisfying needs by relying on an arbitrary combination of uncontrolled air infiltration and window opening.

satisfactory environment in even quite complex buildings.

Natural ventilation is most suited to buildings located in mild to moderate climates, away from inner city locations. Essentially, natural ventilation operates in 'mixing' and pollutant 'dilution' mode; there is insufficient flow control to achieve 'displacement' or 'piston' flow, although non-critical flow patterns between 'clean' and 'contaminated' zones are possible. Subject to climatic and outside noise constraints, typical applications include:

• low rise dwellings,

• small to medium size offices,

• schools,

• recreational buildings,

• public buildings,

• warehouses,

• light industrial premises.

Specialised natural ventilation systems may be applicable to a wider range of climatic conditions and buildings including large commercial buildings; much depends on individual circumstances and requirements. A bibliography on natural ventilation and its applications has been produced by Limb (1994a).

Natural Ventilation Mechanisms

Despite the variability of natural driving forces it is often possible for satisfactory design solutions to be developed.

For a given configuration of openings, the rate of natural ventilation varies according to the prevailing driving forces of wind and indoor/outdoor temperature difference. Despite this variability, it is nevertheless possible for satisfactory design solutions to be developed, provided that flexibility in indoor air temperature, air flow rate and instantaneous ventilation rate can be accommodated.

Driving Forces

Natural ventilation is driven by wind and thermally (stack) generated pressures (see Chapter 12). Designing for natural ventilation is concerned with harnessing these forces by the careful sizing and positioning of openings.

Wind pressure: Wind striking a rectangular shaped building induces a positive pressure on the windward face and negative pressures on opposing faces and in the wake region of the side faces. This causes air to enter openings and pass through the building from the high pressure windward areas to the low pressure downwind areas (see Figure 5.1(a)). Calculation guide-lines for estimating wind pressure distribution are given in Chapter

12. Normally very simplistic assumptions must be made about the wind pressure distribution. If more detail is required, such as the pressure distribution acting on complex structures, it may be necessary to resort to wind tunnel methods (see Chapter 11).

Stack pressure: Stack effect is developed as a result of differences in air temperature, and hence air density, between the inside and outside of the building. This produces an imbalance in the pressure gradients of the internal and external air masses which results in a vertical pressure difference. When the inside air temperature is greater than the outside air temperature, air enters through openings in the lower part of the building and escapes through openings at a higher level (see Figure 5.1(b)). The flow direction is reversed when the inside air temperature is lower than the outside air temperature. Calculation of stack pressure is based on the temperature difference between the two air masses and the vertical spacing between openings (see Chapter 12).

Systems need to be designed to ensure that the effects of wind and stack action complement rather than oppose each other.

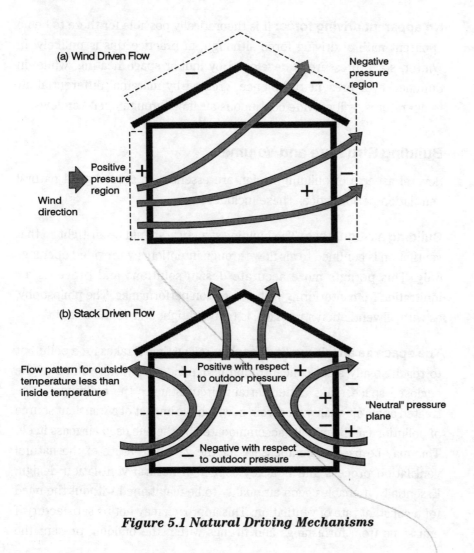

Figure 5.1 Natural Driving Mechanisms

Complementary and combined use of wind and stack pressures:
Systems need to be designed to ensure that the effects of wind and stack action complement rather than oppose each other. This is accomplished by understanding and exploiting the pressure distribution developed by each mechanism and locating openings to best advantage. Passive stack and atria designs seek to accomplish this objective. Alternatively, the driving forces may be modified by careful inlet design or by providing a shelter belt to reduce wind effect. The typical interaction of wind and stack pressure is illustrated in Figure 5.2. Ventilation rate at low wind speeds is dominated by the stack effect. As the wind speed increases, wind dominated ventilation takes over. At certain wind speeds, wind pressure may act in complete opposition to stack forces at specific openings, resulting in a small drop in the total ventilation rate. The application of 'network' calculation techniques, combined with representative weather data for the building locality, enables the natural ventilation performance of individual design solutions to be evaluated (see Chapter 12).

No apparent driving force: It is theoretically possible for there to be no apparent natural driving force although, in practice this is unlikely. In Winter, stack pressure is developed by indoor space heating, while, in Summer, ever present turbulence, created by marginal differential air temperatures, will provide continuous air flow through open windows.

Building Structure and Volume

Several aspects of building design are essential to secure good natural ventilation performance. These include:

Building air-tightness: The building structure should be air-tight so that ventilation is confined to air flow through intentionally provided openings only. This permits more accurate design solutions and prevents air infiltration from interfering with ventilation performance. The philosophy, as with all ventilation strategies, is to 'build tight and ventilate right'.

Under certain circumstances the building can be treated as an "air quality reservoir" in which the impact of a transient source of pollution can be initially accommodated by the enclosed air mass itself.

The space as an 'air quality' reservoir: The time it takes for a pollutant to reach steady state concentration is dependent on the volume of the enclosed space. Thus under certain circumstances the building can be treated as an 'air quality reservoir' in which the impact of a transient source of pollution can be initially accommodated by the enclosed air mass itself. This may be used to compensate for the variable nature of the natural ventilation process and is a key aspect of natural ventilation design. Essentially, it enables good air quality to be maintained without the need for a constant rate of ventilation. This approach may not be satisfactory if emissions from furnishings and fittings within the building present the

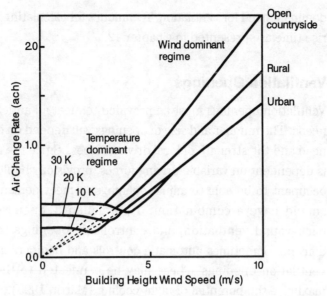

Impact of wind and temperature difference on natural ventilation

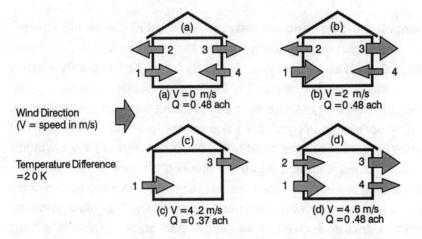

Wind Direction
(V = speed in m/s)

Temperature Difference
= 20 K

(a) V = 0 m/s
Q = 0.48 ach

(b) V = 2 m/s
Q = 0.48 ach

(c) V = 4.2 m/s
Q = 0.37 ach

(d) V = 4.6 m/s
Q = 0.48 ach

Influence of wind and temperature (stack effect) on
ventilation rate and air flow pattern

While the rate of ventilation can be held almost constant for a range of weather conditions, the pattern of air flow changes.

In (a) below, ventilation is dominated by temperature (temperature dominant regime). Air enters through the lower openings (1 and 4) and leaves through the upper openings (2 and 3).

As the wind increases, (b), wind pressure reinforces stack pressure at the windward lower openings (1) leeward upper openings (3), while opposing the stack pressure at the other openings (2 and 4). Although the pattern and magnitude of flow essentially remains unaltered, the flow rate through each opening changes.

At (c) the wind exactly opposes stack pressure at openings (2 and 4), leaving flow only through openings (1 and 3). The effective reduction in the number of openings reduces slightly the overall air change rate. This effect is less pronounced as the number of openings increase since it is unlikely that a significant proportion of them would simultaneously experience exactly opposing pressures.

At greater wind speeds, (d), flow enters the building through the windward side of the building (1 and 2), and flows out through leeward openings (3 and 4). This marks the start of the wind dominant regime.

Figure 5.2 Combined Effect of Wind and Temperature Difference on Ventilation Rate and Air Flow Pattern

dominant need for ventilation. Techniques for calculating the concentration rise time are presented in Chapter 12.

Ventilation Openings

Ventilation openings must be provided to meet all anticipated ventilation needs. The number and size of openings will depend on overall ventilation need and the strength of local driving forces. Since the rate of ventilation is dependent on variable driving forces, provision should be made for the occupant to be able to adjust openings to meet demand. A good design should have a combination of permanently open vents, to provide background ventilation, and controllable openings to meet transient demand. Sometimes automatic controls and dampers are used to adjust ventilation openings. These may be connected to thermal sensors to maximise the potential of night cooling (Martin 1995).

Natural ventilation components include:

Openable windows and louvres: In many buildings, openable windows are the principal component of natural ventilation. They permit the passage of large flows of air for purging or Summer cooling. Unfortunately, window designs aimed at maximising air flow for Summer cooling can cause extreme discomfort and energy waste during the heating season if good control of window opening is not possible. Sometimes losses are exacerbated if heating systems are over sized and have poor controls, since window opening is then used as a means to moderate indoor air temperature. Vertical sash or sliding windows are able to provide air above the occupied zone to prevent low level draughting. Louvres and 'top hung' windows provide a greater degree of flow control than large opening side hung windows.

Air vents and 'trickle' ventilators: Unnecessary air change can be avoided by using 'trickle' ventilators (small air vents) in place of window opening for Winter ventilation. They typically have an effective area of opening of between 4000 and 8000 mm^2. Ideally they should be permanent openings although some incorporate manual adjusters. When used by themselves, trickle ventilators provide limited but 'uncontrolled' ventilation. At least one vent per room is normally recommended for naturally ventilated dwellings. United Kingdom recommendations for office buildings are 4000mm^2 of opening for each 10m^2 of floor space (BRE, 1994). Openable windows or other large openings are needed for Summer cooling and rapid air purging. Trickle ventilators should be positioned to promote the entry and rapid mixing of outdoor air. This is necessary to ensure good air distribution and to prevent localised areas of cooling. To prevent discomfort, it is often recommended that vents are located at a high level, i.e. above the window and possibly integrated into the window frame. Sometimes ventilators are positioned directly behind wall mounted heaters or even ducted directly to the heating system. This prevents unauthorised access to the vents and enables the incoming air to be pre-heated before reaching the occupied zone.

Automatic (variable area) inlets: Some air inlets respond automatically to various air quality and climate parameters. These are usually intended for use with passive stack (or mechanical extract) ventilation systems. Typical systems include:

Temperature sensitive vents

The area of opening of the temperature sensitive vent reduces as the outside air temperature falls. This limits the impact of stack ventilation and prevents a rise in air flow rate as the stack pressure increases.

Humidity sensitive vents

The humidity sensitive vent opens in response to increased room humidity to assist in moisture removal. These are popular in some countries.

Pressure-sensitive vents

Various pressure-sensitive vents have been developed but they are usually too insensitive for reliable operation at the normal driving pressures of natural ventilation (i.e. < 10 Pa) By contrast, the vent illustrated in Figure 5.3 (Knoll, 1993) has been specifically designed for robust operation at pressure differences as low as 1 Pa. This enables an almost uniform flow

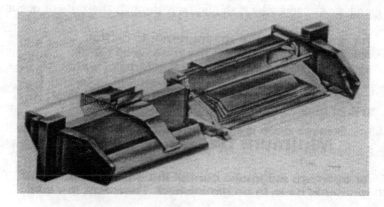

Figure 5.3 Pressure-Sensitive Air Inlet
(Courtesy B Knoll, TNO , The Netherlands)

rate to be achieved throughout a wide pressure range, thus permitting good control of natural ventilation. The main disadvantage, at present, is cost.

Passive stacks: Passive stacks are vertical ducts that penetrate a room at ceiling level and terminate above roof level. The purpose of such a stack is to enhance temperature difference or stack driven air flow. Ideally the roof opening is located where wind action induces a suction pressure, so that air flow is reinforced by wind action (see Passive stack ventilation) Cowels may be fitted at the roof opening to promote wind induced suction pressure and prevent back-draughting. Passive stacks are an important element of controlled natural ventilation systems, especially in dwellings.

Air vents for combustion appliances: Often building Regulations specify a minimum area of permanently openable vents which must be included in dwelling rooms fitted with an open combustion appliance. This is needed to secure combustion supply air and to prevent excessive suction pressures from being developed if a mechanical extractor is in use. It is an essential safety measure, but these vents add to the air change process and can therefore cause additional energy loss. Whenever possible, room sealed combustion appliances incorporating balanced flues or externally supplied and exhausted air should be installed. Open combustion appliances can be incompatible with energy efficient building design.

Natural Ventilation Techniques

Various techniques or combinations of techniques are used to provide natural ventilation; these include:

Cross flow ventilation: Cross flow ventilation relies on establishing a clearly defined and unimpeded air flow path between the incoming and outgoing air streams which should pass through the zone of occupancy. Such an air flow pattern is impeded if the building is compartmentalised. Consequently, an 'open plan' interior is recommended. Examples of cross flow ventilation configurations are illustrated in Figure 5.4. Since there is a practical limit that naturally provided ventilation air may be expected to penetrate the building from an opening, limits are applied to the maximum distance from openings. In the past, this limit has been taken as between 2 to 2.5 times the ceiling height (a depth of typically 6m), although some studies (BRE 1994) have shown that it may be possible to extend this limit to 10m.

Single-sided ventilation: Sometimes ventilation design appears to be 'single sided' in that the only obvious openings are positioned along just one side of the room. True single sided ventilation through a small opening (see Figure 5.5(a)) is driven by random 'turbulent fluctuations'. At best, this type of single sided approach is unreliable and is not recommended as part of a controlled natural ventilation strategy.

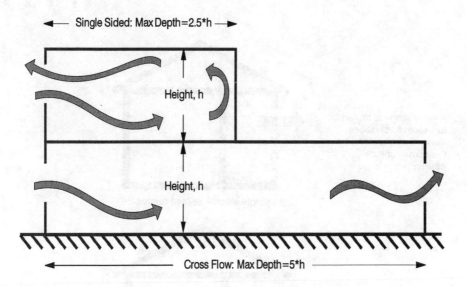

Figure 5.4 Cross Flow Ventilation

Generally, more than one opening may be placed on a single side or a single opening is large enough for air to flow simultaneously through it in both directions, (see Figure 5.5(b)). Ventilation is then driven by the normal process of wind and stack forces. For these configurations, flow rates may be calculated using standard network calculation techniques (see Chapter 12). Good spacing between openings is needed to generate reliable air change for practical applications.

Often apparent 'single sided' ventilation turns out to be 'cross flow' ventilation as illustrated in Figure 5.5(c). In this example, a second flow path exists through joints around internal partitioning. Quite fortuitously, many rooms experience this type of background cross flow. Internal air vents or open doors will assist this process.

Passive stack ventilation: Passive stack systems have been used in many parts of Scandinavia and in other locations throughout Europe primarily for the ventilation of dwellings and, sometimes, non-domestic buildings. Normally they are used to promote the extraction of air from 'wet' rooms. Air flow is driven through the stack by a combination of stack pressure and wind induced suction pressure. Although the rate of air flow is variable, some control of the pattern of air flow is possible, with air predominantly entering through purpose provided 'trickle' ventilators and exhausted through the stack. A separate stack is needed for each room. Occasional 'back-draughting' will occur when the pressure generated in the stack cannot overcome the static pressure of cold outside air sitting above it. This flow reversal, if it does occur, is normally temporary and should not normally present an air quality or health problem. Sometimes 'shunt' ducts

Air flow is driven through the stack by a combination of stack pressure and wind induced suction pressure. Although the rate of air flow is variable, some control of the pattern of air flow is possible, with air predominantly entering through purpose provided "trickle" ventilators and exhausted

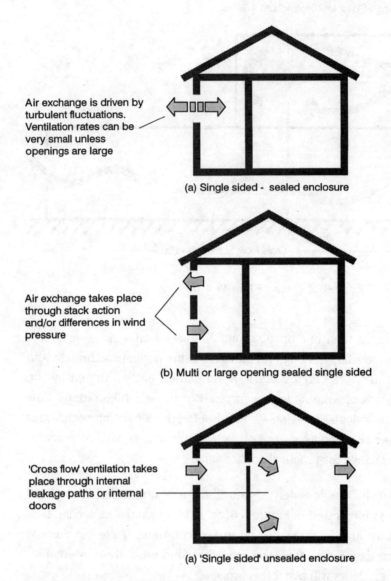

Air exchange is driven by turbulent fluctuations. Ventilation rates can be very small unless openings are large

(a) Single sided - sealed enclosure

Air exchange takes place through stack action and/or differences in wind pressure

(b) Multi or large opening sealed single sided

'Cross flow' ventilation takes place through internal leakage paths or internal doors

(a) 'Single sided' unsealed enclosure

Figure 5.5 Single-sided Ventilation

Passive stacks are most suitable for moderate to medium cold climates, where a consistent winter time driving force can be developed.

from individual rooms or apartments are connected to a central stack but there is a serious risk of cross contamination between connected locations.

Careful design is required if passive stacks are to perform correctly. A configuration for a single family house is illustrated in Figure 5.6. Stack diameter is typically between 100 and 150mm. Since frictional losses must be minimised, it is preferable for the stack to be completely straight and vertical. At most there should be no more than two bends and these should not exceed 45°. If flexible ducting is used it must be cut to the exact length needed to prevent any excess from being coiled. Stacks passing through unheated spaces must be insulated to prevent condensation. A separate stack is needed for each room in which extraction is necessary.

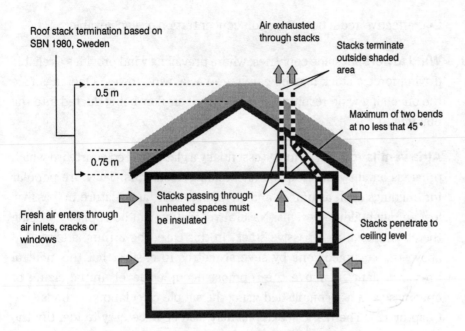

Figure 5.6 Stack Ventilation (dwellings)

Make up air should be provided through intentional openings. The stack must terminate in the 'negative' pressure region above the roof space. Basic sizing and flow analysis can be undertaken using the mathematical principles outlined in Chapter 12.

Passive stacks are most suitable for moderate to medium cold climates, where a consistent winter time driving force can be developed. Studies and further information on the performance of passive stack systems are described by Shepherd et al (1994), Villenave et al (1994). Stack systems are also used to mitigate radon concentration by venting beneath a building's foundations. Measurements reported by Saum et al (1990) show

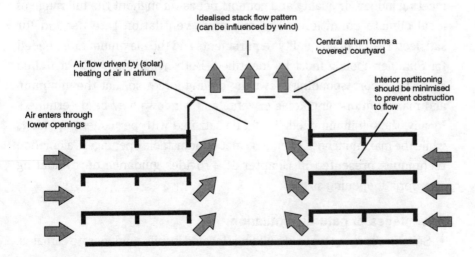

Figure 5.7 Stack Ventilation (atrium)

that effective reductions in radon concentration are achievable.

Wind towers: In some countries, where prevailing wind provides a reliable driving force a stack may be configured as a 'wind tower'. Openings face the oncoming wind resulting in wind driven air flow being ducted into the building.

Atria ventilation: An atrium is essentially a glass covered courtyard which provides an all weather space for building occupants. They are popular for buildings such as offices and shopping malls, and feature in 'passive' low energy building designs. Natural ventilation can be applied by using the atrium itself as a passive stack. In this case, the atrium is extended above the occupied zone by several metres to ensure that the 'neutral pressure plane' is above the topmost occupied level. Initial sizing of openings can be accomplished using the simple calculation methods (see Chapter 12). Thermal calculations may also be necessary to identify the total heat gain. Some designers use computational fluid dynamics to predict the air flow pattern within the structure.

The basic concepts of natural atrium ventilation are summarised in Figure 5.7. Building joints must be well sealed to prevent uncontrolled air change and high velocity draughting. Flow patterns can be disrupted by wind induced pressures. Automatic damper controls may be needed to adjust inaccessible top openings. Successful examples of large buildings based on natural ventilation of the atrium space are described by Holmes (1985) and Guntermann (1994).

Robustness of Natural Ventilation Design

Natural ventilation solutions should be shown to be robust and capable of meeting indoor air quality and comfort needs throughout the full range of local climate conditions.

Natural ventilation solutions should be shown to be robust and capable of meeting indoor air quality and comfort needs throughout the full range of local climate conditions. The minimum ventilation rate needed for satisfactory indoor air quality requirements and the maximum rate needed for Summer cooling must be identified. Both needs should be matched against the corresponding prevailing driving forces so that the minimum and maximum opening areas of vents and windows may be determined. Ideally, the minimum need should be satisfied with permanent openings while the maximum need should be met by adjustable openings. Calculation techniques presented in Chapter 12 provides guidance on evaluating appropriate opening sizes.

Advantages of natural ventilation:
- Suitable for many types of buildings located in mild or moderate climates.
- The 'open window' environment associated with natural ventilation is

often popular, especially in pleasant locations and mild climates.

- Natural ventilation is usually inexpensive when compared to the capital, operational and maintenance costs of mechanical systems.

- High air flow rates for cooling and purging are possible if there are plenty of openings.

- Short periods of discomfort during periods of warm weather can usually be tolerated.

- No plant room space is needed.

- Minimum maintenance.

Disadvantages of natural ventilation:

- Inadequate control over ventilation rate could lead to indoor air quality problems and excessive heat loss. Air flow rates and the pattern of air flow are not constant.

- Fresh air delivery and air distribution in large, deep plan and multi-roomed buildings may not be possible.

- High heat gains may mean that mechanical cooling and air handling will prevent the use of natural ventilation.

- Natural ventilation is unsuited to noisy and polluted locations.

- Some designs may present a security risk.

- Heat recovery from exhaust air is technically feasible (Shultz, 1993) but not generally practicable.

- Natural ventilation may not be suitable in severe climatic regions.

- Occupants must normally adjust openings to suit prevailing demand.

- Filtration or cleaning of incoming air is not usually practicable.

- Ducted systems require large diameter ducts and restrictions on routing.

5.2 Mechanical Ventilation

Background and Applications

Mechanical ventilation systems are capable of providing controlled ventilation to a space. In large commercial type buildings, especially, they may be combined with heating, cooling and filtration systems. Many systems operate in 'mixing' mode to dilute pollutants while others operate in 'displacement' mode to remove pollutants without mixing. Some systems incorporate exhaust air heat recovery techniques to reduce ventilation heat loss. Well designed systems installed in good quality buildings can be unaffected by climatic driving forces. Benefits have to be balanced against capital and operational costs, on-going maintenance needs and eventual replacement. It is often this balance between cost and performance benefit

Mechanical systems need to be designed to meet the specific needs of the building in which it is to operate. An integrated design philosophy ensures optimum performance combined with maximum energy efficiency.

that dictates the approach to ventilation. Mechanical systems need to be designed to meet the specific needs of the building in which it is to operate. An integrated design philosophy ensures optimum performance combined with maximum energy efficiency.

Applications include:
- large commercial buildings in almost any climatic region,
- apartments,
- single family dwellings and other smaller buildings located in severe climatic regions,
- local intermittent extract ventilation is frequently used to support natural ventilation.

Mechanical Ventilation Components

Mechanical systems are made up of various components; these include:

Fans: Fans are used to provide the motivating force for mechanical ventilation. Common types are propeller fans, for low capacity, and centrifugal and axial fans for high capacity and lengthy duct runs. Fans operate by consuming electrical energy. This energy can represent a very significant factor in the energy budget of a commercial building air conditioning system. Work reported by BRECSU (1993) indicates that the fan can account for more than half of the system's energy consumption. Energy consumption is dependent on flow rate, pressure drop across the fan (or circulation pump), fan efficiency and motor efficiency. Fan power is approximately proportional to the cube of the air velocity. This means that halving the velocity of air through a duct will result in an eight fold decrease in fan power. Large cross-sectional area ducting can therefore be beneficial but must be assessed in the context of additional capital costs and space needs. Further control strategies for minimising fan energy are reviewed by Steimle (1994).

Ducts: Ducting is used to transfer air. Ducts impose a resistance to air flow, thus influencing performance and energy need. The amount of resistance depends on:

- the air flow rate through the duct,
- cross sectional area,
- the length of the duct run,
- the number and angle of bends,
- surface roughness.

The greater the flow resistance, the greater is the fan capacity and electrical energy which is needed to drive a mechanical ventilation system. Transport energy may be reduced by minimising resistance to air movement. This is achieved by using low loss fittings and minimising flow impedances presented by filters and cooling coils etc. Ducting which passes through unconditioned spaces should be insulated to prevent thermal losses and condensation risk. They should also be well sealed to prevent the loss of conditioned air. Good systems require electrical power at 1 Watt or less for each litre/s of air flow. Poorly designed systems might need 3 Watts or more to deliver the same air flow rate.

Diffusers: Diffusers are used to discharge mechanically supplied air into the ventilated space. Considerable design effort is needed to ensure that they do not cause uncomfortable draughts. Design specification covers the emission rate, discharge velocity and turbulent intensity. Examples are reviewed by Nielsen (1989).

Air intakes: Air intakes are the openings at which outdoor air is collected for ducting to a ventilation system. Problems occur if air intakes are located close to contaminant sources (e.g. traffic fumes or local industry or building exhausts).

Problems occur if air intakes are located close to contaminant sources (e.g. traffic fumes or local industry or building exhausts).

Air inlets: Air inlets are 'passive' openings which are used to provide 'make up' air to a space. They may consist of trickle ventilators or air bricks as used for natural ventilation.

Air grilles: Air grilles are used to capture exhaust air from a space.

Silencers (noise attenuators): Noise in mechanical ventilation systems can present considerable discomfort. A concise summary of the problem and cures is presented by Op t' Veld (1993). Direct noise is generated by the system itself including fan noise, duct propagation, poor mountings, control valves and aerodynamic noise (through grilles). A system may also be influenced by the transfer through the system of outdoor noise. Efforts to reduce noise include the sound proofing of ducts with sound absorbing material and the use of 'silencers'. These consist of a perforated inner duct, surrounded by mineral wool packing which is enclosed by an outer duct. Both techniques increase flow resistance and therefore incur an energy penalty. Active noise filters are also in the course of development (Leventhall et al 1995). These create an 'anti phase' noise in a space aimed at cancelling out existing noise. A microphone placed in the duct, downstream of the fan, detects any generated sound and converts the pressure waves into an electrical signal. An active filter and sound analysis network is used to produce an anti-phase audio signal into a loudspeaker positioned further upstream to cancel out the system noise.

Mechanical Ventilation Strategies

Various configurations of mechanical ventilation are in use. These include:

Optimum operational efficiency is achieved by contriving to keep the mechanical pressure at a slightly greater level than the weather induced pressure.

Mechanical Extract Ventilation: A fan is used to mechanically remove air from a space. This induces a 'suction' or 'under' pressure which promotes the flow of an equal mass of 'make-up' or 'fresh' air into the space through purpose provided air inlets or infiltration openings. If the under-pressure created by the extract process is greater than that developed by wind and temperature, the flow process is dominated by the mechanical system. If the under-pressure is weaker, then the flow process is dominated by air infiltration. Optimum operational efficiency is achieved by contriving to keep the mechanical pressure at a slightly greater level than the weather induced pressure. In common with natural ventilation design, best control is established by ensuring that the structure is air tight and that purpose provided air inlets are used to supply make-up air. However, since 'natural' or 'passive' openings are needed, this approach can tolerate a small amount of infiltration opening. Extract systems include:

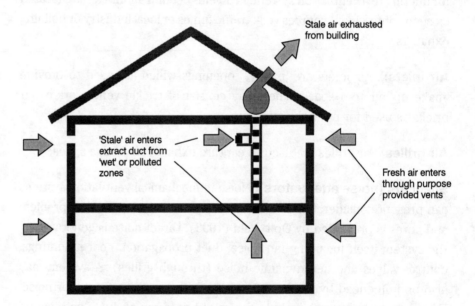

Stale air exhausted from building

'Stale' air enters extract duct from 'wet' or polluted zones

Fresh air enters through purpose provided vents

Figure 5.8 Central Mechanical Extract Ventilation (dwellings)

Local extract: Local extract systems are common in many smaller buildings where they are used to extract pollutants (often moisture) from the source of production. These are typically low capacity wall, window and cooker (range) hood fans which vent the contaminated air directly to outside. Typical capacities are 25-50 l/s. Local extractors are frequently used to support natural ventilation. Operation is normally intended to be intermittent and may include a time switch or humidity sensor for automatic control. Propeller type fans are often used. Duct lengths as short as 1 metre can impair performance considerably.

Centralised ducted extract: Ducted systems provide complete ventilation to a building. The system is operated by a central fan which is connected to extract grilles via a network of ducting (see Figure 5.8). These systems are used in single family and apartment dwellings, particularly in cold climates. Extract systems are also used in industry and in hospital environments where suction pressures are applied to prevent the spread of chemical or microbiological contaminants. In dwellings, extract grilles are located in 'wet' rooms while air inlets are located in living and bedrooms. This configuration is especially beneficial in preventing water vapour from penetrating and condensing in the building fabric. In industrial locations extract points are located above heat or polluting sources.

Extract ventilation with heat recovery: Waste heat from the exhaust air may be recovered using an air to liquid heat pump (see Chapter 6). These are able to recover between 20 and 40% of the energy in the exhaust air for pre-heating of the domestic hot water. Up to 95% of hot water needs may be satisfied in this way (Knoll 1992). Further energy may be extracted if used in conjunction with a 'wet' central heating system.

Applications: Mechanical extract systems are used when it is important to prevent localised pollutant sources from contaminating occupied spaces or where cross contamination from 'clean' to contaminated zones is to be avoided. Examples include:

Dwellings
Central and local extract systems are used in dwellings. Sometimes they form part of a building retrofit in which passive ventilation ducts are used to carry the extract air.

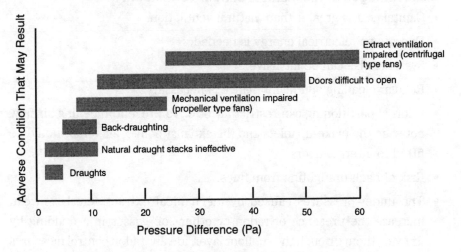

Figure 5.9 Adverse Effects of Under-pressure

Factories and Laboratories

Extract fume hoods are used to capture contaminants from polluting processes and prevent them entering occupied spaces.

Excessive under-pressures must be avoided. If the building is too tight or there are insufficient make-up openings, either the suction pressure (and hence electrical load) will rise or the fan will be unable to deliver the desired air flow rate.

Limitations and Design Precautions: Excessive under-pressures must be avoided. If the building is too tight or there are insufficient make-up openings, either the suction pressure (and hence electrical energy load) will rise or the fan will be unable to deliver the desired air flow rate. High under-pressures may cause combustion flues to backdraught and radon or other soil gases to enter the building; they may also cause noise and high velocity draughts. The adverse effect of excessive suction pressures is summarised in Figure 5.9 (HAMA, 1959). Strict controls usually apply to the installation of ducted extract systems in buildings fitted with open combustion appliances. Canadian Standard CAN/C95B-51.71-95 (1995) requires that for dwellings fitted with open combustion appliances, the under-pressure should not be allowed to exceed 5 Pa. The sizing of openings for optimum under-pressure is a very straightforward exercise based on the relationship between pressure drop and flow rate through an opening (see Chapter 12).

Potential benefits of extract ventilation must be equated against cost, operational energy and long term maintenance needs.

Advantages of mechanical extract ventilation:
- Controlled ventilation rates are possible.
- Extraction of pollutants at source reduce the risk of pollutant ingress into occupied spaces.
- The risk of moisture entering walls is reduced.
- Heat recovery from the exhaust air stream is possible.

Disadvantages of mechanical extract ventilation:
- Capital cost is greater than natural ventilation.
- Operational electrical energy is needed.
- System noise can be intrusive.
- Regular cleaning and maintenance is necessary.
- Internal partitioning can restrict air flow. To prevent impeding air flow between the make-up inlets and the exhaust points, air vents should be fitted to internal doors.
- Risk of back-draughting from flues.
- The under-pressures caused by mechanical extract ventilation can increase the presence of radon or other soil gasses in a building by drawing them through the subfloor layer. Ideally, radon control measures

should, in any event, be incorporated into buildings located in high radon areas (Saum et al, 1990).

- Fixed air inlets may result in the ventilation rate being influenced by weather conditions. The installation of pressure-sensitive air inlets such as illustrated in Figure 5.3 can assist in providing a constant air flow rate by further reducing the influence of climate forces.

- Adjustment to individual air inlets could affect flow through other branches of the system.

Mechanical Supply Ventilation

Supply (outdoor air) is mechanically introduced into the building where it mixes with the existing air. This process induces a positive (i.e. above

Supply ventilation inhibits the ingress of infiltrating air and therefore enable all the incoming air to be pre-cleaned and thermally conditioned.

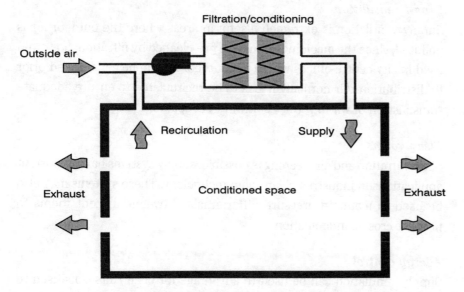

Figure 5.10 Central Mechanical Supply Ventilation

atmospheric) pressure in the building. Indoor air is displaced through purpose provided and/or infiltration openings. If the system is well designed and good fabric air-tightness is achieved, supply ventilation inhibits the ingress of infiltrating air and therefore enables all the incoming air to be pre-cleaned and thermally conditioned.

Ducted systems: Typically the system is ducted, and may be incorporated as part of an air heating or cooling distribution system (see Figure 5.10). Normally the air is filtered to reduce dust and particulate concentrations (see Chapter 8). A proportion of the room air escapes through leakage openings and/or purpose provided openings, while the remainder is recirculated for thermal comfort and blended with incoming outdoor air (see also Balanced ventilation). Problems have arisen in the past when the fresh air supply dampers have been closed to reduce energy consumption. The same air-tightness and vent conditions are needed as for extract ventilation. Optimum performance is maintained by sizing the system to operate just beyond the pressure range developed by wind and temperature.

Task supply ventilation: Sometimes supply air is ducted directly to individual occupants where flow rate and comfort conditions can be manually adjusted. Task ventilation is often incorporated into work station 'booths' (Arens et al, 1990).

Applications: Supply ventilation has several important applications where a building needs to be pressurised; these include:

Urban ventilation
Supply ventilation is extremely useful in areas where the outdoor air is polluted, since the incoming air may be pre-cleaned by filtration. It is often used in city centre offices where the outdoor air can be conditioned prior to distribution. Air normally needs to be recirculated to ensure adequate transmission of warmth (or 'coolth') to occupants.

Clean rooms
Since filtration and air cleaning is possible, supply systems have important applications in industrial clean room technology. These systems may also be used to maintain pressure differentials between adjacent rooms to prevent cross-contamination

Since filtration and air cleaning is possible, supply systems have important applications in industrial clean room technology.

Allergy control
Supply ventilation can be used to advantage for occupants sensitised to pollutants from outdoor sources (e.g. pollen, industrial emissions etc.). When used in the home, care is needed to prevent moisture, generated in the dwelling, from penetrating and condensing in the building fabric. This means ensuring that outlet grilles and local extractors are located in these areas and that the internal walls are well sealed.

Limitations and design precautions: Although the pressurisation characteristics of supply ventilation can inhibit the adventitious entry of pollutants and soil gases into a space, and can minimise the risk of back-draughting, they are not normally recommended for dwellings since there is a risk that indoor generated water vapour can penetrate and condense in the building fabric.

Extreme care is needed over the siting of air intakes to avoid drawing in outdoor pollutants from local sources (see Chapter 2). Air intakes must not be obstructed or blocked.

Advantages of mechanical supply ventilation:

- Outdoor air can be pre-cleaned and conditioned.
- Good air control is possible.
- Entry of outside pollutants and soil gases is inhibited.
- Flue back-draughting risk is reduced.
- Infiltration can be restricted, provided the structure is fairly air tight.

Disadvantages of mechanical supply ventilation:

- Problems occur if air intake dampers are blocked or closed, or if air intakes are close to pollutant sources.
- Indoor moisture sources may be driven into the building fabric at risk of condensation. Thus this method is not normally recommended for dwellings.
- Heat recovery is not possible.
- Removal of pollutants at source is not possible.

Mechanical Balanced 'Mixing' Ventilation

Balanced 'mixing' ventilation combines extract and supply systems as separately ducted networks. Typically, air is supplied and mixed into

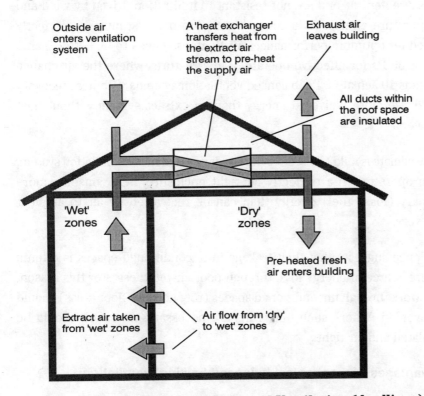

Figure 5.11 Mechanical Balanced Ventilation (dwellings)

Balanced systems almost always incorporate heat recovery using a plate heat recovery unit or similar air to air system (see Chapter 6). It is this potential for heat recovery that is often used to justify the additional capital and operating costs.

'occupied' zones and is extracted from 'polluted' zones (see Figure 5.11). An air flow pattern is established between the supply to the extract areas which should be supported by air transfer grilles between rooms. Balanced systems almost always incorporate heat recovery using a plate heat recovery unit or similar air to air system (see Chapter 6). This enables 'free' pre - heating of the incoming air. It is this potential for heat recovery that is often used to justify the additional capital and operating costs. Sometimes an intentional flow imbalance may be introduced to put the building in a slight negative pressure (dwellings) or positive pressure (commercial buildings).

Applications
Dwellings
Balanced ventilation systems are popular in both high and low rise dwellings, especially, in extreme climatic regions where worthwhile heat recovery is possible.

Offices and commercial buildings
Balanced type systems combined with filtration, air conditioning and heat recovery are used in office and commercial buildings. Background information on typical configurations for offices is presented by Limb (1994b).

Limitations and design precautions: Balanced systems are usually 'pressure neutral' and are not resistant to infiltration driven by wind and temperature effects. As a consequence, the building must be perfectly sealed for optimum performance. Air-tightness needs to be better than 1 ach at 50 Pa for effective operation. In structures where the air change exceeds 10 ach at 50 Pa, balanced ventilation systems with heat recovery could use more delivered energy than an extract system without heat recovery.

If the climate is mild (i.e. < 2500 degree days) a balanced ventilation system, even operating in a perfectly air tight enclosure, may consume more primary (fossil fuel) energy than can be recovered by air to air heat recovery.

Evidence suggests that duct leakage in unconditioned spaces is often a severe source of energy loss, through poor air-tightness. For this reason, ductwork through unconditioned spaces (roof and sub-floor areas) should be avoided.

Evidence suggests that duct leakage in unconditioned spaces is often a severe source of energy loss, through poor air-tightness. For this reason, ductwork through unconditioned spaces (roof and sub-floor areas) should be avoided. Where such duct runs are necessary, ductwork should be insulated and air tight.

Advantages of mechanical balanced 'mixing' ventilation:

• Allows heat recovery and pre-heating of supply air.

Figure 5.12 Balanced 'Displacement' Ventilation (office)
(Courtesy FGK, Germany)

- Supply air is targeted to occupied zones, while air is extracted from polluted zones.

- Absence of high suction pressures reduces the risk of back-draughting as well as the entry of radon or soil gas.

- Filtration of the incoming air is possible.

Disadvantages of mechanical balanced 'mixing' ventilation:

- Two systems are present, thus doubling installation and operational costs.

- The systems have been shown to require regular long term maintenance.

- For correct operation, these systems must be installed in air-tight enclosures. This reduces safety margins if the system fails to operate correctly or if the occupant unwittingly introduces high polluting sources into the building.

Mechanical Balanced 'Displacement' Ventilation

Displacement ventilation is a form of balanced ventilation in which the supply air 'displaces' rather than mixes with the room air. Pre-conditioned air at 2 to 3 K below ambient room temperature is introduced to the space at low level and at a very low velocity (typically 0.1 to 0.3m/s). Gravitational effects encourage the incoming air to creep at floor level until it reaches a thermal source (occupant, electrical load, etc.). The air then rises around the heat source and into the breathing zone prior to extraction at ceiling level. (See Figure 5.12). This approach is designed to avoid the mixing of air, instead it 'displaces' the air already present within the space. It therefore has a high 'air change efficiency' (see Chapter 9). Air supply diffusers are

Displacement ventilation is designed to avoid the mixing of air, instead, it "displaces" the air already present within the space.

usually either free standing or are located in the floor. A large total area of diffuser over which the air is uniformly discharged is needed to accomplish the required volume flow rate at low supply velocity.

Applications: Displacement systems have become popular, especially in some Scandinavian and European countries, for applications in offices and public buildings.

Advantages of mechanical balanced 'displacement' ventilation:
- Potentially an energy efficient ventilation system.
- Smoke control is possible, maintaining the areas close to the floor free of smoke.

Disadvantages of balanced 'displacement' ventilation:
- The availability of floor space is reduced since occupants must be kept at some distance from floor standing diffusers and must not place obstructions over diffusers located in the floor. This space restriction puts displacement systems at a disadvantage compared with systems with ceiling mounted mixing diffusers.
- Precise temperature and air flow control is needed to establish correct operating conditions.
- Upstream pollutants must be avoided. Since there is reduced mixing, pollutants upstream of the breathing zone can become extremely concentrated. Possibilities include floor level contaminants (e.g. from dirty carpets) and emissions from electrical equipment in the vicinity of an operator.
- Limited heating or cooling capacity of distributed air means that a separate system (e.g. radiant panels) may be needed for heating and cooling. (See Chapter 7).

Demand Controlled Ventilation

Demand controlled ventilation (DCV) systems provide a means by which the rate of ventilation is automatically controlled in response to variations in indoor air quality.

Demand controlled ventilation (DCV) systems provide a means by which the rate of ventilation is automatically controlled in response to variations in indoor air quality. Ventilation is therefore provided only when and where it is needed while, at other times, it may be reduced to minimise space heating or cooling losses. Essentially, a 'sensor' is used to track indoor air quality and to modulate the rate of ventilation to ensure air quality does not deteriorate. Ideally a 'total' air quality sensor is needed which is capable of detecting all pollutants and react as soon as the concentration of any individual component exceeds a pre-determined threshold level.

In reality, technology has yet to reach this stage, while cost imposes a further limitation. However, where a dominant pollutant can be identified, demand

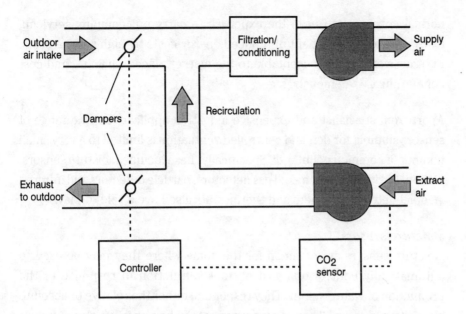

Figure 5.13 Demand Controlled Ventilation (office)

controlled ventilation has proved to be extremely effective. Specific examples include the control of moisture in 'wet' rooms, carbon dioxide sensing in transiently occupied buildings and carbon monoxide linked systems in parking garages. Systems are reviewed in detail by Raatschen (1990) and Mansson et al (1992) as part of the work of IEA Annex 18.

Elements of the system: A demand controlled system comprises three essential elements (see Figure 5.13). These are:

- a sensor or group of sensors, designed to monitor the dominant pollutant (or pollutants),
- a control system for adjusting the ventilation rate in response to need,
- a conventional (usually mechanical) ventilation system.

Demand controlled ventilation is effective when there is a 'dominant' pollutant specific to a type of activity or locality, that can be monitored and controlled. Often, when sufficient ventilation is provided to dilute or remove the dominant pollutant, other, less easily definable pollutants are, themselves, controlled. The first step of demand controlled ventilation is to identify the dominant pollutant or pollutants.

Demand controlled ventilation is effective when there is a "dominant" pollutant specific to a type of activity or locality, that can be monitored and controlled.

Sensors: Sensors are predominantly specific to individual pollutants. The system must therefore be tailored to the dominant pollutant or, if there is more than one potential pollutant, several sensors may be necessary with each sensitive to a different range of pollutants. For demand control systems to be effective, sensors must be maintenance free and should not require post-installation calibration since it is unrealistic to expect the normal consumer to have the expertise to carry out complex servicing tasks or to lose the benefit of reduced energy costs by high service costs. In other words, to be acceptable to the market place, reliability and cost benefit must be demonstrated.

Apart from specialist and expensive industrial applications, the range of sensors suitable for demand controlled ventilation is limited to a very small number of common pollutants. Specifically these include moisture sensors, carbon dioxide sensors, mixed gas detectors, particle detectors and infrared 'people' detectors. Timers and thermostats also have a role to play.

Moisture sensors

Moisture sensors are common for the home where they may be used to automatically control or boost extract ventilation in response to the production of water vapour. They respond to either the relative or absolute humidity in a space. They are inappropriate in homes in which the indoor air temperature is allowed to fall below approximately 15°C since ventilation for moisture control becomes ineffective at low temperatures.

Carbon dioxide sensors

This is a valuable approach in densely populated buildings, such as offices and public buildings and in transiently occupied buildings such as shops, theatres and schools.

While carbon dioxide is itself non toxic and harmless, even at quite high concentrations, the measurement of CO_2 can provide a useful indicator to the adequacy of ventilation. This is because in environments in which the only source of CO_2 production is metabolic, there is a close correlation between the steady state concentration of CO_2 and the rate of ventilation (see Chapter 2). Carbon dioxide sensors are therefore useful for controlling ventilation in certain occupied environments. This is a particularly valuable approach in densely populated buildings, such as offices and public buildings and in transiently occupied buildings such as shops, theatres and schools. Typical set point or control levels are in the region of 600 to 1000 ppm. This compares with ambient outdoor levels of between 350 to 400 ppm. Carbon dioxide systems are unsuitable in areas of smoking, where the dominant pollutant becomes the combustion products of tobacco. Additionally, it is not normally appropriate for the home, where low occupancy densities mean that CO_2 levels do not normally rise significantly. Although domestic CO_2 levels as high as 4000 ppm have been measured in bedrooms, these are associated with much more fundamental problems concerning the adequacy of domestic ventilation.

Particle sensors

Particle sensors monitor the particulate levels within zones. These may be of value in function rooms and other meeting zones in which heavy smoking may take place. Cost, however, is often prohibitively high.

Infra-red presence sensors

Instead of monitoring pollutants directly, infra-red presence detectors have been used to control ventilation systems. In principle, they monitor the movement of people in and out of a space and adjust the ventilation rate accordingly. Such sensors are extremely inexpensive. Results to date (Raatchen 1990) have not been promising, partly because it is difficult for these sensors to maintain a reliable count of the number of persons present.

Mixed gas sensors

A number of mixed gas detectors have been designed to monitor overall 'air quality'. These sensors respond to various reactive gases such as hydrogen sulphide, carbon monoxide and various volatile organic compounds. They can indicate the presence of occupants or animals but do not distinguish between individual gases and thus, from an air quality perspective, are not necessarily effective for demand controlled systems.

Sensor Location

Sensors need to be located in the polluting zone and in locations where pollutants are a hazard, either to the building occupant or to the building fabric. Often, the number of sensors that may be used is restricted by the constraint of cost with the result that siting becomes a compromise. Any compromise that will leave a locality at risk must be avoided.

In buildings with good mixing ventilation, the sensor location is not critical and should be placed for convenience. Sometimes it is placed in the exhaust duct although this is only satisfactory if air is continuously extracted. Carbon dioxide sensors should not be placed too close to the 'breathing' zone since CO_2 concentration is likely to be artificially high in this region. Moisture sensors should be located in the vicinity of the pollutant source, i.e. integral with cooking, washing or drying appliances and/or located in the vicinity of room extractors.

In buildings with good mixing ventilation, the sensor location is not critical and should be placed for convenience.

Sensors for displacement systems should be located close to the 'breathing zone', at the transition from 'clean' to 'polluted' air. They can also be located in continuously operated exhaust ducts but the set point must reflect the air quality of the 'breathing zone'.

Control systems: The control system relays information from the air quality sensor to the ventilation system. In its most rudimentary form this is simply a switch which is connected to the fan of the ventilation system. When the sensor indicates a need for ventilation, the ventilation fan is switched on.

Ventilation systems: The ventilation system is usually of conventional

DCV can be retrofitted into many existing ventilation systems.

mechanical design to which the demand controlled system is attached. This means that DCV can be retrofitted into many existing ventilation systems. Some demand controlled sensors can be used in conjunction with natural ventilation.

Applications: Demand controlled systems have been developed for all types of buildings. They are particularly beneficial in locations of transient occupancy or where pollutant loads, specific to an environment, vary over time. The effectiveness of demand controlled systems depends on identifying the dominant need for ventilation and providing a reliable sensor which is able to track this need.

Demand controlled systems are effective when:

- Outdoor air supply can be controlled (i.e. minimum infiltration or other losses).
- The occupancy pattern or dominant pollutant (see Chapter 2) is variable.
- Space heating or cooling energy loads can be minimised.
- The controlled pollutant (or pollutants) are dominant.

Advantages of demand controlled ventilation:

- Ventilation rate can be optimised to meet prevailing need.

Disadvantages of demand controlled ventilation:

- Sensors and control systems can be expensive.
- Currently methods are essentially restricted to carbon dioxide and humidity control.
- While "mixed gas" sensors can provide general control, the individual cocktail of gas is uncertain.
- High concentration of harmful pollutants could go undetected.

References

Arens E A, Bauman F S, Johnston L P, Zhang H, *Tests of localized ventilation systems in a new controlled environment chamber*, Proc 11th AIVC Conference, *Ventilation System Performance*, Vol 1, 1990.

BRE *Natural ventilation in non-domestic buildings*, BRE Digest 399, Building Research Establishment, (UK), 1994.

BRECSU *Selecting air conditioning systems – a guide for building clients and their advisers*, Good Practice Guide 71, Building Research Energy Technology Support Unit, UK, 1993.

CAN/CGSB-51.71-95, *The spillage test*, National Standards of Canada, 1995.

Guntermann K, *Experimental and numerical study on natural ventilation of atrium buildings*, proceedings of Roomvent '94: Air Distribution in Rooms, Volume 1, Fourth International Conference, air-tight 1994.

Hama G, *When and where is make-up air necessary*, Air Conditioning, Heating and Ventilation, November 1959.

Holmes M J, *Design for ventilation*, Proc 6th AIC Conference *Ventilation Strategies and Measurement Techniques*, Air Infiltration Centre, 1985.

Knoll B, *Advanced ventilation systems, state of the art review*, AIVC Technical Note 35, Air Infiltration and Ventilation Centre, 1992.

Knoll B,. *A new low pressure controlled air inlet*, Air Infiltration Review, Vol 14, No. 4, Air infiltration and Ventilation Centre, 1993.

Leventhall H G, Wise S S, Dineen S, *Active attenuation of noise in HVAC systems*, Acoustics, Part 1, Building Services Engineering Research and Technology Vol 16, No.1, CIBSE, 1995.

Limb M, *Natural ventilation, an annotated bibliography*, Air Infiltration and Ventilation Centre, Report No. BIB3, 1994a.

Limb M, *Current ventilation and air conditioning systems and strategies*, Air Infiltration and Ventilation Centre, Tech Note 42, 1994b.

Mansson L G, Svennberg S A, *Demand controlled ventilating systems – source book*, IEA Annex 18 Report, 1992.

Martin A J, *Control of natural ventilation*, Tech Note 11/95, BSRIA, ISBN 0 86022 406 6 1995.

Nielsen P V, *Representation of boundary conditions at supply openings*, Aalborg University, IEA Annex 20 report, February 1989.

Opt 't Veld P J M, *Noise aspects of ventilation systems*, IEA Annex 27 *Evaluation of domestic ventilation systems*, Report No 910767-1, 1993.

Raatschen W, *Demand controlled ventilating system: state of the art review*, Swedish Council for Building Research, Report D9:1990, IEA Energy Conservation in Buildings and Community Systems Programme, Annex 18,

Saum D W, Osborne M C, *Radon mitigation effects of passive stacks in*

residential new construction, Proceedings of the 5th International
Conference on Indoor Air Quality and Climate, Toronto, Volume 3, 1990.

Shepherd T, Parkins L, Cripps A *Effects of passive and mechanical ventilation on kitchen moisture levels*, proceedings of CIBSE National Conference 1994, held Brighton Conference Centre, Volume 2, 1994.

Schultz J M, *Natural ventilation with heat recovery. Naturlig ventilation med varmeganvinding* Tekniske Hojskole, Laboratoriet for Varmeisolering, Meddelelse nr. 249, December 1993.

Steimle F, *Volume control of fans to reduce the energy demand of ventilation systems*, Proc. 15th AIVC Conference, Vol 2, 1994.

Villenave J G, Millet J-R, Riberon J, *Two-zones model for predicting passive stack ventilation in multi-storey dwellings* proceedings of 15th AIVC Conference, *The Role of Ventilation*, Volume 2, September 1994.

6   Ventilation Heat Recovery

Definitions Relating to Heat Recovery
Ventilation Heat Recovery Techniques
Air-to-air Heat Recovery
Techniques Using Heat Pumps
Novel Heat Recovery Systems

Summary and Introduction

Ventilation heat recovery is the process by which thermal energy is recovered from exhaust air for re-use within the building. Since the scale of ventilation heat loss is often considerable, much effort has been devoted to the design and development of heat recovery systems. These have attracted much interest for applications in industry, offices and the home. Popular methods include 'air-to-air' systems, in which heat recovered from the exhaust air stream is used to pre-condition incoming fresh air, and heat pumps, in which heat from the exhaust air stream is used to pre-heat the building's hot water or space heating system. 'Dynamic' insulation methods are also under development. These effectively recover ventilation heat loss by passing exhaust air through the building insulation. Although not strictly ventilation air heat recovery, a further pre-conditioning approach is based on the use of underground ducting through which supply air is passed.

Ventilation heat recovery is the process by which thermal energy is recovered from exhaust air for re-use within the building

The theoretical heat transfer efficiencies of heat recovery systems can be quite high (typically 70% for air-to-air systems) thus adding to the attractiveness of this approach. It is nevertheless important to understand that, while the heat recovery system can appear to be extremely efficient, benefits must always be equated against the primary energy needed to drive the process and increased capital and maintenance costs. Various hidden losses such as air infiltration must also be included in any energy analysis. Without careful design and construction of the building envelope, total energy performance will be considerably impaired and, in some instances, more energy could be expended by the recovery process than is actually recovered. Climate also influences the appropriateness of heat recovery. Since the operating cost of a system is largely dependent on capacity, the benefit of heat recovery improves as the outdoor climate becomes more

Climate influences the appropriateness of heat recovery.

severe. As with any other efficiency measure, the successful implementation of heat recovery systems depends on several factors, these include:

- careful equipment selection,
- proper integration of that equipment into the ventilating system,,
- good commissioning,
- proper maintenance,
- air tight building construction.

The purpose of this Chapter is to review heat recovery systems and to outline the applications and conditions under which they can be expected to perform.

6.1 Definitions Relating to Heat Recovery

Important terms related to heat recovery include:

Coefficient of performance: The coefficient of performance (COP) is the ratio between the useful energy extracted from the heat recovery system and the energy used in the extraction process. Strictly this should be calculated in terms of primary rather than delivered energy.

Efficiency (or thermal efficiency): Thermal efficiency relates to the proportion of waste or 'lost' heat (sensible and latent) usefully recovered by the heat recovery process (usually expressed as a percentage).

Latent heat recovery: Latent heat recovery is the recovery of heat released by the condensation of vapour (usually water vapour).

Sensible (dry air) heat recovery: Sensible heat recovery is the recovery of waste heat from dry air.

6.2 Ventilation Heat Recovery Techniques

Various forms of heat recovery systems are available with each having their own set of applications, advantages and disadvantages. Principal methods include:

- air-to-air heat recovery,
- flue gas heat recovery,
- exhaust air heat pumps,
- combined air-to-air heat recovery with heat pumps,
- dynamic insulation,
- pre-conditioning of supply air using buried or 'ground' ducting.

6.3 Air-to-Air Heat Recovery

Air-to-air heat recovery systems are used to transfer heat from the exhaust air of a ventilation system to the supply air. Various approaches to air-to-air heat recovery are in use and are reviewed in detail by Irving (1994). Some systems are able to transfer latent heat, while others can work in reverse mode for space cooling applications. Air-to-air heat recovery systems are used in conjunction with mechanical balanced ventilation incorporating separate supply and exhaust networks. A demonstration system based on natural stack driven ventilation has been developed (Schultz,1993). Systems include:

Air -to-air heat recovery systems are used to transfer heat from the exhaust air of a ventilation system to the supply air.

Plate Heat Exchangers

Plate heat exchangers are static devices (i.e. they contain no moving parts). They consist of layers of separated, interleaved flow channels through which the supply and exhaust air flows. The channel walls or plates are constructed of very high conducting material (usually metal but also various types of plastic may be used) across which heat rapidly transfers. Systems incorporating polymer membranes for latent heat recovery have also being developed (Rose,1992).

The efficiency of a plate heat exchanger is primarily associated with the flow configuration of exhaust and supply air, the spacing between plates, the surface area and the type of surface (e.g. roughness can promote turbulence and enhance heat transfer coefficients). Example flow configurations are illustrated in Figure 6.1(a to c). Parallel, counter flow can produce a maximum theoretical heat recovery of 100% (less fan energy), while performance is reduced to a maximum of 50% if exhaust and supply air flow runs in the same direction. For optimum heat recovery, combined with ease of manufacture and installation, a cross flow system is commonly used. These can have efficiencies in excess of 70%. A typical configuration is illustrated in Figure 6.1(d). Fans are usually located on the supply and extract side, such that air is pulled through the heat exchanger. This minimises the pressure difference between the two air streams and, therefore, reduces the risk of cross contamination. Heat generated by the extract fan, however, is lost to the outgoing air stream. To prevent Summer overheating, a by-pass damper should be fitted, however the fan load will not be reduced unless controls are introduced to respond to the resultant fall in pressure drop.

Plate heat exchangers are used in dwellings (single family and apartments) and in other environments in which the supply and exhaust ducts can be brought closer together.

Applications: Plate heat exchangers are used in dwellings (single family and apartments) and in other environments in which the supply and exhaust ducts can be brought closer together. They are very popular in countries with severely cold climates (e.g. Scandinavia and Canada).

Advantages of plate heat exchangers:

• These systems are simple and reliable.

• The absence of moving parts minimises maintenance needs, although filters must be regularly replaced.

• If properly constructed, there is little possibility of cross contamination between air streams.

Disadvantages of plate heat exchangers:

• Unless a by-pass is provided there may be Summer overheating.

• Heat exchangers present an extra flow resistance, therefore increased fan energy over that needed by a balanced system without heat recovery is needed.

• Poorly designed or installed systems can add to system generated noise.

• Cross leakage can occur if there are faulty seals or damage has occurred.

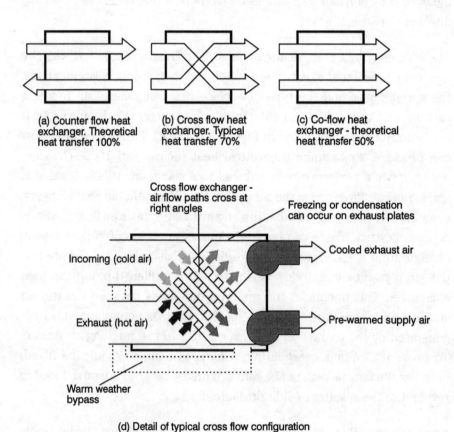

(a) Counter flow heat exchanger. Theoretical heat transfer 100%

(b) Cross flow heat exchanger. Typical heat transfer 70%

(c) Co-flow heat exchanger - theoretical heat transfer 50%

Cross flow exchanger - air flow paths cross at right angles

Freezing or condensation can occur on exhaust plates

Incoming (cold air)

Cooled exhaust air

Exhaust (hot air)

Pre-warmed supply air

Warm weather bypass

(d) Detail of typical cross flow configuration

Figure 6.1 Plate Heat Exchange System

Run-around Coils

Run-around coils comprise two fin type heat exchangers, one of which is installed in the supply air and the other in the exhaust (see Figure 6.2). A liquid (normally a water/glycol solution) is used as the heat transfer medium and is continuously pumped between the exchangers using a circulation pump. Heat in the exhaust air stream is thus transferred to the supply air via the heat exchangers. Performance is primarily related to the number of coil rows although, eventually, there is a trade off between the benefit of additional coil rows and the extra fan energy needed to overcome increasing pressure drop. Direct transfer efficiency must always, therefore, be compared against fan losses.

Run-around coils comprise two fin type heat exchangers, one of which is installed in the supply air and the other in the exhaust.

Applications: This approach is useful when fresh air and exhaust ducts are not adjacent to each other and hence often have important retrofit applications. Multiple supply and exhaust systems can be combined by a single loop. Total isolation means that heat can be recovered from industrial processes for use elsewhere.

Advantages of run-around Coils:

• The supply and exhaust air streams are totally separated, therefore the risk of cross contamination is eliminated.

Disadvantages of run-around coils:

• This type of system can only generally transfer sensible heat and has a relatively low efficiency (40 to 60%).

• The additional energy needed to operate the circulation pump has to be offset against predicted energy savings; typically this represents 5% of the energy available for heat recovery.

• The circulation pump presents additional maintenance requirements. Because heat is transferred from one coil to another, through interconnecting pipe-work, it is essential that it is protected from freezing. For this reason, a glycol solution is often used. Typically a glycol mix of 20% gives freeze protection down to -10°C but it increases the water loop pressure drop by 15% and reduces thermal transfer efficiency by 10 to 20%. For this reason alternative forms of frost protection may be considered such as trace heating, immersion heating or continuous pump operation. Where a system is operating at close to maximum duty, it is possible for condensation to occur. Although this can be transferred as sensible heat to the supply coil, condensation build-up will add to air flow resistance with pressure drops increasing by as much as 30%. This can also result in freezing problems in extreme climates. If condensation is likely to occur, drop eliminators are recommended to avoid damage to the coils. Again, however, these devices add to flow path resistance.

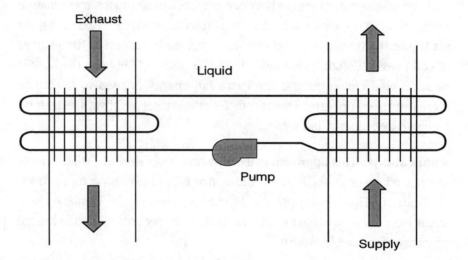

Figure 6.2 Run-around Coil System

Thermal Wheels

A thermal wheel is essentially a revolving cylinder divided into a number of segments packed with coarsely knitted metal mesh or some other inert material. It operates by rotating at between 10 and 20 revolutions per minute picking up heat in the warmer exhaust stream and discharging it into the cooler supply air stream (see Figure 6.3). Some thermal wheels contain desiccant materials which enable latent heat transfer to take place. This is especially useful in an air conditioned environment where the system can be operated in reverse mode to dry and cool incoming air. Since it is not possible for the wheel to provide a perfect barrier between the exhaust and supply air, some cross contamination is inevitable. This may be reduced by incorporating a small 'purging zone' in which the portion of outdoor air that passes through the section of wheel element that is closest to the exhaust air zone is purged before it enters the supply duct.

Thermal wheel performance is largely a function of the packing material. Different packing materials are applied according to need (e.g. latent heat recovery). This is a unique benefit of thermal wheels. Thermal wheels also have the highest efficiency of all devices which, combined with a low air side pressure drop will tend to maximise net energy savings.

Applications: Thermal wheels tend to be used in large commercial or public buildings where they form an integral part of the HVAC system.

They can be constructed to meet the most demanding of ventilation capacity.

Advantages of thermal wheels:

- Depending on the medium, thermal wheels can transfer latent heat as well as sensible heat.
- A variable speed drive enables the efficiency of the device to be varied.
- The wide range of available matrix materials enable the system to be designed to suit many applications.
- Static pressure drop across the system tends to be low, this minimises the use of fan energy.

A thermal wheel is essentially a revolving cylinder divided into a number of segments packed with coarsely knitted metal mesh or some other inert material.

Disadvantages of thermal wheels:

- Exhaust and supply ducts must be adjacent.
- The drive motor increases energy penalty.
- A purge section reduces thermal efficiency and, even when fitted some cross contamination is unavoidable, and so thermal wheels cannot be used where noxious fumes are exhausted, or where the presence of any exhaust air in the supply stream is unacceptable.

Heat Recovery from Air and Flue Gases

Some systems provide for the recovery of waste heat from the flue gases of a gas heating system in addition to that from the exhaust ventilation air. Flue gas heat is passed through a conventional plate air-to-air heat exchanger as part of a balanced ventilation system. Examples of the application and performance of this technique are described by Etheridge (1985) and Steimle et al (1992).

Applications: This method is principally aimed at dwellings with gas fired warm air or 'wet' central heating systems.

Advantages of heat recovery from air and flue gases:

- Waste heat is extracted from flue gas.

Disadvantages of heat recovery from air and flue gases:

- Care must be taken to avoid the risk of flue gas contaminating the supply air.

- To accomplish this, the extract duct must, at all times, be below room pressure, and this is normally achieved by placing the extract fan at the flue discharge point.

- Pressure sensors must automatically shut off the gas supply to the appliances should extract pressure rise through a fault condition.

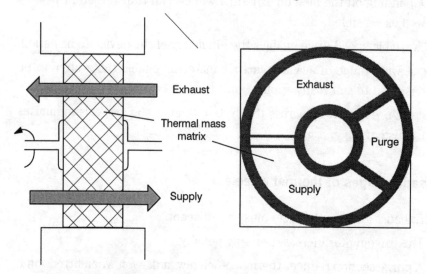

Figure 6.3 Thermal Wheel
(Courtesy - FGK, Germany)

Heat Recuperators

Under development are 'cyclical' heat recuperators (see Figure 6.4) This system uses a chamber with a significant thermal capacity and a damper to cycle the supply and exhaust flows between two halves of the chamber. In the first part of the cycle, the exhaust air flowing through one half of the chamber heats up the thermal mass. The damper is then moved so that the supply air now flows through that part of the chamber, absorbing the heat from the structure and reducing its temperature for the beginning of the next cycle. Efficiencies can be quite high for these systems.

Heat Recovery Performance

Heat is only recovered from the air that passes through the heat recovery system. Heat lost through other openings is not recovered and, if significant, will have a considerable impact on the energy performance of a heat recovery system. In the case of balanced ventilation systems, air exchange through infiltration adds directly to that through the balanced system itself. It is therefore imperative that infiltration losses are minimised. An example is illustrated in Figure 6.5 in which a design ventilation rate of 0.5 ach is specified. In Figure 6.5(a), the entire design air flow is assumed to pass through the heat recovery system, resulting in a worthwhile 70% energy recovery. In Figure 6.5(b) the system has been installed in a leaky structure in which the air infiltration rate is, itself, 0.5 ach Now the net heat recovery is only 35%. Worse, the total energy loss is 15% greater than if the system had not been installed. This is because air infiltration has resulted in doubling the design air change rate. Calculation methods outlining the energy and cost performance of air-to-air heat recovery systems are given in Chapter 12.

Heat is only recovered from the air that passes through the heat recovery system. Heat lost through other openings is not recovered and, if significant, will have a considerable impact on the energy performance of a heat recovery system.

6.4 Heat Pumps

Ventilation Exhaust Air Heat Pumps

Ventilation exhaust air heat pumps provide a further method by which waste heat from the exhaust air may be recovered. These have become popular in some countries because a balanced mechanical supply air system is unnecessary since the waste heat is used to pre-heat domestic or space heating hot water.

Three configurations are common; these are:

- air to liquid systems for the preheating of hot water supply for domestic hot water and/or 'wet' central space heating,
- air to both liquid and air for combined hot water heating and warm air space heating,

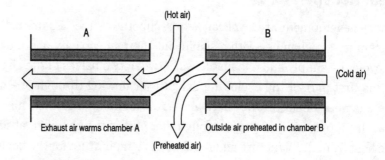

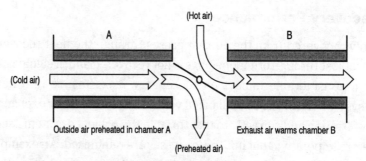

Figure 6.4 Heat Recuperator System
(Courtesy J Brunsell, Norwegian Building Research Institute)

- air-to-air systems to supplement air-to-air heat recovery.

Typically an 'air to liquid' heat pump is used in which the evaporator is located in the exhaust air stream, to extract heat from the outgoing air, while the condenser is located in a reservoir tank, to boost water temperature. Sometimes the condenser may be located in a fan coil unit through which indoor air is continuously recirculated and heated (an air-to-air heat pump system). To extract maximum efficiency, heat pump output may be split between space heating and domestic hot water heating.

Applications: Ventilation heat recovery heat pump systems can be found in many types of buildings demanding continuous occupancy. These include schools, hospitals, apartment buildings and single family dwellings. They have, for example, been used in retrofit applications to replace a passive stack type or exhaust only ventilation system. Numerous examples and case studies of installed systems now exist. In Scandinavia, a study by Nilson (1987) on nine Gothenburg apartment buildings showed that the annual net energy savings arising from the fitting of heat pumps for extract ventilation heat recovery amounted to 35 kWh/m^2. In the Ontario region of Canada, Cane (1992) reported that systems installed in hospitals and apartments had a payback period of between four to six years. Systems for single family homes yielded electrical savings of between 1500 and

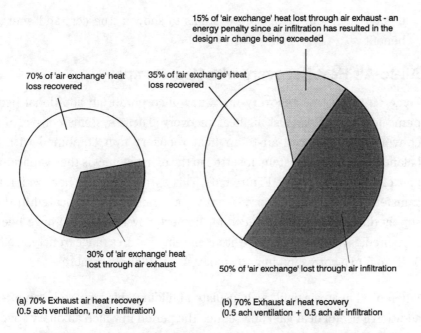

15% of 'air exchange' heat lost through air exhaust - an energy penalty since air infiltration has resulted in the design air change being exceeded

70% of 'air exchange' heat loss recovered

35% of 'air exchange' heat loss recovered

30% of 'air exchange' heat lost through air exhaust

50% of 'air exchange' lost through air infiltration

(a) 70% Exhaust air heat recovery (0.5 ach ventilation, no air infiltration)

(b) 70% Exhaust air heat recovery (0.5 ach ventilation + 0.5 ach air infiltration

Figure 6.5 Influence of Air Infiltration on Air to Air Heat Recovery Performance

3000kWh/yr. Wallman et al (1990) showed that energy savings for all electric homes fitted with dual condenser systems (i.e. one for hot water and one for warm air heating) in Portland, USA were estimated to be 6000 to 7000kWh less than an equivalent all electric home.

Advantages of ventilation exhaust air heat pumps:

• Heat may be recovered from the exhaust air stream without the need for a balanced supply air system.

• This can considerably reduce ventilation system costs and reduce the space needed for ductwork.

• Exhaust only systems or passive stack ventilation systems can be upgraded to incorporate heat pumps.

• Also extract ventilation systems provide some protection against air infiltration thus enabling some air leakage to be tolerated.

• Acceptable air leakage values including infiltration and purpose provided openings should not exceed 3 to 5 ach at 50 Pa induced pressure.

Disadvantages of ventilation exhaust air heat pumps:

• Heat pumps are relatively costly and require operational energy.

• The energy benefit must be carefully evaluated.

• Coefficient of Performance (COP) values need to be high, probably greater than four or five, for systems to show a true cost and energy benefit.

Air-to-Air Heat Recovery with Heat Pumps

Some air-to-air heat recovery units now incorporate an additional heat pump for further exhaust air heat recovery. These systems consist of a conventional balanced air-to-air heat recovery unit combined with a balanced ventilation system.

Some air-to-air heat recovery units now incorporate an additional heat pump for further exhaust air heat recovery. These systems consist of a conventional balanced air-to-air heat recovery unit combined with a balanced ventilation system. Inserted in the exhaust duct is the evaporator unit of a heat pump (see Figure 6.6). This extracts further heat which is transferred to the supply air stream via a condenser unit located in the supply duct. Typical COP values for domestic systems of 3.0 have been measured, Siviour et al(1993). Output air temperatures range from typically 30°C to 50°C, corresponding to an output of 1000Wh or more.

When used in an air tight, well insulated building, this approach can offer additional useful heat gain and reduce the period in which auxiliary space heating becomes necessary. Efficient use depends on a good control strategy that prevents the operation of conventional space heating, while sufficient heat is being supplied by the heat recovery unit. Air distribution must also be controlled for optimum performance. This means satisfying ventilation needs of each room and providing sufficient air flow to meet thermal requirements.

Advantages of air-to-air heat recovery with heat pumps:

• additional heat recovery is possible from the exhaust air stream.

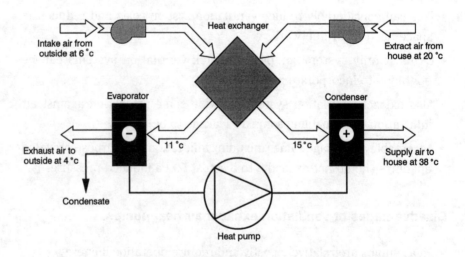

Figure 6.6 Plate Heat Exchanger with Heat Pump

Disadvantages of air-to-air heat recovery with heat pumps:

- Disadvantages are similar to those of air-to-air heat recovery systems in that air tight construction is essential and cost in terms of operation and maintenance must be considered.
- Also extra capital cost and maintenance need will be incurred resulting in a lengthened pay back period.

6.5 Dynamic Insulation

Dynamic insulation is a means by which ventilation air is passed through the fabric of the building to effectively reduce fabric heat loss. The resultant total heat loss from the building, due to ventilation and conduction, becomes less than that which would be due to ventilation loss and conduction loss.

Dynamic insulation is a means by which ventilation air is passed through the fabric of the building to effectively reduce fabric heat loss.

Several configurations are available. These include:

Counter-flow (extract ventilation): A conventional extract ventilation system is used to extract air from the building. The resultant under pressure is used to draw air in through the building fabric in a counter or opposite flow direction to conduction heat loss. Heat from the building fabric is absorbed by the incoming air which is thus pre-heated. In theory, as the air flow rate increases and captures more of the heat from the fabric insulation, the 'U' value of the insulation reduces, hence the term 'dynamic' insulation'. Maximum performance occurs when all the available conduction heat is captured and is only possible at high ventilation rates.

Co-flow (supply ventilation): Supply ventilation is used to pressurise the building. The resultant over pressure induces air to flow out of the building through the building fabric. Assuming that the outdoor air temperature is below that of the indoor air temperature, the direction of airborne heat transport is the same as that of conduction heat transport. Heat in the departing air stream is absorbed by the fabric insulation, thereby effectively reducing conduction loss by modifying the temperature gradient at the interface between the inside space and the envelope. There is a danger, however, as the departing air stream loses heat, moisture in the extract air may condense into the fabric insulation.

Combined counter and co-flow systems: Maximum theoretical heat recovery is possible by combining the two systems such that half the fabric area provides a counter flow approach, while the other half provides a co flow approach. This behaves rather as a balanced ventilation system in which the supply air is pre-heated while the exhaust air is able to surrender its heat.

Alternating combined counter and co-flow systems: A further method to maximise the heat exchange is to alternate the direction of supply and extract airflow.

Theoretical performance: An analytical study has been made by Jensen (1993) of the energy performance of dynamic insulation. This combines the classical conduction and heat transfer theory. Jensen introduces the concept of relative heat loss reduction, which he defines as the ratio between combined ventilation and conduction heat loss, based on using dynamic insulation compared with the heat loss resulting from the direct addition of ventilation and conduction heat loss. Heat loss reduction is shown to be a function of the ratio between normal ventilation heat loss and normal conduction loss.

For counter or co-flow, performance peaks at 0.23 at a ventilation to conduction ratio of 1.79 and for combined counter and co flow performance peaks at 0.35 for a ratio of 1.15. It is also shown that when applied to heat recovery efficiency of the ventilation air, this translates to a maximum performance of 0.5 heat recovery for counter or co-flow and 1.0 for combined flow. It is theoretically possible to optimise the ventilation to conduction ratio to satisfy particular design needs.

Practical examples: A number of buildings have been constructed to evaluate the potential of dynamic ventilation. Brunsell (1994), for example, presents the results from a set of row-houses designed with dynamic insulation in the roof (see Figure 6.7). These dwellings have been carefully designed to take full advantage of dynamic insulation. A 10 Pa pressure difference was planned resulting in a velocity of 2 m/h through the roof insulation. This was designed to be equivalent to 0.8 ach for the whole house. Assuming an air leakage value of < 1 ach at 50 Pa, air from the remainder of the structure would account for a further 0.3 ach at 10 Pa of ventilation resulting in a total design ventilation rate of 1.1 ach. Measurements on the houses revealed that a slightly smaller proportion of ventilation air came from the roof space than was intended as a consequence of the dwelling being leakier than the design value. Nevertheless, it was found that ventilation could be drawn through the dynamic insulation without creating draughts and that the heat loss through the insulation could be reduced to almost zero. No particulate or fibres were found in the insulation.

Advantages of dynamic insulation:

• Heat recovery is potentially possible.

• A counter flow system could be used to pre-heat incoming air, while a heat pump, inserted in the exhaust air duct, could recover heat from the outgoing air stream.

Disadvantages of dynamic insulation:

• Performance is subject to very specific operating conditions requiring careful design and precision engineering. This will add to capital and construction costs.

• Co-flow or combined flow systems could result in moisture condensation damage and could not, therefore, be recommended as a practical option.

• Counter flow systems have an operational efficiency below that which can be accomplished with an ordinary air-to-air heat recovery system.

• Inevitable clogging of the insulation, as air is passed through it, will impair performance.

• The incoming air might be contaminated with insulation products or gases.

It is unlikely that this approach will offer a practical alternative to conventional heat recovery methods in the near future.

6.6 'Ground' Pre-heat Recovery

It is possible to pre-condition ventilation air by using earth-laid pipes as

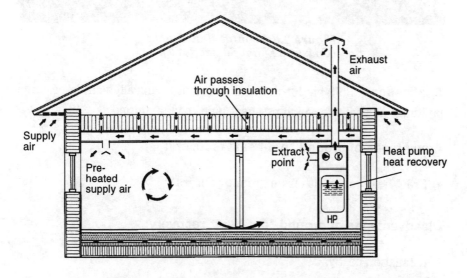

Figure 6.7 Dynamic Insulation
(Courtesy J Brunsell, Norwegian Building Research Institute)

It is possible to pre-condition ventilation air by using earth-laid pipes as part of a mechanical ventilation supply duct (see Figure 6.8)

part of a mechanical ventilation supply duct (see Figure 6.8). In Winter these systems take advantage of the thermal energy stored in the ground, while, in Summer, the ground can absorb excess heat from the supply air. Trumper et al (1991) describes a system for a single family dwelling which incorporates 42m of 125mm diameter tubing. 140 m3/h of supply air is provided using a 50W fan. In a demonstration study, 421 kWh of total cooling (sensible + latent) at a cost of 36 kWh of electrical energy was achieved. In Winter, 923 kWh of useful heat was provided at the expense of 127 kWh of electrical energy. The optimum depth of piping depends on the thermal characteristics of the ground. Typical depths are 3 to 4.5 m. These results indicate that very high 'coefficients of performance' are feasible.

Figure 6.8 Ground Heat Ducts
(Courtesy EMPA Switzerland)

Applications: Suitable for both small and mechanically ventilated large buildings adjacent to which pre-heat pipes can be buried.

Advantages of ground "pre-heat" recovery:

• "Free" heat and coolth from ground sources.

Disadvantages of ground "pre-heat" recovery:

• Installation costly.
• Extra fan capacity.
• Maintenance/replacement strategy needed.

References

Brunsell J T, *The performance of dynamic insulation in two residential buildings*, Proc 15th AIVC Conference, Buxton, Great Britain (supplement).

Cane R L D, Clemes B, Forgas D, *Electricity savings through heat pump heat recovery in buildings*, IEA Heat Pump Centre Newsletter, Vol 10, No 2, June 1992.

Etheridge D, *Signs of recovery*, Watson House Bulletin, Vol 49, No 3, 1985

Irving S J, *Air-to-air heat recovery in ventilation*, AIVC Tech Note 45, 1994.

Jensen L, *The energy impact of ventilation and dynamic insulation*, Proc 14th AIVC Conference, Copenhagen, Denmark, pp251-260, 1993.

Nilson A, *Evaluation of energy savings by measurements when implementing extensive energy conservation measures in nine blocks of flats*, Proc Third International Congress on Building Energy Management ICBEM'87, Vol 2, 1987.

Rose W B *An efficient enthalpy exchanger for economical ventilation*, Proc 13th AIVC Conference, 1992.

Schultz J M, *Natural ventilation with heat recovery. Naturlig ventilation med varmeganvinding*, Tekniske Hojskole, Laboratoriet for Varmeisolering, Meddelelse nr. 249, December 1993,

Siviour J B, Bertinat M P, *Performance of a heat pump ventilation unit (HPVU) in a United Kingdom house*, Proc ASHRAE, *Building design technology and occupant well-being in temperate climates*. International conference, 1993.

Steimle F, Roeben J, *Ventilation requirements in modern buildings*, Proc. 13th AIVC Conference, 1992.

Trumper H, Albers K-J , *Preheating and cooling of the incoming air of dwellings using an earth-laid pipe*, Proc AIVC 12th Conference, *Air Movement and Ventilation Control within Buildings*, Vol 2, September 1991.

Wallman P H, Fisk W J, *Exhaust-air heat-pump performance with unsteady-state operation*, Heat Recovery Systems & CHP, Vol 10, No 3, 1990.

AIVC Guide to Ventilation

7 Ventilation and Cooling

Cooling in Relation to Ventilation Strategy
Passive and Mixed Mode Techniques
Reducing the Need for Cooling

Summary and Introduction

While active cooling can provide reliable thermal comfort, its use adds considerably to building energy need. Such cooling is often essential in hot and humid climates but it is also used to remedy high internal and solar heat gains that may arise from inappropriate architectural design or excessive thermal loads from electrical equipment and other indoor sources. Energy savings are possible in all climates by minimising unnecessary heat loads. Where heat gains are from predominantly indoor sources it should often be possible to replace active cooling by passive cooling methods involving ventilation. By so doing, conditioning energy need is eliminated. A problem with passive cooling is that a stable thermal climate cannot be guaranteed, instead some flexibility in indoor conditions must be accepted. Often this flexibility is expressed in terms of acceptable periods of deviation from notional design conditions.

As demand for good comfort conditions in both the home and workplace has increased, there has been a steady growth in the use of such systems.

Cooling is needed when the indoor environment becomes excessively hot or humid. This may occur as a result of high outdoor temperatures or as a consequence of excessive solar or internal heat gains. High internal gain is a particular problem in large non-domestic buildings where the volume to surface area ratio rapidly rises causing generated heat to be trapped in the space. This difficulty is made worse if solar gain is concentrated by large areas of glazing. Traditionally, cooling needs have been met by the use of refrigerative air conditioning systems and, as demand for good comfort conditions in both the home and workplace has increased, there has been a steady growth in the use of such systems. This demand is adding to energy use in buildings.

When the need for cooling is dictated by internal heat gains rather than outside temperature and humidity, much can be accomplished to reduce the need for, or eliminate altogether, active cooling systems. Solutions depend on climate but include cooling by ventilation (passive cooling), designing for reduced solar gains, the use of thermal mass and restricting internal heat loads.

A complete analysis of air conditioning and cooling systems is beyond the scope of this Guide. Instead, a background to cooling is presented in relation to the role that ventilation plays in interacting with cooling needs. Essentially, two distinct roles for ventilation can be identified. In the first it provides a mechanism by which air from a cooling system is distributed to a space. In this respect, its role is no different from that applied to meeting the needs of heating. In particular, excessive air change must be avoided since this will result in energy waste or may prevent cooling from being achieved. In its second role, ventilation is used as a mechanism to flush hot air from a building to be replaced by cooler outdoor air. 'Flushing' may further be used, especially at night, to cool the structure or fabric of the building itself (night cooling). This method of cooling is attractive since the 'active' conditioning of air (by refrigerative or evaporative techniques) may be avoided. Unlike mechanical cooling, this role demands a high air change rate which is commonly met by window opening or also by the use of stacks and atria.

In many cases the choice between "mechanical" or "passive" cooling is well defined with much depending on building type and climate.

In many cases the choice between 'mechanical' or 'passive' cooling is well defined with much depending on building type and climate. On the other hand there is a very significant 'intermediate' zone where the choice is less well defined. Much research is taking place in this area to extend the 'balance point' at which 'passive' rather than 'active' cooling techniques can be employed.

7.1 Cooling in Relation to Ventilation Strategy

'Mechanical' ('active') cooling

Mechanical cooling strategies vary according to need (i.e. 'sensible' or combined 'sensible' and 'latent' cooling) and according to ventilation strategy (i.e. 'mixing' or 'displacement'). These methods are usually used in conjunction with mechanical ventilation although some systems operate independently of ventilation strategy. Cooling techniques include:

Evaporative cooling: Sensible 'evaporative' cooling is appropriate to hot dry climates in which cooling can take place without relative humidity rising above comfort levels (see Chapter 2, Chapter 3 and Colliver 1995). With 'direct' systems, ventilation air is passed through the path of a water spray. Heat for evaporation is taken from the air supply thus reducing its temperature. In so doing, the water content of the ventilation air is increased. In 'indirect' systems, the air is passed through a network of tubes, the outside surfaces of which are kept moistened with a fine water spray. This prevents additional humidification. Furthermore, this system can form part of an air recirculation system to retain conditioned air within the building. Liveris (1995) reports that evaporative cooling is appropriate to climates in which the mid-day Summer relative humidity does not exceed

40%. Sometimes evaporative cooling is used in conjunction with passive 'night' cooling. Bollinger et al (1993), for example, indicate that evaporative cooling combined with passive 'night' cooling can exclusively deal with a thermal load of up to 55 W/m2 provided the outside air temperature does not exceed 28°C.

Refrigerative cooling: Refrigerative cooling methods provide for both the cooling and dehumidification of indoor air. They are used when the outdoor air temperature and relative humidity are above comfort levels (see Chapter 2) and when solar and internal heat gains are high. Techniques are based on the mechanical compression (liquification) and evaporation by expansion of refrigerant gases. The latent heat of vapourisation depresses the temperature of cooling coils over which the air to be cooled is passed. Dehumidification takes place at the cooling coils where the local air temperature is brought below the dew point temperature of the air. In the majority of applications, relative humidity can be permitted to float between approximately 30-60% (see Chapter 2) but, in some applications, much tighter control may be necessary. Although humidity levels can be allowed to vary, in some climatic regions, humidity control can nevertheless be the most significant effect in determining the energy consumption of air conditioning. This is because air has to be cooled to below its dew point. Once the required moisture content has been achieved, further energy is needed to bring the air back to the supply temperature.

Refrigerative cooling methods provide for both the cooling and dehumidification of indoor air.

Refrigerative cooling systems are popular because good control of the internal environment is possible and because they can be designed to meet a wide range of needs. Unfortunately, refrigerative cooling is energy intensive and is therefore actively discouraged in some countries. When such cooling is necessary, much can be accomplished by good design and maintenance to ensure efficient operation. A key aspect is the space cooling load which represents the energy that must be removed to achieve and maintain the desired temperature and humidity levels within the building. This in turn is based on the amount of energy needed for sensible (dry air) cooling and humidity treatment (either dehumidification or humidification). It is this cooling load that dictates energy consumption, since all the relevant energy flows are related to this load. Consequently, good design must aim to minimise the space cooling load as much as possible by eliminating unnecessary heat gains.

Cooling with 'Mixing' Ventilation

Refrigerative cooling combined with mixing ventilation can be sized to meet almost any heat gain problem. It is commonly applied to many commercial and large buildings in a variety of climatic zones. Typical

Refrigerative cooling combined with mixing ventilation can be sized to meet almost any heat gain problem.

methods include:

Centralised air distribution cooling systems: Systems installed in large office complexes are traditionally centralised and combined with the heating and 'mixing' ventilation system. Incoming outdoor air is blended with recirculated air, filtered and conditioned for temperature and humidity. This air is distributed to occupied zones via a ducted distribution network. During periods in which the outdoor air temperature and relative humidity are below set point values, outdoor air may be introduced, without refrigeration.

Supply air temperatures for mixing ventilation systems can be typically provided at 10 to 12K below room air temperature. This combined with the cooling load requirement may be used to set the total volume flow rate of air needed to satisfy cooling needs. Since the resultant air flow rate for cooling is usually considerably in excess of that required to satisfy fresh air needs, recirculation and/or thermal recovery is essential.

Distribution of the chilled air by variable air volume 'VAV' is widely used, especially in buildings requiring all year cooling. Air is supplied at a constant temperature, with the volume of air to each zone of the building being varied to match cooling need. Alternative distribution systems include constant volume (suitable for buildings in which the cooling load is uniform) and dual systems (for very accurate temperature control) based on a combination of constant and variable air volume methods. Sometimes, further conditioning of the air is accomplished locally by means of additional room heating or cooling coils.

Localised air cooling systems: Local cooling systems are available to meet the cooling needs of individual rooms or zones such as in small offices or homes. They do not form part of the ventilation system and therefore can be used with either mechanical or natural ventilation methods. Cooling takes place by continuously circulating room air across the chiller coils of a refrigeration unit. Captured heat is dissipated into the outside air stream. Systems may either be 'single unit' or 'split'. Single systems incorporate the refrigeration section, chiller coil and air distribution fan as a wall or window mounted unit while split systems have their fan coil unit separated from the compressor. Several such fan coil units can be connected to the same compressor which may be situated at a convenient outside location. Some systems act as reversible heat pumps that are able to provide both heating and cooling.

Cooling with 'Displacement' Ventilation

Chilled ceilings: The cooling capacity of displacement ventilation systems is limited by the need for a low temperature difference between the supply and room air (typically 2K) and the need to supply air at a low discharge velocity (see Chapter 5). Normally the requirements of humidity treatment can be satisfied by the air distribution system but sensible cooling is limited to a maximum heat load of approximately 50 W/m2 Any additional sensible cooling must be met by alternative means that do not introduce air mixing into the displacement ventilation process. This difficulty has been overcome by the use of 'chilled' ceilings which can bring cooling capacity up to approximately 100 W/m2 of floor surface. These provide cooling by radiation and/or convection, Mertz (1993). Radiation cooling systems generally form part of a pre-cast or plastered ceiling containing pipes through which coolant (usually water) is circulated. Convective ceilings consist of a network of horizontal or vertical fins, located beneath ceiling level. Observations show that convective down-draughts created by chilled ceilings need not necessarily conflict with the upward motion of displacement ventilation (Dickson 1994). Control strategies are needed to avoid the risk of condensation on the ceiling or convective elements. This involves ensuring that the coolant temperature remains above dew point temperature.

7.2 Passive and Mixed Mode Techniques

'Passive' Cooling

In response to environmental concerns over greenhouse gas emissions and ozone depletion, there has been a trend to move towards more passive and hybrid approaches to cooling (Annex 28). Designing for ventilation cooling is an enormous subject in its own right. It requires very close integration of the architectural and HVAC designs. Firstly, particular attention has to be given to envelope performance to minimise the heat gains the system has to deal with. Secondly, the organisation of the building should be such as to promote enhanced natural flows during periods of high cooling requirement. Considerable attention has been given to such features as atria and solar chimneys to enhance stack effects to provide the required building air change rates (see Chapter 5). Methods and examples of natural and low energy cooling methods for buildings are presented by Liveris (1995). Studies by BSRIA (Martin 1995) indicate that cooling up to approximately 40 W/m2 can be accomplished by passive cooling. Essentially, techniques are based on 'traditional' methods that have been used by civilisations throughout history. These incorporate:

Designing for ventilation cooling is an enormous subject in its own right. It requires very close integration of the architectural and HVAC designs.

Natural ventilation: Natural ventilation is used to purge the building of hot air and cool the building fabric. Methods may include window opening, wind towers, solar chimneys and atria. In each case the system is designed to take advantage of prevailing driving forces. Air movement is also an important aspect of ventilation cooling since it offsets increases in temperature while maintaining comfort, provided that the increased air velocities are under occupant control e.g. through task ventilation or user control of opening windows.

Thermal mass: A particular problem of passive cooling is that the cooling potential of the outside air is at a minimum when the heat gains are at a maximum. Techniques to overcome this difficulty focus on the use of thermal mass. This has the effect of reducing diurnal temperature variations and limiting radiant temperature. Peak temperatures may be reduced by 2 to 3 K.

Night cooling: To achieve the potential of thermal mass, emphasis is placed on night cooling, in which either mechanically or naturally provided ventilation air is used to cool down structural elements in the building fabric. During the day time advantage may be taken of reduced radiant temperatures and depressed ventilation air temperatures for improved comfort.

Applications: These methods are primarily intended for climates in which high outdoor air temperatures and humidity levels do not present the main need for cooling, although even in such climates useful reductions in active cooling are possible.

Advantages of passive and mixed mode techniques:

• Passive cooling eliminates or minimises the periods in which active cooling is needed. This significantly reduces the need for conditioning energy.

Disadvantages of passive and mixed mode techniques:

• Specific thermal conditions cannot be maintained by passive cooling.
• Instead some flexibility in conditions must be accepted.
• Such flexibility may be expressed in terms of permitted periods of deviation from notional design conditions.

'Mixed Mode' Cooling

Sometimes ventilation cooling techniques (mechanical or passive) are used to reduce the periods in which mechanical cooling is needed.

Sometimes ventilation cooling techniques (mechanical or passive) are used to reduce the periods in which mechanical cooling is needed. Such buildings are operated in 'mixed' mode. Variable air volume systems, for example, can take advantage of a dramatic reduction in fan energy use at reduced air flow rates when the cooling load is below peak design conditions. At any cooling load less than the design duty, the option is available to cool the air to the design room temperature either by using refrigeration or by using a greater volume of out door air. For maximum energy efficiency, a balance has to be found between increased fan power and chiller consumption.

Examples in the literature, Channer (1994) and Brister (1995) describe predominantly naturally ventilated 'mixed mode' buildings at both ends of the development spectrum. The first is the 23 storey GSW tower in Berlin, whereas the second is a much smaller office building. In both cases, mixed mode is seen as providing substantial energy benefit and provides the occupants with a measure of environmental control.

Applications: Mixed mode design is an extension of good design practice to minimise unnecessary heat gains during periods when cooling becomes necessary. All buildings which are likely to need active cooling should adopt mixed mode design guidelines.

Advantages of mixed mode cooling:

• The need for active cooling energy can be significantly reduced.

Disadvantages of mixed mode cooling:

• There is a risk of improper use in which 'passive' ventilation air change operates in conjunction with active cooling, e.g. windows and vents left open during periods of refrigerative cooling.

• This will result in a poor thermal environment and an expensive loss of conditioned air.

• Extra expense of combined cooling method.

7.3 Reducing the Need for Cooling

Control of Heat Gains

Minimising the need for mechanical cooling and extending the range of passive cooling is dependent on good control over thermal gains. Sources of heat gain include conduction through the building fabric, infiltration of ambient air, solar gains through window glazing, and internal gains from lights, equipment and occupants. Clearly the higher these gains, the greater will be the cooling load to achieve a desired thermal condition within the building. It is therefore important to consider how these gains may be minimised or controlled in the Summer months to reduce the energy requirement for cooling.

It is important to consider how these gains may be minimised or controlled in the Summer months to reduce the energy requirement for cooling.

Major sources of heat gain include:

Outdoor climate: In many climates, outdoor conditions present a major reason for cooling. Gains arise from high outdoor air temperatures (thermal gain) and from solar radiation (solar gains).

Thermal gains: Thermal gain occurs as a result of high outdoor air temperature and humidity conditions. This is essentially an unavoidable condition which is dependent on geographical location. The impact of outdoor thermal conditions on both heating and cooling needs has been analysed by Colliver (1995). This study focused on an analysis of hourly weather data for representative weather years from over forty sites throughout Europe and North America. These data were used to evaluate the energy needed to condition the outdoor air to various set point temperature and humidity levels. The results and methodology enable the need for cooling, as a consequence of outdoor conditions, to be assessed for any location. This approach also enables the most appropriate cooling strategy to be identified (see Chapter 3).

Solar gains: Solar gain occurs as a result of the absorption of infra-red radiation by surfaces exposed to sunlight. The temperature of these surfaces can rise considerably, resulting in heat transfer to the surrounding air stream. Solar gain is used to advantage in 'passive' solar designs to provide 'free' heat during periods when space heating would otherwise be needed. On the other hand, excessive Summer time solar gain frequently leads to overheating of buildings and the unnecessary use of air conditioning systems. If building design is poor, overheating is possible, even when outdoor ambient air temperatures are relatively low. In addition, solar gain may cause discomfort to occupants who are exposed to direct radiation. Methods to reduce solar gain include minimising glazing, using special coatings.

These problems may be overcome by implementing good architectural design aimed at balancing the need for minimising excessive solar gain against the need to provide daylight and a view for occupants of the outside world. Architectural features to minimise solar gains include window recesses and self shading by different parts of the building (e.g. overhanging roof eaves). Other methods include coated glazing, and the use of external blinds and shutters. Once solar radiation has penetrated glazing, little can be done to reduce its impact on indoor air temperature.

Many buildings situated in climates that would otherwise not warrant refrigerative cooling, require cooling as a consequence of internal gains.

Internal heat loads: The need for cooling is greatly influenced by the magnitude of internal heat gains. These are affected by the use to which the building is put. Many buildings situated in climates that would otherwise not warrant refrigerative cooling, require cooling as a consequence of internal gains. Principal gains are from electrical sources such as lighting and office equipment and from occupants themselves.

Electrical appliances: Although the use of both domestic and office electrical appliances has risen in recent years, the energy usage of individual appliances has steadily reduced. One major factor involved in the over-specification of air conditioning is excessive assumptions about the levels of heat gain from office equipment. In general, name plate ratings are a poor estimate of the actual heat output from the appliance. Over generous allowances leads to oversized air conditioning equipment, which then runs for extended periods at part load. This is wasteful on capital costs, as well as energy costs, Parsloe et al (1992). Some electrical appliances have automatic power saving features to minimise electrical and heat loads, while various PC manufacturers now produce 'low energy machines' that assist in reducing heat gain to the space. Furthermore, some furniture manufacturers are providing integrated desks that enable heat emitted from PC's to be removed with the extract air, thereby reducing the cooling load. Further reductions are achieved by ensuring that all unused appliances are switched off.

Lighting gains: The required lighting levels for the tasks to be carried out in the building, will largely determine the gains from lighting. Good daylighting, the use of low energy light sources and good lighting control are all beneficial. Control of lighting gains is especially important when cooling is necessary since a reduction in lighting gain not only saves electricity directly, but also indirectly by reducing cooling demand. Another important contribution to reducing heat gain from lighting is to use air handling luminaires from which ventilation air is extracted which remove a significant proportion of the heat at source. The energy needed to provide the same level of illumination varies considerably according to the lighting system used, with values, for example, varying from 8 to 10 W/m2 for triphosphor to 33 W/m2 for standard fluorescent to achieve 500 lux of light intensity.

Occupants: Occupants make an important contribution to heat load, especially in densely occupied buildings. Total heat emission for a sedentary occupant averages approximately 100 Watts.

Control of Building Services

Various other performance factors influence and reduce the need for cooling energy. These include:

Flexible environmental set point: Flexibility in setpoint values for

Flexibility in setpoint values for temperature and humidity can have a major impact on energy performance as can permitted short term transient drifts from the comfort zone.

temperature and humidity can have a major impact on energy performance as can permitted short term transient drifts from the comfort zone. Allowances in set point values can also enable reductions in the design cooling load thus enabling a reduction in plant size. Handel et al (1992) demonstrate that a useful energy reduction of at least 10% is possible by permitting a flexible rather than fixed environmental set point. Colliver (1995) also demonstrates that energy requirements, especially for cooling, are highly sensitive to environmental set points.

Other factors observed by Handel included increased energy impact due to inadequate maintenance and poor controls. Improper use of sun blinds resulted in a temperature increase of 7K while a wrongly designed variable air volume (VAV) system contributed to an increase in energy consumption of 10% to 15%. Further problems identified included simultaneous heating and cooling, and filter and duct clogging.

Avoiding distribution losses: Distribution losses include leakage of conditioned air to the outside or to unconditioned spaces. These losses can be enormous and completely destroy any benefit of air conditioning. Modera (1989), for example, emphasises the problems associated with air leakage from poor quality ducting in housing which can account for air infiltration increases of 30 to 70%. Often, the fabric of the building or the quality of installation is too inadequate to provide for efficient cooling, with conditioned air being lost through exfiltration. Resulting insufficient cooling can encourage occupants to open windows and doors, thus further adding to poor performance and wasted energy. Good air-tightness and ventilation design, therefore, plays an important role in securing energy efficient cooling.

Economiser cycles: Savings are possible by introducing an 'economiser' cycle. This varies the proportions of outside and recirculated air to minimise cooling plant energy consumption. In simplistic terms, the strategy aims to take advantage of any cooling capacity of outdoor air by blending it with return air in suitable proportions to satisfy cooling requirements with the minimum need for refrigeration. This means that for parts of the year no plant heating or cooling may be required.

References

Bollinger A, Roth H, *Benefits and limits of free cooling in non-residential buildings*, Proc. 14th AIVC Conference, *Energy Impact of Ventilation and Air Infiltration*, held Copenhagen, Denmark, 1993.

Brister A, *Chilled beams provide perpetual cooling*, Building Services, January 1995.

Channer G R, *A mixed mode ventilation system for an office tower which addresses the problems of infiltration, internal comfort and energy consumption*, Proc CIBSE National Conference Vol 2, 1994.

Colliver D G, *Energy requirements for the conditioning of ventilation air*, AIVC Technical Note 47, 1995.

Dickson D, *A testing time for chilled ceilings*, Building Services, June 1994.

Handel C, Lederer S, Roth, H W, *Energy consumption and comfort of modern air conditioning systems for office buildings*, Proc. 13th AIVC Conference, Ventilation for Energy Efficiency and Optimum Indoor Air Quality, 1992.

Liveris P, *Natural and low energy cooling in buildings*, Thermie Programme Action Report, The European Commission Directorate, DG XVII, 1995.

Martin A J, *Control of natural ventilation*, TN 11/95 BSRIA, UK, ISBN 0 86022 406 6, 1995

Mertz G, *Cooling ceiling systems and displacement flow*, Proc 14th AIVC Conference, Energy Impact of Ventilation and Air Infiltration, 1993.

Modera M P, *Residential duct system leakage: magnitude, impacts and potential for reduction*, ASHRAE Transactions, Vol 95, Pt 2, 1989.

Parsloe C, Hejab, *Small power loads*, TN 8/92 BSRIA (UK), 1992.

8 Air Cleaning by Filtration

Particulates
Depositions
Filtration Performance
Mechanisms
Gas Adsorption
Performance Specifications

Summary and Introduction

Filtration is a method by which particulates and, sometimes, gaseous pollutants may be removed from the air by passing the contaminated air through a medium. The filter intercepts the pollutant while allowing clean air to pass through. This method of air cleaning is especially necessary when high concentrations of particulates are present or when the outside air is contaminated. A brief review of filtration methods is presented in this Chapter. Filtration is most effective at controlling pollutants (especially particulates) associated with a specific air quality problem. It is not a substitute for the ventilation necessary to meet the metabolic needs of occupants, since filtration does not replenish oxygen or normally remove metabolic carbon dioxide from the air stream. To be effective, filtration systems must be capable of trapping the smallest of particles and of handling large air flow volumes.

Filtration is a method by which particulates and, sometimes, gaseous pollutants may be removed from the air by passing the contaminated air through a medium.

Filtration systems are most effective at dealing with individual particulate pollutant problems (e.g. pollen, environmental tobacco smoke etc.). Systems based on a multi-filter approach are likely to provide an optimum solution. These are based on a coarse pre-filter, to remove large dust particles, followed by an efficient fibrous or electrostatic filter, to remove respirable particles, and, possibly, charcoal filter, to remove odour.

8.1 Particulates

Particulates are an important source of contaminant which can have serious health implications. They also deposit on surfaces where they cause unsightly staining. Their physical properties depend very much on size. As with other contaminants, particulates are drawn from both indoor and outside sources. Typical outdoor particles include pollens, fungal spores, carbon and fibres. Indoor sources include smoke particles, spores, biological fragments, fibres and household products such as hair sprays and talcum

Particulates are an important source of contaminant which can have serious health implications.

powder etc. Examples of common particulates and properties, based on material published by CIBSE (1988), ASHRAE (1989) and the US Environmental Protection Agency (Owen et al 1990), are summarised in Figure 8.1. Large or heavy particles settle rapidly, while small particles tend to remain in the air and exhibit diffusion properties, similar to gaseous compounds. Microscopic particles can settle in the lungs causing health related problems.

Particulate Size and Concentration

Particles present in the atmosphere can range in size from less than 0.01µm to over 100µm. These comprise smoke products, vegetable matter, viruses, bacteria, fungal spores and insect fragments, traffic fumes, mineral substances and fibres. The concentration of particulate matter is commonly expressed in terms of mass of particulates/unit volume of air (mg/m^3). This is defined as the total suspended particulate concentration. Values for rural and suburban outdoor air would be in the range of 0.05 to 0.5 mg/m^3 whereas industrial areas could have concentrations in excess of 10 mg/m^3.

Deposition and Discoloration

Physical characteristics are dependent on size, mass and shape. Particles of less than 2.5 to 3.0µm in size are largely uninfluenced by gravitational forces. They tend to remain in suspension by continual molecular bombardment (Brownian motion) and display diffusion properties similar to a gas. Depending on concentration, these small particles may coagulate to form larger particles or adhere to other particles. Deposition or the eventual settling of these small particles occur on both vertical and horizontal surfaces where they can cause unsightly staining which is frequently difficult to remove. Fine particles tend to cause the most discoloration and are the most difficult to remove from the air stream.

Larger particles remain in the air stream for shorter periods and tend to settle on horizontal surfaces as dust. Typical settling velocities are summarised in Figure 8.1. Above about 50 to 100µg, particles attain their terminal velocity rapidly and can be expected to settle in a few seconds, although they are easily disturbed by draughts, dusting or sweeping to be re-entrained into the air stream.

Although deposition represents a mechanism by which particulate concentration can be reduced, reliability depends on particle size and favours the heavier of particulate matter. More harmful, small particles, will tend to remain in suspension for longer or be more easily disturbed. Therefore, the concentration characteristics presented in this Chapter, are based on the assumption of minimal (worst case) deposition. This topic

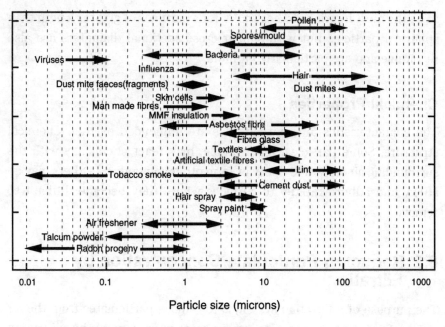

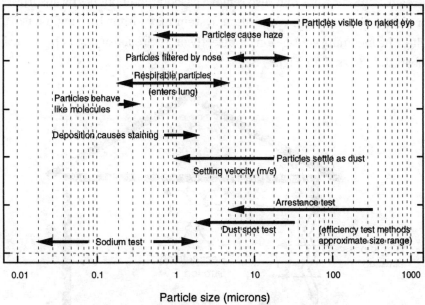

Figure 8.1 Common Particulates and Properties

is the subject of much current research. Further information on deposition is presented by Riffat et al (1994) and Byrne et al (1995).

Inhalable and Respirable Particles

Particles below approximately 30μm are inhalable i.e. they are drawn in through the nose. Those above approximately 10μm in diameter are filtered by the nose and wind pipe while those between approximately 0.2 to 10μm are respirable, i.e. they can enter and lodge in the lung. These are thought to be the most injurious to health. Fibrous particles of greater length than spherical particles but with similar cross sectional diameters are also respirable and are particularly harmful.

Chemical Properties

The characteristics of some particles are influenced by their chemical structure. Some particles, for example, may react chemically with the surrounding air stream to decay or form other compounds. Others may be sticky and adhere rapidly to surfaces where they become difficult to remove.

8.2 Reducing Particulate Concentration by Filtration

The purpose of a filtration system is to remove particulates from the air stream. Some systems may also remove gaseous components by adsorption or chemical treatment.

The purpose of a filtration system is to remove particulates from the air stream. Some systems may also remove gaseous components by adsorption or chemical treatment. A filtration system may either be 'single pass' to filter the incoming ventilation air directly or 'recirculatory' to continuously clean the internal air Figure 8.2.

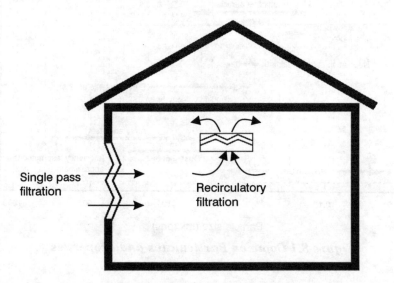

Single pass filtration

Recirculatory filtration

Figure 8.2 Single Pass and Recirculatory Filtration Methods

Defining Filtration Performance

Key definitions relating to the contaminant removal performance of filtration systems include:

Filter efficiency: The efficiency of a filter is normally expressed in terms of the proportion of particles of a given size range (or gaseous pollutant) that is intercepted by the filter in a single pass of air.

Arrestance: This is the reduction in the mass of particulates in the air after being passed through a filter. Since the bulk of the mass of atmospheric particulates is in the size range above 1μm while the highest concentrations are in the size range below 1μm, arrestance is usually used to describe the performance of low performance 'dust' filters.

Effective flow rate: The effective flow rate is defined as the rate of air flow through the filter multiplied by the filter efficiency. Thus an air flow rate through a filter of 90% efficiency removes the same quantity of pollutant as twice the air flow rate through a filter of 45% efficiency. It is for this reason that recirculatory filtration provide some compensation for low filter efficiency.

The efficiency of a filter is normally expressed in terms of the proportion of particles of a given size range (or gaseous pollutant) that is intercepted by the filter in a single pass of air.

Filter Mechanisms and Types

Particles are either trapped by fibrous filters or are electrically charged and collected on high voltage electrodes. Gaseous pollutants are removed by adsorption (reversible) or chemical reaction (irreversible). A numerical analysis of filtration performance is summarised in Chapter 12.

Fibrous filters (panel, pleated and bag): Common filters are constructed of fibrous matting or mesh through which air can pass but in which particulate matter is trapped. Particles of greater size than the mesh are trapped by direct straining. Coarse filters intended to strain out large particles may be included as a pre-filter to prevent clogging of the main filter. Particles of smaller size than the filter mesh may be intercepted by inertial deposition, diffusion or electrostatic deposition. Inertial deposition occurs when the air stream in which the particle is present is deflected by the filter medium. The relatively heavy particle is unable to follow the air stream and, instead, impacts on to the filter medium. Diffusion applies to very small particles subjected to Brownian motion. As the particles are bombarded by molecules, they attach themselves to the filter material. A concentration gradient of particles is established which enhances this process. Electrostatic attraction relies on charged particles being attracted to collection plates of opposite charge.

Filters presenting the least resistance to air flow require the least energy to operate but tend to have wide mesh spacing and hence poor efficiencies. The most basic of fibrous filter is the panel filter. This is a relatively coarse filter of mesh spacing between 15 to 60μm made from glass fibre, open cell foam or metal. It may be coated with an adhesive to improve efficiency. This is a low cost filter which is characterised by high porosity and, hence, low resistance to air flow. It is commonly used in warm air heating systems and air to air heat recovery units to intercept dust and other large particles.

Efficiency is dependent on the coarseness of the filter and the construction material. They can be constructed to achieve efficiencies of 90% for particles down to 10µm although, more often they are intended for collecting large particles, in which case their overall efficiency is low.

Improved efficiency is available from filters based on 'dry media' design in which the fibres are much smaller and densely packed. Filtration efficiency may range from between 15 to 98% according to fibre spacing and material. A pleated design is used to increase the surface area of the filter while extra depth (bag filter) may be incorporated to increase capacity. The most efficient fibrous filters incorporate mats comprising fibres of spacing 0.5-2.0µm.

Electrostatic filters: Electrostatic filters operate by charging particles using a high intensity electric field. The charged particles then pass through a grid system of alternately earthed and high voltage plates, where the resultant electric field attracts the particles to the charged plates. This is commonly called a charged plate system. For efficient operation, these plates must be regularly washed and cleaned. Typical charging voltage is 12000 volts followed by an attraction plate voltage of 6000 volts. These filters offer little impedance to flow and are therefore electrically efficient. They are especially suited to attracting small smoke particles and therefore often form the basis of recirculatory office or club air cleaning systems. A charcoal filter is also often incorporated to adsorb odours and gaseous pollutants.

Charged media filters: This type of filter is a combined fibrous and electrostatic system. It comprises a disposable dry fibrous filter which is charged by a grid of alternately earthed and high potential electrodes. Airborne particles are polarised by the electric field and are attracted to the fibres of the filter.

Adsorption is the process by which a gas molecule is attracted to and held on to the surface of an "adsorbent" material. This property enables various gaseous pollutants to be removed from a space.

Gas adsorption filter: Adsorption is the process by which a gas molecule is attracted to and held on to the surface of an 'adsorbent' material. This property enables various gaseous pollutants to be removed from a space. Since this is a surface action, it is necessary to maximise the surface area of adsorbent to achieve good efficiency. Granular activated carbon is the most common of adsorbants used for the filtration of gaseous pollutants.

Chemical gas filters: Adsorbants are not effective at capturing all gases. A method of improving performance is to impregnate the adsorbant material with chemicals that will react with individual polluting gases. This reaction either produces a more readily adsorbable gas or removes the pollutant entirely by forming a stable compound. A common broad spectrum chemical impregnant is potassium permanganate which is often used with activates alumina. Sometimes a dual approach based on potassium permanganate impregnated alumina combined with granular activated carbon is used to provide a very broad spectrum gas filter. More information on gas filtration is presented by Muller et al (1995).

Filtration Systems

The characteristics of filtration are dependent on the source of contaminant.

Removing outdoor pollutants: If high concentrations of outdoor pollutants are present for an extended period, control must be by filtration. Single pass filtration of the incoming air stream leads to a reduction in pollutant concentration which is directly proportional to the filter efficiency for the appropriate particulate or gaseous pollutant (see Figure 8.3).

If the air is filtered by a recirculatory system, located within the building, then the reduction pattern is more complex as illustrated in Figure 8.4. To reduce the inside concentration to 50% of the outside value, an effective filtration rate equivalent to the incoming ventilation rate is necessary. To reduce the concentration to 25% of the outdoor value, the effective filtration flow rate must be increased to three times the ventilation rate.

Removing indoor pollutants: While it is possible to control internally generated particulates by dilution ventilation, if the generation rate is high and unavoidable, the amount of ventilation needed may become excessive.

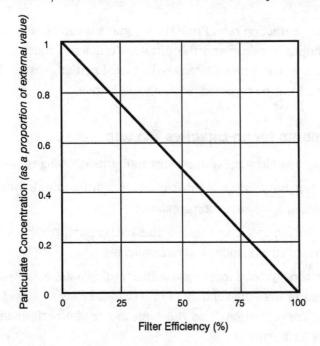

Figure 8.3 Influence of Single Pass Filtration on Outdoor Pollutants

In these circumstances, particulate pollutants may be controlled with recirculatory air filters. Examples of particulate reduction are illustrated in Figure 8.5. Filtration augments the dilution ventilation process. An effective filtration rate equivalent to the ventilation rate halves the pollution concentration. This is further reduced to 25% of the level achievable by ventilation alone by increasing the effective filtration rate to three times

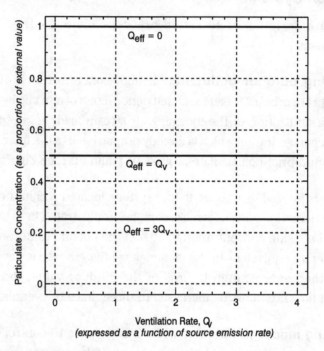

Figure 8.4 Influence of Recirculatory Filtration on Outdoor Pollutants

the fresh air ventilation rate. From these figures it can be seen that both the air handling capacity and the filtration efficiency must be high to accomplish a worthwhile pollutant reduction. For this reason, desk top 'air purifiers' must be regarded as totally ineffective.

Requirements for an Effective System

To be effective, a filtration system must fulfil the following requirements:

- It must not be used as a substitute for ventilation air needed for occupants, or for combustion appliances.

- It must be designed to remove the particular problem pollutant (e.g. tobacco smoke, industrial emissions etc.).

- Recirculatory systems must have sufficient flow rate, e.g. two to three times greater than the ventilation rate to make a sensible reduction of pollutant concentration. This rules out any useful performance from desk top 'air fresheners'.

- It must be well sited to intercept the polluted air.

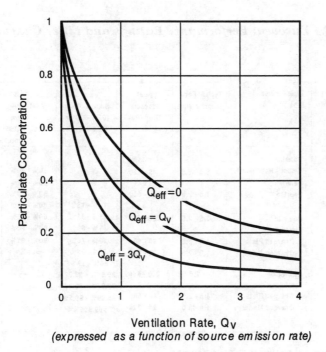

Figure 8.5 Influence of Recirculatory Filtration on Indoor Pollutants

- It must be inexpensive and easy to maintain, and preferably give a clear indication of when filter replacement or cleaning is needed.

- It should be free of operational noise.

- It should be energy efficient.

- It should not cause excessive draughts.

- It should be designed to ensure that filtered air is not directly short circuited back into the air intake.

- It should conform to relevant requirements and performance standards.

- Filters should be well sealed into the assembly frame to ensure that particles do not bypass the filter.

- Ductwork should have provision for cleaning. Contamination of a building with dust and bacteriological products can occur if ductwork and filters are not regularly cleaned (see Chapter 10).

- Air distribution across a filter should be uniform, otherwise local clogging and premature filter failure will occur.

> *Contamination of a building with dust and bacteriological products can occur if ductwork and filters are not regularly cleaned (see Chapter 10)*

Performance Specification

Several criteria are used to define the performance of a filtration system. Standards cover efficiency, pressure drop and dust holding capacity. In Europe, efficiency Standards are covered by an 'EU' rating; these are summarised in Table 8.1 and include:

Table 8.1 Eurovent Performance Ratings and Filter Characteristics

Euro Rating	Typical Filter Type	Typical Face Velocity (m/s)	Typical Pressure Drop (Pa)	Efficiency		
				Sodium Flame (0.02 -2.0 µm) BS 3928 Test	Dust Spot > ˜2 µm	Arrestance > ˜ 5 µm
					BS6540 Test (Approximate Size)	
EU1	Panel:			-		
EU2	Viscous Impingement	1.5 - 2.5	40 - 160	-	10% - 20%	65% - 80%
EU3	Panel:			-	20% - 30%	80% - 90%
EU4	Pleated	1.5 - 2.5	50 - 250	-	30% - 40%	>90%
EU5				10% - 15%	40% - 60%	-
EU6	Bag and	1.5 - 2.5	200 - 350	15% - 35%	60% - 80%	-
EU7	Electrostatic:			35% - 50%	80% - 90%	-
EU8	Charged Plate	1.5 - 2.5	40 - 60	50% - 75%	90% - 95%	-
EU9	Charged Media	1.0 - 2.0	25 - 125	75% - 95%	>95%	-
EU10				95% - 99.95%	-	-
EU11	HEPA and	2.5	250 - 650	99.95% - 99.97%	-	-
EU12	Electrostatic:			99.97% - 99.99%	-	-
EU13	Charged Plate	1.5 - 2.5	40 - 60	99.99% - 99.999%	-	-
EU14	Charged Media	1.0 - 2.0	25 - 125	>99.999%	-	-

Data Based on CIBSE Guide (Part B 1986) and ASHRAE Equipment Guide (1992)
* Approximate Efficiencies Only (Not a Test Result)

EU1 - EU4: Filters in this range are intended for low efficiency, general purpose applications. Performance evaluation is based on arrestance testing by measuring the mass of particles intercepted by the filter. A standard mass of synthetic dust is introduced into the filter air stream and the mass passing through the filter is measured.

Ratings EU5 - EU9: These are higher performance filters that are evaluated on the basis of 'dust spot' efficiency. This is aimed at assessing filter performance at intercepting particles down to approximately 2 µm in size. Performance is evaluated on the basis of the degree of staining of a filter paper placed down stream of the filter, compared with the amount of staining on an upstream filter paper. The greater the staining of the downstream target, the poorer is the efficiency of the filter at removing small particles.

Ratings EU10 -EU14: Filters in this range are high performance 'HEPA' filters. Capture efficiencies are greater than 98% for particles in the size range 0.02-2.0 µm. Particles in this size range are generated from sodium chloride and the proportion penetrating the filter is measured using flame photometry. This is a technique by which the concentration of sodium in the air stream is determined by the intensity of sodium light emitted when ignited.

References

ASHRAE Standard 62-1989, *Ventilation for acceptable indoor air quality*, American Society of Heating, Refrigerating and Air Conditioning Engineers, Inc., 1989.

Byrne M A, Goddard A J H, Lockwood F C, Nasrullah M, *Particulate deposition on indoor surfaces - its role, with ventilation, in indoor air quality prediction*, Proc. 16th AIVC Conf. Vol.2, 1995.

CIBSE *Ventilation and air conditioning*, CIBSE Guide Vol B Section 3, *Systems, equipment and air conditioning*, 1988.

Muller C O, England W G, *Achieving your indoor air quality goal, which filtration system works best?*, ASHRAE Journal, February 1995.

Owen M K, Ensor D S, Sparks L E, *Airborne particle sizes and sources found in indoor air*, Proc. Indoor Air '90, Vol 2, 1990.

Riffat S B, Cheong K W, Adam N, Shao L, *Measurement and CFD modelling of aerosol particles in buildings*, Nottingham School of Architecture, 1994.

9 Ventilation Efficiency

Summary and Introduction

Ventilation efficiency may be regarded as a series of indices or parameters which characterise the mixing behaviour of air and the distribution of contaminants within a space. These concepts may be subdivided into air change efficiency and contaminant removal effectiveness. Air change efficiency characterises the mixing of incoming air with that which is already present. Contaminant or pollutant removal effectiveness quantifies the efficiency with which internal pollutant is diluted and removed.

At present, values of ventilation efficiency parameters are normally determined by measurement. This can be restrictive, since the flow and pollutant fields are unique to each enclosed space. The evolution of computational fluid dynamics for flow field analysis provides an opportunity to apply ventilation efficiency concepts at the design stage. However, further validation and boundary data are needed before these CFD methods can be more generally applied.

Ventilation efficiency concepts are difficult to apply to naturally ventilated or leaky structures because the rate and pattern of air flow varies with climatic driving force. The subject of ventilation efficiency is made unnecessarily complex by the lack of uniformity in terminology. Frequently, terms are interchanged or different terms are used to describe the same concepts. Therefore it is important to check definitions carefully.

The subject of ventilation efficiency is made unnecessarily complex by the lack of uniformity in terminology. Frequently, terms are interchanged or different terms are used to describe the same concepts

Some indices are based on room averaged values, while others refer to conditions at specific points or locations within the space. Room values provide guidance to the overall performance of a ventilation system while point values are necessary to indicate regions where ventilation might be inadequate. The concepts of ventilation efficiency may be applied to entire buildings, single zones or locations within a single zone (e.g. the 'breathing zone').

9.1 Concepts of Ventilation Efficiency

Early work on the study of ventilation efficiency was undertaken by Sandberg (1981, 1983) and Skaret (1984). The main concepts of ventilation efficiency are:

Mixing of air: Often the mixing of air is not uniform and spaces may exist within an enclosed space where ventilation air does not penetrate. The concepts of ventilation efficiency are particularly important when, either by design or otherwise, air does not uniformly mix within a space.

The adequacy of a ventilation system in satisfying fresh air needs is influenced by the rate of supply and by the mixing behaviour of air. In reality, much can happen to prevent the desired mixing pattern from being achieved. Mixing characteristics depend on many parameters, including:

- the scale of turbulence,
- room layout, dimensions and partitioning,
- the distribution and size of infiltration paths,
- inlet and outlet configuration,
- diffuser characteristics,
- inlet air velocity and supply rate,
- the location and size of heat sources and sinks.

Hence the pattern of air flow is influenced by a combination of room characteristics and ventilation system characteristics. As a consequence, this pattern will almost always be unique to an individual space and will continuously vary in response to changes in ventilation rate, infiltration rate and thermal variations (buoyancy forces). The concepts of air change efficiency provide a measure of the degree to which the mixing of air takes place under a given set of conditions.

Pollutant distribution: Pollutant distribution is also unique to an individual space. Factors affecting the spatial distribution of a pollutant include:

- the pattern of air flow (air change efficiency),
- the location of the source of a contaminant within a space,
- pollutant emission characteristics,
- absorption or chemical decay behaviour of a pollutant,

- pollutant density.

Pollutant dilution and removal is described in terms of contaminant or pollutant removal effectiveness.

9.2 Air Change Efficiency

Air change efficiency indices are independent of the distribution or emission characteristics of pollutants. They are expressions of the spatial distribution and 'age' of air. A complete derivation and measurement description of terms associated with air change efficiency is summarised by Sutcliffe (1990). Important indices include:

Specific flow: This is an alternative expression for 'air change rate'. It is used to avoid the erroneous impression that air in a space is completely replaced at the given air change rate by clean, incoming air. While incoming ventilation air to a space is ideally 'fresh', the 'displaced' air is normally a mixture of 'old' and 'new' air.

Nominal time constant: The time in which air is present at a location holds the key to virtually all aspects of ventilation efficiency. A long presence (old air) can normally be associated with a greater risk of poor indoor air quality. All enclosure spaces have a time constant which represents the minimum time in which air, once entering the space, will remain. This is the 'nominal time constant' and is given by the inverse of the specific flow. The nominal time constant is completely derivable from basic knowledge of the ventilation rate and the volume of enclosure. It is a constant, regardless of internal flow pattern or pollutant properties.

The 'age' of air: Once air enters an enclosure, it is assumed to 'age'. For example, air is 30 minutes 'old' when it has been inside a space for 30 minutes. The following 'ages' have important applications:

- *Local mean age:* The local mean age of air at an arbitrary point or location in a space is the average time it takes for air, once entering an enclosure (time = 0), to reach that location.

- *Room mean age:* The room mean age of air is the average age of air in the room, i.e. it is the average of the local mean ages for all points.

- *Air change time:* The air change time is the time it takes for air, once entering a space, to be completely replaced. The air change time is equal to twice the room mean age of air.

Air change efficiency: Air change efficiency is the ratio, expressed as a percentage, between the nominal time constant and the air change time.

Since the minimum possible air change time is equal to the nominal time constant, all other values will be less than 100%.

Coefficient of air change performance: The coefficient of air change performance is defined as the percentage ratio of the nominal time constant to the room mean age. Since room mean age is equal to half the air change time, it follows that the coefficient of air change performance is twice the value of air change efficiency and can, therefore, have a maximum value of 200%. This term is equivalent to the definition of 'ventilation efficiency' given in ASHRAE Standard 62 (1989).

These basic air change efficiency terms are summarised in Figure 9.1. Figure 9.1(a) illustrates a 'piston' flow pattern in which no mixing takes place. The incoming air 'displaces' the air which is already present and the local mean age of air increases linearly as it flows horizontally through the enclosure. Assuming a nominal time constant of one hour, the room mean age is 0.5 hours, the air change time is one hour and the air change efficiency is 100%. Figure 9.1(b) refers to an example of 'perfect mixing'. The nominal time constant is again 1 hour but the local mean age is uniform throughout the space at the room mean age of one hour. The air change time is two hours and the air change efficiency falls to 50%. Figure 9.1(c) illustrates an example of variable mixing. 'New' air can completely bypass the poor mixing zone, resulting in the age of air within this zone becoming large. The room mean age and, hence, the air change time will also increase, resulting in an air change efficiency of less than 50%. It is important to note that, while the room mean age will indicate a problem, only knowledge of the local mean age throughout the entire space will reveal the location of poor mixing.

9.3 Contaminant Removal Effectiveness

Indices of contaminant removal effectiveness are dependent on both the characteristics of air flow (air change efficiency) and on the characteristics of the pollutant.

Contaminant removal effectiveness is concerned with the movement and dilution of contaminants within a space. Indices of contaminant removal effectiveness are dependent on both the characteristics of air flow (air change efficiency) and on the characteristics of the pollutant. Definitions of contaminant removal effectiveness are largely analogous to those of air change efficiency. Key indices are described in this section, while a more rigorous review is presented by Brouns and Waters (1991).

Nominal time constant of contaminant: The nominal time constant of contaminant is the average time it takes for contaminant to flow from its source to the exhaust duct or outlet. It is equivalent to the ratio of the volume (or mass) of contaminant in the enclosure and the volumetric (or mass) injection rate.

Local air quality index: The local air quality index is the ratio between the concentration of pollutant at any point within the enclosure and the concentration at the exhaust.

Contaminant removal effectiveness: Contaminant removal effectiveness is a room average or zone average value given by the ratio between the steady state concentration of contaminant at the exhaust and the room or zone average value. For complete mixing, the contaminant concentration is uniformly distributed and thus the contaminant removal effectiveness is unity or 100%. For piston flow, the contaminant removal effectiveness will be greater or equal to unity, depending on the location of the pollutant

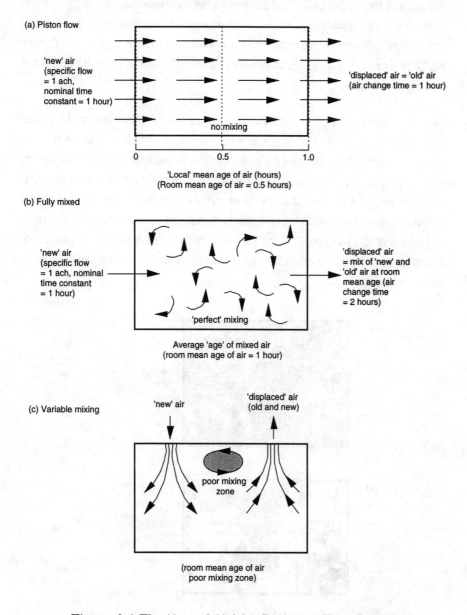

Figure 9.1 The 'Age of Air' for Different Flow Patterns

source. When short circuiting occurs, the room average pollutant concentration will tend to be greater than that at the exhaust point, and thus the contaminant removal effectiveness will range between zero and unity.

Contaminant removal efficiency: The contaminant removal efficiency is a normalised version of the contaminant removal effectiveness. Complete mixing of pollutant within the space gives a value of 0.5; piston flow gives a value between 0.5 and unity; short circuiting gives a value between zero and 0.5.

Complete mixing of pollutant within the space gives a value of 0.5; piston flow gives a value between 0.5 and unity; short circuiting gives a value between zero and 0.5.

Remaining indices of pollutant removal effectiveness may be derived from these basic definitions. Examples of the application of indices of pollutant removal effectiveness are depicted for two idealised flow regimes in Figure 9.2. This illustrates an office in which an item of equipment emits pollutant at a constant rate.

Two occupants are present within the space, one of whom is standing over the equipment, while the other is some distance away. In Figure 9.2(a), uniform mixing is assumed. The local air quality index is uniform throughout the space and the contaminant removal effectiveness is unity. In practice, this means that both occupants receive the same dose of pollutant and the pollutant strength is dependent on the ventilation rate. In the second example (Figure 9.2(b)), vertical piston flow is assumed. The pollution from the equipment is now entrained in a plume of relatively high concentration.

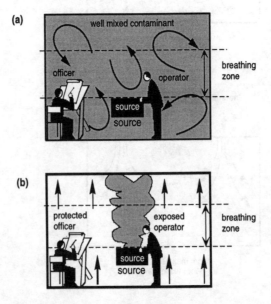

Figure 9.2 The Influence of Ventilation Strategy on the Distribution of Contaminant Concentration

The air quality index in the vicinity of the equipment operator reduces substantially, since he is now receiving a considerable increase in pollution. On the other hand, the remote occupant is experiencing a much higher air quality index since very little pollutant is present elsewhere in the room.

This example emphasises the need to plan the approach to ventilation very carefully. It also stresses the need to consider local efficiency indices in addition to room averaged values. These two very idealised examples represent the limit of analysis that is possible without introducing measurement or calculation methods to determine air flow and pollutant behaviour.

Indices of ventilation efficiency have largely been developed through observation and measurement. More recently, numerical techniques have been introduced to evaluate these parameters.

9.4 Evaluating Ventilation Efficiency Parameters

Measuring ventilation efficiency: Indices of ventilation efficiency have largely been developed through observation and measurement. Basic measurement methods are described in Chapter 11, Section 1. These are based on the use of 'tracer' gas to represent the inflow of fresh air and emissions from pollutant sources (see Figure 9.3). Although measurement methods provide much useful information about the interaction of air flow and pollutant distribution within a particular space, the uniqueness of each environment often restricts the wider application of results. Measurement methods, therefore, tend to be restricted to basic research applications and diagnostic analysis.

Although measurement methods provide much useful information about the interaction of air flow and pollutant distribution within a particular space, the uniqueness of each environment often restricts the wider application of results.

Calculating ventilation efficiency: Recently, computational fluid dynamics (CFD) have become available to predict air flow and pollutant transport throughout a space (see Chapter 12, Section 7). These approximate the space by a grid system containing many control volumes or elements to which numerical equations of flow are applied. In theory, all ventilation efficiency parameters can be derived from the results of CFD simulations. The calculation steps are outlined in Figure 9.4 and are virtually identical to the measurement steps shown in Figure 9.3. Since calculation, rather than measurement is involved, it is possible to undertake analysis as part of the design process. At present, still much development and evaluation of CFD methods is needed before they can be applied with confidence. Particular problems are associated with defining the boundary conditions and developing a sufficiently fine grid system to present an accurate evaluation of the flow field within the limitations of available computer power.

At present, still much development and evaluation of CFD methods is needed before they can be applied with confidence.

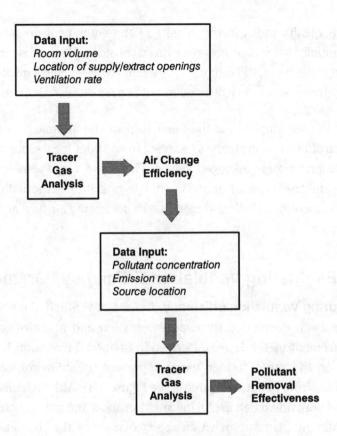

Figure 9.3 Measurement Parameters

9.5 Examples of Applying Concepts of Ventilation Efficiency

Many practical examples of the application of ventilation effectiveness concepts can be found in the literature. Breum et al (1994) compares the performance of mixing and displacement ventilation systems in a clothing factory, while Jiang et al (1993), compare the performance of mixing and displacement systems in partitioned offices. Persily et al (1994) also report on comprehensive measurements made in general office buildings. Shaw et al (1993) reports on the effect of diffuser types and layouts on ventilation effectiveness in work station environments. Faulkner et al (1993) use these concepts to quantify the performance of desk top ventilation systems. In the home, Sateri et al (1991) compare the efficiency of natural, mechanical extract and balanced ventilation systems in over 250 high rise and single family dwellings. Geerinckx et al (1992) reviews the performance of cooker hoods and defines a pollution index that can be used to indicate pollutant level according to hood collection efficiency. Other buildings in which these concepts have been applied include garages (Koskela et al 1991 and Stankanus et al 1989), airport terminals (Guthrie et al 1992), hospitals (Grot et al 1991) and operating theatres (Rock 1995).

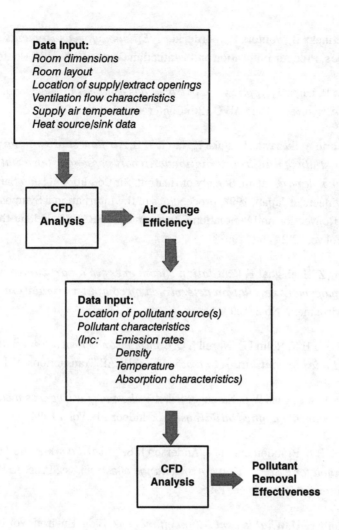

Figure 9.4 Calculation Parameters

References

ASHRAE Standard 62 *Minimum ventilation for acceptable indoor air quality*, (1989, new revision 1996/7)

Breum N O, Orhede E, *Dilution versus displacement ventilation - environmental conditions in a garment sewing plant*, AM Ind. Hyg. Assoc. Journal, vol 55, no 2, 1994.

Brouns C, and Waters R, *A guide to contaminant removal effectiveness*, Technical Note AIVC 28.2. Air Infiltration and Ventilation Centre. Warwick, UK. December 1991.

Faulkner D, Fisk W J, Sullivan D P, *Indoor airflow and pollutant removal in a room with desktop ventilation*, ASHRAE Transactions, Vol 99, Part 2, 1993.

Geerinckx B, Wouters P, Voordecker P, *Efficiency measurements of kitchen hoods*, Proc Air Infiltration and Ventilation Centre 13th AIVC Conference, 1992.

Grot R, Lagus P, *Application of tracer gas analysis to industrial hygiene investigations*, Proc AIVC 12th Conference, Vol 1, 1991.

Guthrie A, Ikezawa H, Otaka K, Yau R M H, *Air flow studies in larger spaces: a case study of Kansai International Airport passenger terminal building, Osaka, Japan*, Japan, Society of Heating, Air Conditioning and Sanitary Engineers of Japan, 1992, proceedings of the International Symposium on Room Air Convection and Ventilation Effectiveness - ISRACVE, held at the University of Tokyo, 22-24 July, 1992.

Jiang Z, Haghighat F, *Ventilation effectiveness in a partitioned office with displacement ventilation determined by computer simulation*, Indoor Environment, No 2, 1993.

Koskela H K, Rolin I E, Norell L O, *Comparison between forced-displacement and mixing ventilation in a garage*, ASHRAE Transactions, Vol 97, Pt 2, 1991.

Persily A K, Dols W S, Nabinger S J, *Air change effectiveness measurements in two modern office buildings*, Proc Indoor Air, Vol 4 1994.

Rock B A, Brandemuehl M J, Anderson R S, *Toward a simplified design method for determining the air change effectiveness*, Proc. ASHRAE Centennial Conference, 1995.

Sandberg M, *What is ventilation efficiency?*, Bldg. Environ. Vol.16 no.2, 1981.

Sandberg M, *Ventilation efficiency as a guide to design*, ASHRAE Transactions 1983 vol.89 pt.2A and B.

Sateri J O, Seppanen O A, Majanen A T, *Ventilation effectiveness in residential buildings with various ventilation systems*, ASHRAE Transactions, Vol 97, Pt 2, 1991.

Shaw C Y, Zhang J S, Said M N, Vaculik F, Magee R J, *Effect of air diffuser layout on the ventilation conditions of a workstation, part II: air change efficiency and ventilation efficiency*, ASHRAE Transactions, Vol 99, Part 2, 1993.

Skaret E, *Contaminant removal performance in terms of ventilation effectiveness*, Proc Indoor Air. Vol.5, 1984.

Sutcliffe H, 1990, *A guide to air change efficiency*, Technical Note AIVC 28. Air Infiltration and Ventilation Centre, Coventry, UK. February 1990.

10 Maintenance and Designing for Maintenance

Design for Ease of Maintenance
Maintenance of Specific Components
Maintenance Design for Large Buildings
Maintenance Regulations and Standards

Summary and Introduction

Evidence suggests that the maintenance of ventilation systems is often inadequate and that the need for maintenance may even be ignored in the course of building design. Examples of poor design and maintenance have been widely reported in many countries. Inaccessibility of system components, poor durability and a lack of awareness of servicing needs have all contributed to reduced ventilation performance. These concerns and problems have resulted in much more specific guidelines being developed. Efficiently operating ventilation systems are essential to ensure good indoor air quality and energy efficiency.

Evidence suggests, however, that maintenance is often inadequate and that the need for maintenance may even be ignored in the course of building design.

Complex ventilation systems require regular maintenance to ensure optimum performance. In a Finnish study, (Pallari et al 1993), on the long term performance of mechanical ventilation systems in apartments and single family homes, servicing was found to be inadequate. Typical problems included worn gaskets, dirty fans and grilles, and ill-fitting and clogged filters. In some homes, maintenance was the responsibility of occupants, yet they did not have the tools or knowledge to undertake this task. Sometimes components were located in the ceiling where they were either completely inaccessible or presented a hazard to safety. This study also found control systems to be a problem. They were frequently inaccessible and, in any case, occupants were given no knowledge of the correct settings. Information on using the ventilation systems had, often, long disappeared.

Similar results have been reported in a German study (Werner et al, 1994) where an examination of buildings with mechanical ventilation systems revealed that access to fans and filters for maintenance was poor, primarily due to a total lack of planning. In one case filter replacement was impossible because access was prevented by a hot-water installation. In many cases dirt was found in fans and ducting dating from the time of installation. Frequently fans, filters and vents were not clean, resulting in increased electrical power consumption, reduced air flow rates and a deterioration in indoor air quality. Poor design of many of the investigated systems also resulted in unnecessary pressure drops in the ductwork, producing a further energy penalty. Ducts were often poorly fitted and/or jointed and, in some cases, ducts were completely disjointed. In almost all instances there was a lack of operating and maintenance instructions.

Inspections of offices and homes in Sweden, (Granqvist et al 1994), also show evidence of poor maintenance. Ducts and grilles were often found to be very dirty, resulting in reduced air flow rates and an imbalance in ventilation systems. Again, operating and maintenance instructions were frequently found to be missing. In the United States, Rask (1989) has reported on inadequate maintenance and its impact on sick building syndrome. Examples cited include missing filters, ductwork caked with dirt and dust, entry of sewer gas into the HVAC system, rusted ductwork, fungal infestations, contaminated inlet air and disconnected controls. Inadequate attention to ventilation systems was blamed on slashed maintenance budgets and inadequately trained maintenance staff.

Further examples of poor design and maintenance have also been widely reported in other countries. This concern has resulted in much more specific guidelines being developed for the maintenance of ventilation systems. Some of these aspects are discussed in this Chapter.

10.1 Design for Ease of Maintenance

The ease with which a system can be maintained is strongly influenced by the degree to which the issue has been considered at the design stage.

Maintenance is needed to ensure the reliability of the ventilation system and to secure the economic operation of the ventilation plant. Only by correct functioning can a ventilation system be relied upon to meet the indoor air quality needs of a building. In the past, systems have often been installed without a clear idea of how maintenance is to be accomplished. The ease with which a system can be maintained is strongly influenced by the degree to which the issue has been considered at the design stage. It is for this reason that an increasing number of Standards and Codes of Practice focus on designing for maintenance.

Nordic maintenance guidelines: Comprehensive guidelines have been developed to improve the design and maintenance of mechanical ventilation systems. The Nordic Committee on Building Regulations (NKB, 1991) for example, has produced the following guidelines for ventilation systems:

Controls

Controls shall be easy to reach, understand and operate.

Siting of components

Components which require attendance shall be sited so that they are readily accessible and replaceable, and are mounted so that work can be carried out easily and safely.

Cleanability

It shall be possible for both supply and extract ventilation air installations to be cleaned in their entirety. Installations shall be cleaned sufficiently frequently to ensure that neither the magnitude of air flows nor the quality is adversely affected by deposited dirt.

Components and materials

Components shall be made of materials which stand up to the intended use and maintenance and do not emit pollutants such as particles or gases which may adversely affect the quality of the supply air. The choice of materials and construction shall be such that the growth of micro-organisms is prevented.

Air tightness and pressure conditions

Experience has shown that ventilation installations are very leaky and that rotary heat exchangers have incorrectly fitted fans and dampers such that as much as 50% of the exhaust air can be unintentionally recirculated. In view of this it has been recommended that installations shall have the required air tightness. Pressure conditions between supply and extract air installations shall be adjusted so that there is no unintentional flow from the extract air to the supply air.

Commissioning

Ventilation systems shall be balanced so that the intended flow rates and tolerances are obtained. When an installation is handed over, it shall be demonstrated that it has been constructed and functions in the way intended. The installation shall be handed over in a clean state ready for operation.

Documentation

The necessary drawings and specifications shall be produced for a building and the ventilation installation. The materials used including make and type designation shall be documented. Air flow rates through individual rooms shall be specified. Instructions for the operation and maintenance of the ventilation installation shall be prepared and shall be available when

Instructions for the operation and maintenance of the ventilation installation shall be prepared and shall be available when the building is put into service.

the building is put into service. User instructions in easily understandable language, which provide information on attendance, cleaning and maintenance, shall be affixed within easy reach of each terminal or appliance which is capable of being controlled by the user.

Inspection

At all stages of the design, construction and operation of a building, checks shall be made to ensure that the intended quality is secured. Buildings shall be regularly inspected to ensure the correct functioning of the ventilation system and of other factors which influence good indoor climate.

10.2 Maintenance of Specific Components

Reliable ventilation system performance depends on maintenance of the component parts.

Reliable ventilation system performance depends on maintenance of the component parts. Major items include:

Fans: There are a number of basic health and safety requirements associated with all fan installations. For example, they must be properly guarded to avoid access to rotating parts, and they must be capable of being isolated electrically before any work is commenced. There are also a wide range of basic maintenance activities which will be common to most pieces of mechanical plant (lubrication of bearings, adjustment of drive belts for tightness and alignment, checking anti-vibration mounts etc.). Specific items for fans would include cleaning the impeller to avoid build up of dust. This can be a particular problem in extract fans from a dirty or greasy environment (e.g. a kitchen). Build up of dirt on the impeller blades may cause out-of-balance problems resulting in excessive bearing wear and noise. It may also affect aerodynamic performance. Care must be taken when cleaning the blades, since mechanical damage or distortion of the impeller can also result in performance penalties.

Air filters: Filters are a very important part of a ventilation system, and the grade of filter should be selected with due consideration to the particle size range of the particulates in the inlet air. Using lower grade filters may result in a reduction in the frequency of required filter change, but will also lead to reduced performance (e.g. staining on ceilings and near grilles, and potential IAQ problems for occupants).

Good design and installation practice can reduce the demands on a filtration system. Locating air inlets away from dirty or dusty areas will reduce the load. Inlet ducts should ideally slope downwards towards the external louvre, and the filter should be protected by bird and insect screens. Extract systems should be sealed off until all internal builders work is completed, to avoid dust being pulled into the system.

No attempt should be made to clean and re-use filter elements unless this is specifically allowed for by the manufacturer. Some systems use a measurement of high differential pressure across the filter to indicate the need for replacement of the element. The pressure sensing should not be relied on as the sole criteria for filter replacement – regular visual checks should also be made. For example, on a roll band filter, the high pressure may be the result of too low a band speed. Long term readings of low pressure drop may not indicate that the filter is working satisfactorily, it may indicate that the filter element is mechanically damaged, and is not doing its job at all!

Accumulation of dust in the downstream ventilation system could result in increased potential for the development of fungal spore and other microbiological activity. It may also affect other components (e.g. dampers and the finned surfaces of coils), leading to an overall degradation of performance. There is a wider issue in that there may be increased fire hazard, particularly if the air is grease laden. This carry over of greasy/dirty air may also cause clogging of automatic fire dampers, and this combination of factors may result in a significant safety risk.

Accumulation of dust in the downstream ventilation system could result in increased potential for the development of fungal spore and other microbiological activity.

Inevitably, used filters contain considerable amounts of dust, and therefore precautions should be taken when handling to minimise exposure to dust hazards. This should include use of protective clothing and dust masks. Additional safety precautions will need to be taken for those air handling systems used in hazardous areas (e.g. fume cupboard extracts, clinical areas etc.).

Ductwork and Air Distribution Systems: There are a number of energy and air quality issues which are related to the proper maintenance of ductwork systems. The primary ones are the mechanical integrity of the ductwork (leakage and insulation), and the cleanliness of the internal walls of the ductwork.

Duct leakage can occur as a result of poorly maintained joints, or in the extreme case, physical damage to the ductwork itself. This is most likely in lengths of flexible ductwork, which may also be liable to "kinking" which will cause increased pressure drops. Ductwork leakage can be a source of considerable energy wastage, especially if the leakage occurs to non-conditioned spaces (crawlspaces, service shafts etc.). Not only will the fan have to deliver a greater air quantity to compensate for the leakage loss, the air heating and cooling coils will also be required to condition air unnecessarily. Other problems may also result. For example, warm moist air leaking from the positive pressure side of an extract system may result in fabric damage in unheated spaces.

Mechanical damage to ductwork insulation will obviously result in energy loss. There is also the subsidiary problem with those systems distributing cooled air as part of an air conditioning system. The air in the duct may be cooler than the dew point of the air through which the duct is passing, resulting in condensation and moisture damage.

The cleaning of ductwork systems is a subject which has gained increased attention over recent years. A review by Lloyd (1992) provides a useful overview of the subject. Accumulation of dust within ductwork systems can provide a site for the development of microbiological growth. This can result in bacteria or fungal spores being released into the occupied space with potential impacts on occupant comfort and health.

Control of dust build up will be enhanced by good filtration regimes, but occasional duct cleaning may also be required. To facilitate cleaning, access doors must be provided. To avoid damaging sensors or probes, these should be withdrawn from the duct before cleaning is undertaken. Similarly, care should be taken to avoid damage to dampers and linkages which may be in the ductwork.

Air treatment plant: In many ventilation systems, there will be a number of air treatment components (heaters, coolers, humidifiers, heat recovery devices etc.). The performance of heat exchangers is critically dependent on maintaining good heat transfer coefficients at the surfaces, and this requires regular maintenance. When cleaning coils, the fans should be switched off, so that any dirt that is disturbed is not carried into the ductwork system. In addition to cleaning, the surfaces of coils should be sterilised, especially if coils operate under moist air conditions. Condensate drains should be kept clear, and the drain traps should be filled with water.

Terminal units: Many of the terminal unit types will have filters, coils and/or small local fans in them; the general principles which are defined in previous sections are equally valid to terminal units. The main additional items of concern are the controls, including sensors, actuators and dampers. These should be checked to ensure that they are functioning correctly in order to achieve both occupant comfort and energy efficiency.

10.3 Maintenance Design for Large Buildings

Mechanical ventilation and air handling systems are found in buildings of all sizes. Large buildings, however, present particular problems since the air handling system is necessarily large and the distribution system complex. Ductwork, especially has to be co-ordinated with the needs of other services and structural barriers. Designing for the maintenance of large (non- domestic buildings) is discussed at length by Parsloe (1992) in relation to the following issues.

Plantroom: Allowances must be made at an early stage for the sizing of the plant room and main service runs, so that the general organisation of the building can be determined. It is essential that space is allocated for plant and to provide access for maintenance, plant handling and manoeuvring. There must be an easily accessible route from the point in the building where maintenance materials are stored to the point where they will be used. This is especially important where plantroom access is from within the building, and disruption to building occupants may result. Stepped floors should be avoided, but floors should be laid to fall so that any spillage flows to the drain. Lifting beams should be provided over heavy plant items. Good lighting is essential and power outlets are needed for servicing tools.

It is essential that space is allocated for plant and to provide access for maintenance, plant handling and manoeuvring.

Plant selection: The selection of plant items is a very important factor in determining the future maintainability of the system. The choice of plant will dictate the future maintenance requirements, and the following factors should be borne in mind when selecting equipment:

- the reliability of the manufacturer or supplier,
- the availability of performance data measured according to approved Standards,
- the availability of warranties or guarantees of service life,
- indications of mean time between failure,
- availability and cost of spare parts (will they continue to be manufactured, do they need to be imported?),
- the quality of construction should be suitable for the application (strength, durability, corrosion resistance, fire proofing etc.).

System design: In the case of ventilation systems, a number of specific measures should be considered. These include:

- Access panels should be provided for inspection of such components as dampers, filters and coils. These access panels should be easy to remove and replace.
- Test holes should be provided at regular locations to allow commissioning and monitoring of plant performance.
- Lengths of flexible ductwork should be kept to a minimum.

- Ducts should be as straight as possible. It is especially important that straight lengths are provided at inlets and outlets to fans to ensure flow stability.

Maintenance brief: In establishing a maintenance regime, it is important for the building owner/operator to establish the basic principles which will set the philosophy for the maintenance contractor. Examples of guidelines to help in the development of a maintenance programme have been produced by CIBSE(1990) in the UK and ASHRAE(1993).

In all cases, maintenance must ensure that the relevant health and safety Standards are addressed.

In all cases, maintenance must ensure that the relevant health and safety Standards are addressed. This not only includes the regular testing of safety equipment, but also ensuring that maintenance personnel are properly equipped to carry out their work in a safe way. In many countries there is an increasing obligation on building operators to demonstrate that they are properly addressing these health and safety issues. A well planned maintenance regime will help in this respect.

An essential part of any maintenance planning is a careful analysis of the implications of any particular plant item failing. This will dictate the level of maintenance provision; if the continued running of the plant is essential to the operational requirements of the building, duplicate standby plant may be justified. Less critical components may necessitate guaranteed repair times, which in turn will require access to skilled personnel and a readily available stock of spare parts etc.

A further element of maintenance planning is to ensure economic operation of plant. This relates to both energy efficiency and maximising the economic life of plant. This clearly requires that data be gathered about fuel use, plant running times etc. Monitoring and targeting systems can be a useful tool to help identify plant malfunctions. Sudden changes in the pattern of fuel use may indicate that plant is malfunctioning, enabling remedial action to be taken before failure occurs.

Having set the maintenance philosophy, a decision will need to be taken on whether the maintenance work should be carried out by "in-house" resources, or whether the work should be contracted out. In all cases, management time has to be provided to ensure that the maintenance is carried out as specified, and to continually review whether changes in the maintenance programme are required in the light of changing circumstances.

10.4 Implementing Maintenance Regulations and Standards

Various Standards and Regulations are being introduced to ensure the quality and reliability of ventilation systems.

Swedish Standards: In Swedish buildings the compulsory testing and examination of ventilation systems has been introduced (Granqvisk et al 1994). Inspection periods are dependent on the type of building and installed ventilation system (see Table 10.1). The only exceptions to buildings to be tested are single family and semi-detached homes incorporating natural or mechanical extract ventilation, agricultural buildings, industrial units and defence buildings. These requirements apply to both new and existing buildings.

Inspections require that drawings and design documents are available and have been followed and that ventilation performance and other aspects conform to the Regulations that applied when the system was brought into operation. Any deficiencies must be rectified by the building owner. The inspection schedule must include the following performance checks:

- operation and maintenance instructions,
- air change,
- humidity,
- fans and air handling units,
- recirculated air,
- deposits in ventilation ductwork,
- radon,
- user viewpoints.

Various Standards and Regulations are being introduced to ensure the quality and reliability of ventilation systems.

Table 10.1 Inspection Intervals According to Building Type

Building type	Inspection interval
Single family/semi detached dwellings with natural ventilation	exempt
Single family/semi detached dwellings with mechanical extract ventilation	exempt
Agricultural buildings	exempt
Industrial buildings	exempt
Defence buildings	exempt
Day care centres, schools, health care centres, etc.	2 years
Apartments and office buildings with balanced ventilation	3 Years
Apartments and office buildings with mechanical extract ventilation	6 Years
Apartments and office buildings with natural ventilation	9 Years
Single family/semi detached dwellings with mechanical balanced ventilation	9 years

ASHRAE Standards: In the United States, proposed guidelines for ASHRAE Standard 62 (1996/7) cover the maintenance of HVAC systems to maintain good indoor air quality. Included in the current draft are :

- inspection and maintenance records,
- responsible maintenance manager,
- visual inspection of all major air handling components,
- filter replacement, at least twice yearly,
- annual inspection of outside air dampers and actuators,
- annual inspection of ceiling return plenums,
- annual inspection of heating and cooling coils, cleaning as necessary,
- annual inspection of drain pans,
- measurement (and adjustment) of flow rates on renovation or at five year intervals.

European Standards: Within Europe, maintenance is being addressed by the European Standardisation Organisation (CEN). TC 156 is in charge of ventilation related issues. The work is done by nine different working groups covering a number of aspects including, terminology, domestic ventilation systems, ductwork, terminal units, design criteria, system performance, installation and fire aspects.

References

ASHRAE, *Preparation of operating and maintenance documentation for building systems*, Guideline 4-1993, ASHRAE, 1993.

ASHRAE Standard 62, *Ventilation for acceptable indoor air quality*, American Society of Heating, Refrigerating and Air Conditioning Engineers, Inc., proposes revision 1996/97.

CIBSE, *Building Services maintenance management*, Technical Memoranda 17, CIBSE, UK, 1990.

Granqvist P, Kronvall J, *Checking the performance of ventilation systems: the Swedish approach*, Air Infiltration Review, Vol 15, No 2, March 1994, pp 1-4.

HVCA, *Standard maintenance specification for mechanical services in buildings*, Vol II - Ventilation and Air Conditioning, HVCA, (UK) 1991.

Lloyd S, *Ventilation system hygiene - a review*, Technical Note 18/92, BSRIA, UK, 1992.

NKB, *Indoor Climate - Air Quality*, Nordic Committee on Building Regulations, NKB Publication No 61E, 1991.

Pallari M-L, Luoma M, *Long-term performance of residential ventilation systems*, Proc 14th AIVC Conference, Energy Impact of Ventilation and Air Infiltration, 1993.

Parsloe C, *Design for maintainability*, Application Guide 11/92, BSRIA, 1992

Rask D R, *Resolution of the sick building syndrome*, The human equation: health and comfort, proc IAQ 1989, pp173-178.

Werner J, Rochard U, Zeller J, *A survey of mechanical ventilation systems in 30 low energy dwellings in Germany*, Proc 15th AIVC Conference, *The Role of Ventilation*, Vol, 1994.

11 Measurement Methods

Tracer Gas Methods
Pressurisation Methods
Component Air-tightness Testing
Other Measurement Methods
Instrumentation for Tracer Gas Detection
Theoretical Outline

Summary and Introduction

Measurements provide the means for understanding the mechanics of ventilation and air flow in buildings. They are essential for commissioning, diagnostic analysis, design and research. Many techniques have been developed with each having a specific purpose. Important methods include tracer gas techniques for evaluating ventilation flow rate in buildings and pressurisation testing to determine the air-tightness of components or structures. In addition a wide range of other methods are available to measure and visualise air flow. The intention of this Chapter is to present a summary of measurement methods and to provide guidance on the selection of techniques according to application. Comprehensive information on measurement methods is published by Charlesworth 1988 and Roulet et al 1991.

Measurements are essential for commissioning, diagnostic analysis, design and research.

Typical applications include the evaluation of:

- outdoor air flow rate into a building (ventilation and air infiltration),
- outdoor air flow rate into individual rooms,
- long term 'average' air flow rates into buildings and individual rooms,
- rate and pattern of air flow between rooms,
- the 'age' of air and ventilation efficiency indices,
- qualitative air movement in a space (flow visualisation),
- quantitative air movement in a space (flow velocity, turbulence etc.),
- air flow rate through ducts, grilles and purpose provided openings,
- building air-tightness,
- air-tightness of individual rooms,

- component air-tightness,
- location of leaks,
- driving forces.

11.1 Tracer gas methods

Background

By measuring either the variation in tracer gas concentration over time, or the rate at which tracer gas needs to be released to maintain a target concentration, it is possible to evaluate the rate of air flow between seeded and unseeded zones.

Air that enters a space comes from a combination of infiltrating and intentional sources. While the measurement of air flow rate through identifiable openings is possible by direct flow measurement (see Section 4), it is not practicable to measure air flow through the many unknown gaps and cracks that may appear in the construction of a building, or to measure air flow rate through more than one or two purpose provided openings at a time. It is possible to overcome this problem by using a tracer gas. The technique is performed by seeding an inert gas into a space where its concentration behaviour is observed as it interacts with unseeded, incoming air. By measuring either the variation in tracer gas concentration over time, or the rate at which tracer gas needs to be released to maintain a target concentration, it is possible to evaluate the rate of air flow between seeded and unseeded zones. Depending on specific application, the tracer gas method is conducted using one of the following techniques:

- concentration decay,
- constant concentration.,
- constant emission,
- long term average,
- multi tracer analysis.

Measurements may be 'instantaneous', representing ambient conditions, or 'time averaged', in which the measurement period may span several days or even several weeks. A theoretical summary of the tracer gas technique is presented in Section 11.6.

A tracer gas is an inert gas which is non toxic, measurable at low concentrations and is not normally present in the atmosphere. Typical gases include nitrous oxide (which is detectable in the 0.1 to 25 parts per million (ppm) range), sulphur hexafluoride (detectable in the parts per billion (ppb) range) and various per fluoro tracers (PFTs) (detectable in the parts per trillion (ppt range). Although present in the atmosphere, carbon dioxide gas, either as generated by occupants or released from cylinders, is also used.

Common tracer gases and detection methods are summarised in Table

Table 11.1 Common Tracer Gases and Detection Ranges

Tracer gas	Maximum acceptable concentration	Molecular weight	minimum detectable concentration	Detection method
Carbon dioxide	5000 ppm	44	400 ppm	infra-red
Nitrous oxide	25 ppm	44	0.1 ppm	infra-red
Sulphur hexafluoride	1000 ppm	146	0.1 ppm 1.0 ppb	infra-red electron capture
PFTs	-	200 - 400	0.001 ppb	electron capture

11.1. More information on detection techniques is given in Section 11.5. The amount of tracer gas needed depends on the volume of space to be seeded and the desired target concentration, calculation guide-lines are given in Section 11.6. Apart from ventilation efficiency and air quality measurements, tracer gas has to be well mixed in the test space. This is usually accomplished by using small mixing fans.

Single Tracer Gas Concentration Decay

Applications: The tracer gas concentration decay technique is used to determine the rate at which air enters an enclosed space. It is one of the most straightforward of tracer gas methods, is the least disruptive and requires the minimum of equipment. Specific applications include:

The tracer gas concentration decay technique is used to determine the rate at which air enters an enclosed space.

- measurement of air change rate in small 'single zone' buildings (e.g. <500 m³),
- estimation of ventilation efficiency parameters (see Chapter 9).

Method: Tracer gas is released into the space and thoroughly mixed with small 'desk' type or similar mixing fans. These fans are normally located at each internal door and in the proximity of the tracer release point. The amount of tracer released is calculated on the basis of the maximum start concentration desired (see Section 11.6) and should be released rapidly. To aide mixing, the operator may sometimes release gas from a hand held cylinder while walking through the space. If the building is fitted with an air distribution system, mixing may be accomplished by injecting the tracer gas directly into the air handling unit. Sampling then takes place at the return air duct. Once the desired quantity has been released, the gas supply is turned off and, after a further short period of mixing, the decay in tracer gas concentration is measured over time using a tracer gas analyser (see

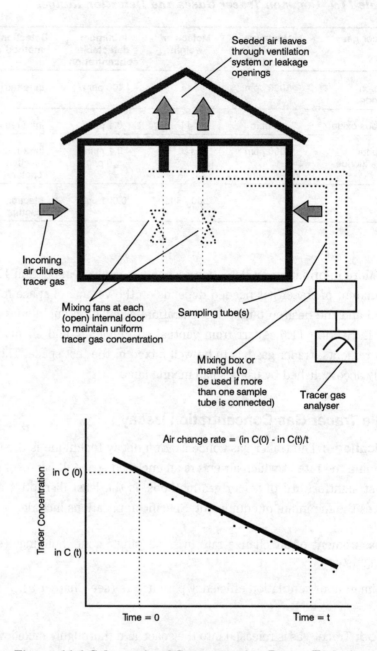

Figure 11.1 Schematic of Concentration Decay Technique

Section 11.5). The measurement period is typically between 15 and 30 minutes. Provided air in the space is well mixed and the forces driving the air change process remain constant, the decay in tracer gas concentration is logarithmic, with the air change rate being directly related to the decay gradient (see Section 11.6). A schematic of the system and a typical decay curve is illustrated in Figure 11.1.

The success of the decay technique is dependent on the validity of following key assumptions:

The mixing of tracer gas into the space is perfect and instantaneous.
Imperfect mixing occurs when air movement is impeded by obstructions or when air is trapped by the effects of stratification or eddies. It can also occur when infiltrating air displaces the air already present without mixing, or when exfiltrating air re-enters the building at another location. The effect is to cause a spatial variation in tracer gas concentration resulting in different parts of the enclosure having apparently different air change rates. Sometimes small deficiencies in mixing can be overcome by sampling the air at several locations. This is achieved by linking each sample location via equal length tubes to a manifold (see Figure 11.1) or by sequentially sampling the gas concentrations at each location. Artificial mixing is not applied to air quality and ventilation efficiency measurements since these seek to identify areas of poor mixing.

Imperfect mixing occurs when air movement is impeded by obstructions or when air is trapped by the effects of stratification or eddies.

The interior of the building is open plan.
An open-plan type space is needed to ensure that tracer gas can be well mixed and uniformly distributed. Internal doors should be kept open. If the decay test is restricted to a single room or zone of a building, then the measured 'air change rate' will be based on components of incoming outdoor air and unseeded air from adjacent rooms. It will not be possible to differentiate between these two sources unless multi-tracer methods are used, (see multi-tracer gas methods).

The 'effective volume' of the enclosure is known.
Accuracy of measurement is dependent on knowledge of the internal or 'effective' volume in which the tracer gas is mixed. This effective volume is often assumed to be the physical volume of the test space (e.g. internal building volume). Inaccuracies occur if there are significant 'dead' spaces in which gas does not penetrate (e.g. cupboards or closed rooms) or if there are additional communicating spaces such as basements, crawl spaces or attics which have been ignored in the volume calculation. Cupboard and room doors should be opened and the volume of all spaces in which tracer gas is intentionally distributed should be identified.

The factors that influence air change remain constant.
Factors influencing air change rate should remain constant throughout the measurement period. These include driving forces (wind, temperature and mechanical ventilation) and window opening. A change in driving forces will result in a non linear gradient in concentration decay curve.

Limitations: Various limitations restrict the range of applicability of this approach, such as:

• The need for good mixing that restricts this technique to small (typically less than 500 m3) open plan structures.

- If decay measurements are applied to a single room of a multi-roomed building, it will not be possible to distinguish between the entry of outdoor air into the room and the entry of non-fresh air from adjacent rooms (see constant concentration techniques and multi-tracer methods).

- Mixing fans may create an artificial environment, i.e. the 'test' mode for the building may not represent the normal occupied operational mode.

- Single measurements may provide a 'snapshot' picture of air change only. In leaky or naturally ventilated buildings the air change rate can vary considerably and hence many measurements representing a wide range of weather conditions and user patterns may be necessary.

Tracer Gas Constant Concentration

The constant concentration method is used to determine the rate of fresh air entry into individual rooms or zones of a multi-room

Applications: The constant concentration method is used to determine the rate of fresh air entry into individual rooms or zones of a multi-room (compartmentalised building). It is designed to adapt to rapidly varying conditions such as window opening or changes in driving force. Constant concentration methods are used to monitor variations in air change rate in occupied buildings for extended periods of time. Air flow to each room is typically calculated at 15 minute intervals, although some instrumentation can operate at 2 minute intervals.

Method: Tracer gas is continuously released into each room within the building in variable amounts such that a near constant concentration is maintained. This is accomplished by sequentially sampling the tracer gas concentration in each zone and calculating the necessary injection rate needed to return the concentration to a target 'set point' value. The volume flow rate of fresh air into each zone is directly proportional to the injection rate of tracer gas (see Section 11.6). Unlike the concentration decay method, no knowledge is required of room or building volume to determine the amount of fresh air entering the space. A micro processor or computer controlled feedback and injection system is needed to control the process (see Figure 11.2). Examples of constant tracer gas equipment are described by Etheridge (1985) and Grot (1980). A commercial package is reviewed by Grieve (1989).

Injection and sampling must take place independently in each room. The time interval between sampling should be as short as possible and is typically one to two minutes. This is necessary to avoid any drift in tracer gas concentration. Normally PFT type tracers combined with electron capture detection are used so that only very minute concentrations of tracer gas are needed. Air in each room should be mixed using mixing fans. The maximum number of zones that can be injected with gas is approximately ten. Beyond this, the sequential sampling frequency

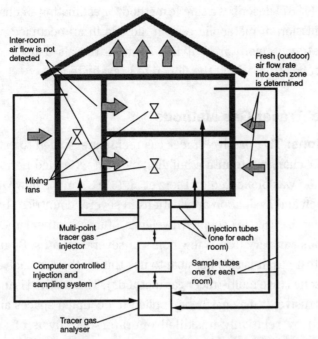

Figure 11.2 Schematic of Constant Concentration Technique

becomes too long and the instrumentation and software too complex. Injection takes place only in rooms in which fresh unseeded air enters and dilutes the tracer gas. For this reason air flow between rooms is not detected.

Limitations:

- Inter room air flow cannot be detected or measured using this approach.

- Instrumentation is bulky, has many trailing injection and sample tubes and it is a difficult and time consuming test to perform.

- Equipment is not widely available for general use and measurements are normally restricted to research purposes.

Tracer Gas Constant Emissions

A simplification of the constant concentration approach is constant tracer gas emission. If ventilation conditions remain unchanged and tracer gas is injected at a constant rate, then an equilibrium (constant) tracer gas concentration will eventually be reached. At equilibrium, the air flow rate into the space is calculated on the basis of equilibrium concentration and emission rate using the same analysis as for the constant concentration method. Difficulties include reaching equilibrium, especially in large spaces, and avoiding excessive tracer gas concentrations and/or excessive use of tracer gas. The use of constant emission for short term measurements is not widely used.

A simplification of the constant concentration approach is constant tracer gas emission.

Sandberg (1987) describes a simple method for estimating air change based on the emission of metabolic carbon dioxide in an occupied space. CO_2 concentration is monitored at fixed time intervals using inexpensive detector tubes from which the flow rate is evaluated.

'Passive' Tracer Gas Methods

The 'passive' tracer gas technique is used to estimate the average air change rate into a building over an extended period of time.

Applications: The 'passive' tracer gas technique is used to estimate the average air change rate into a building over an extended period of time. This method was pioneered by Dietz et al, (1983) and is now widely used for research and evaluation applications in several countries (Sateri et al, 1989). It may be used in occupied dwellings, offices or other large buildings. Test periods can vary from a few hours to several months. By using more than one test gas, it is also possible to use this method to analyse air flow between zones (see multi-tracer gas methods). This method is inexpensive and unobtrusive. It may easily be applied to occupied spaces and may be conducted by relatively unskilled operators. Analysis of samples is undertaken off-site in a laboratory.

Method: Passive techniques are based on the use of volatile per fluoro tracers (PFT's) which may be detected in the air in minute concentrations within the parts per trillion range. Tracer gas is gradually emitted over a period of time within the test space. An exposed sample tube is used to adsorb the gas over the same time period. The air change rate is calculated from the amount of gas emitted and collected by the emission and sample tubes respectively. Analysis of the sample tubes is undertaken in a laboratory using gas chromatograph and electron capture detection (see Section 11.5).

The source (see Figure 11.3(a)) typically consists of approximately 0.4ml of volatile liquid PFT tracer placed in a glass ''emission' tube of approximately 5mm diameter and 30mm length. The liquid gradually evaporates through a porous plug or capillary tube into the test space at a rate which is related to ambient air temperature. Approximately one emission and one detection tube should be used for each 50 m3 of space. The emission tubes should preferably be located in a region of uniform temperature, i.e. areas of extreme heat (e.g. close to light fittings or radiators) or extreme cold (e.g. close to outside walls or regions of draught) should be avoided. Usually the emission rate can be reasonably accurately inferred from records of the average daily indoor air temperature.

The sample tube is of similar dimension to the source tube and, in use, is open at one end (see Figure 11.3(b)). It contains a small quantity of gas adsorbent such as activated charcoal which is contained by a porous mesh.

Passive sampling is initiated by opening one end of the sample tube for a fixed time interval (the measurement time). A diffusive flow of tracer gas

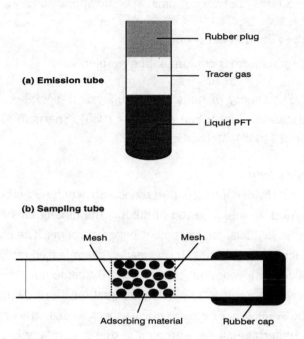

(a) Emission tube

Rubber plug

Tracer gas

Liquid PFT

(b) Sampling tube

Mesh   Mesh

Adsorbing material   Rubber cap

Figure 11.3 'Passive' Sampling Techniques

takes place which is proportional to the concentration gradient between the neck of the tube and the adsorbent. Quick sampling is possible by actively pumping air through the tube at a known flow rate. After the measurement time, the sample and emission tubes are capped and sent in separate packages to a laboratory for analysis.

Limitations:

• This method is only accurate if air change remains reasonably constant over a period of time.

• This approach provides insufficient weighting to peaks in air change, such as those associated with airing, door opening or transient high infiltration driving forces, i.e. transient changes in conditions are not "seen". Arguably, if the objective of the measurement is to estimate the average pollutant dose received by occupants in a space, resulting from a constant emitting pollutant source (e.g. furnishings and fittings), this method provides a reliable result. However, it can ignore the benefit of ventilation for transient pollutant emissions (e.g. airing for washing and cooking) and underestimate ventilation related thermal losses by as much as 40% or even more (see Section 11.6 for more details).

Multi-tracer Gas Methods

Applications: Multi-tracer gases are used to determine the movement of air (and pollutants) between rooms. Specific applications include:

- flow rate evaluation between zones,
- identification of cross contamination problems.

Methods: The theory of multi-tracer analysis is complex. Details and instrumentation are described by Prior (1985), Sherman (1989), Irwin (1989), Sateri (1989). Methods include:

Multi-tracer decay

The building is divided into separate zones, with a unique gas being emitted into each. After an initial period of mixing, the mixing fans are switched off, to prevent artificial air movement between rooms. The concentration decay in each zone, relevant to the seeded gas released into that zone is used to calculate a room air change rate. By combining the air change value for each room in a flow balance equation, the flow rate between each may be evaluated. From a practical aspect, a single tracer gas analyser is used to undertake all measurements, this is normally based on a gas chromatograph that can separate each of the gases in a sample prior to analysis (see Section 11.5). Sometimes gas samples may be collected in bottles for subsequent laboratory analysis.

Multi-tracer Constant concentration

This approach enables the air flow pattern to be continuously observed. A unique tracer gas is seeded into each zone, and between zones, maintained in the seeded zone at a constant concentration, as outlined in Section 11.4. The total air flow rate out of each zone (to adjacent zones or outside) is calculated from the tracer gas injection rate. By combining the air flow rates for each zone, the individual flow rates between zones may be determined.

Multi-tracer passive sampling

The average air flow rate between zones may be determined using passive emission and sampling tubes (see Section 11.5). Each zone is seeded with a different PFT gas and air flow rate between zones is calculated using the flow balancing approach of the previous methods, (Dietz et al 1985, Sateri et al 1989).

Limitations:

The use of multi-tracers greatly amplifies the complexity of the tracer gas test, restricting this approach to the specialist field.

- The use of multi-tracers greatly amplifies the complexity of the tracer gas test, restricting this approach to the specialist field.

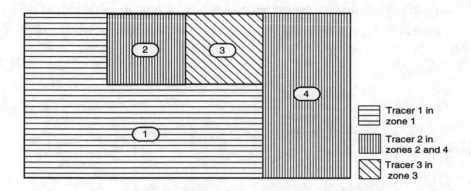

Figure 11.4 Multi-zone Seeding Strategy

- Measurements using more than three tracers are rare and the practical maximum is probably restricted to five.

- This limits the number of zones in which measurements can be made. It is nevertheless possible to analyse buildings with a greater number of zones either by zone reduction (e.g. opening internal doors) or by using a careful seeding strategy which may enable identical tracers to be used in non-adjacent rooms throughout the building without interference (see Figure 11.4). A preliminary test should provide an indication of which rooms are isolated from each other.

Use of a Single Tracer Gas to Measure Air Flow Between Zones

A single tracer may be used to identify a specific cross contamination route by seeding the suspect zone and detecting the gas in adjacent zones. By sequentially seeding each room of a building in turn with a single gas, it is also theoretically possible to build up a complete picture of air flow pattern throughout the building. However, this would be a very lengthy process and it is unlikely that the air flow pattern would remain uniform throughout the test period.

Tracer Gas Methods for the Measurement of Ventilation Efficiency

Applications: Ventilation efficiency measurements are used to assess ventilation performance, room air quality and pollutant distribution. They are useful for diagnostic analysis, and test chamber analysis of ventilation systems. Room estimates of air change and pollution removal effectiveness can be accomplished by simple tracer gas injection methods. The concepts of ventilation efficiency are summarised in Chapter 8.

Room estimates of air change and pollution removal effectiveness can be accomplished by simple tracer gas injection methods

Methods: Detailed reviews of measurement methods have been produced by Sutcliffe (1990) and Brouns and Waters (1991). The basic measurement steps for evaluating air change efficiency parameters are summarised in Figure 11.5. Approaches can apply to single rooms or multi room buildings.

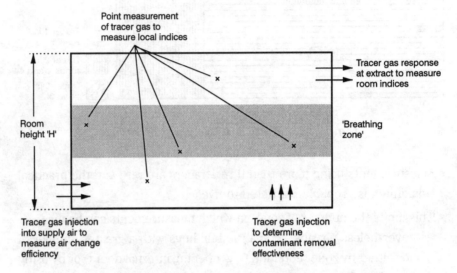

Figure 11.5 Measurement of Ventilation Efficiency Indices

Single room tracer measurements

Tracer gas may be introduced as a pulse into the supply air duct and the time response to tracer concentration at the exhaust may be used to evaluate room average ventilation efficiency parameters. Alternatively, a 'step up' technique is possible in which tracer gas is injected at a uniform rate into the supply air. Zero 'age' is represented by the start of injection. When supply injection is not possible, a tracer decay technique may be used in which an entry time of 'zero age' for the air is represented by the start of the concentration decay. Local indices of ventilation efficiency (see Chapter 9) can only be evaluated by making measurements of the time response of tracer concentration at the locations of interest (e.g. the 'breathing' zone). Contaminant removal effectiveness is similarly evaluated using tracer gas to represent the pollutant source strength and location. Pulse, step-up and decay techniques may be applied.

Multi-room measurements

Similar measurement methods are applied but each room is treated as a well mixed zone. Ventilation efficiency parameters are based on the concentration of tracer gas and the age of air as it passes from room to room.

Limitations:

- Air flow and pollutant patterns are unique to each enclosure and to the thermal and other conditions prevailing at the time of the test. It is difficult, therefore, to make inferences from such tests that can be applied to other situations.

- these techniques and the concepts of ventilation efficiency cannot be applied to systems dominated by window opening and infiltration

- exhaust air locations must be well defined.

11.2 Pressurisation Methods

Background

Pressure testing is used to measure the air-tightness of buildings and components. This is important since, excessive air leakage interferes with the design performance of ventilation systems. Pressurisation test data are used to derive the 'flow' characteristics of buildings and components, e.g. C and n values (see Chapter 12). Techniques are described in the following sections.

Pressure testing is used to measure the air-tightness of buildings and components.

Whole Building Pressurisation

Applications: Whole building pressurisation is needed for the following applications:

- Verification of air-tightness regulations or standards.
- Assessing air-tightness retrofit needs.
- Estimating air infiltration risk.

Method: The purpose of this method is to measure the air-tightness of a building at pressures in excess of those that are developed naturally but not so great that openings are artificially distorted by the pressurisation process itself. Measurements are made by using a fan to create incremental pressures between the inside and outside of a building in the +/- 10 - 100 Pa pressure range. For each pressure increment, the corresponding air flow rate through the fan is measured. The relationship between induced pressure and flow rate is plotted. The instrumentation is frequently built into a door (blower door) which temporarily replaces an existing entrance door (Figure 11.6(a)). It can normally be fitted simply by opening rather than removing the existing door. Alternatively a fan may be sealed into a window opening. Flow rate through the fan is usually measured with a calibrated orifice plate or nozzle that is supplied with the system. Pressure difference is measured with a manometer which is generally connected via a tapping in the blower door. To minimise the effect of naturally

(a) Domestic Blower Door
(Crown copyright - UK Building Research Establishment)

(b) Large Building Multi-fan System
(Crown copyright - UK Building Research Establishment)

Figure 11.6 Pressurisation Test Fans

developed pressures, the test should be conducted during periods of low wind speed. The influence of ambient conditions can be further minimised by connecting the manometer to pressure taps on each face of the building. Access to 'blower' doors for the routine testing of dwellings and other small buildings is now widely available. The maximum volume of enclosure that may be pressurised is governed by the overall air-tightness of the building, its volume and the available fan capacity. Large buildings may require more than one fan (see Figure 11.6(b)). If fitted, it is sometimes possible to use the building's own mechanical ventilation system to carry out a pressurisation test.

When used in conjunction with smoke testing for leak detecting (see Section 11.4), it is possible to weather seal the building at the same time to improve air-tightness. It has become common practice to compare the air-tightness of buildings at a reference pressure of 50 Pa Care must be taken when data are compared to ensure that identical test conditions apply. Normally the method should be applied to 'background' envelope leakage of the 'conditioned' space. All purpose provided openings and chimneys etc. should be sealed.

Limitations: Air-tightness is just one of the parameters that affect air change and ventilation rate. Specific limitations include:

• air-tightness testing which does not provide information on the size of infiltration or ventilation driving forces,

• the measurement of air-tightness which is difficult to perform on large buildings,

• trained specialists who should undertake or supervise the measurement of air-tightness.

Applications: Sometimes air-tightness test results are used to provide guidance on the significance of background leakage on ventilation performance (see Chapter 12).

Air-tightness Testing of Apartments, Individual Rooms and Facades

Applications: Pressurisation testing using more than one fan enables the leakage characteristics of individual walls and the leakage characteristics between rooms to be measured. This enables the air leakage across specific walls including party walls, internal room walls and facade walls to be determined.

Method: One of the most accurate methods of estimating air leakage through party walls or facades is the pressure equalisation or guarded pressurisation technique, using two pressurisation fans (Furbringer et al 1988). An example is illustrated in Figure 11.7. Air leakage is determined as follows:

Step 1: Windows and doors in room 2 and the corridor are opened to the outside. The overall air leakage (e.g. at 50 Pa, of room 1 is determined by conventional fan test.

Step 2: Windows and doors in room 2 are closed, room 1 is retained at the same pressure differential as in Step 1, and room 2 is brought to the same pressure as room 1. The resultant reduced flow rate through fan 1 corresponds to the leakage value of the party wall between rooms 1 and 2.

Step 3: The door between room 2 and the corridor is opened and the door between the corridor and outside is closed. Fan 2 is used to bring the pressure in room 2 and the corridor to the same level as room 1. The flow rate through fan 1 now corresponds to the external wall leakage. The remaining wall leakages may be similarly determined.

Limitations: This measurement is time consuming and involves the use of two fans. Multi-fan testing is usually restricted to research or specialist applications.

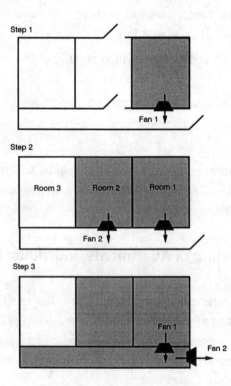

Figure 11.7 Two fan Pressure Testing

11.3 Component Air-tightness Testing

Applications

Air-tightness testing of specific building components is necessary to check compliance with relevant standards and to check the quality of fitting. Standards verification is usually undertaken in the laboratory whereas the quality of fitting must be undertaken as an 'in situ' test.

Methods

Several methods of component testing are available. These include:

Reductive sealing: The building pressurisation test is repeated as components are systematically sealed with tape. This enables the in situ leakage characteristics of individual components to be assessed by deduction.

Pressure testing individual components: A 'pressure' collection chamber is placed over the component (see Figure 11.8(a)) and a standard pressurisation test is performed. For improved accuracy the test room may be pressurised to the same value as the collection chamber (see Figure 11.8(b)). This approach may be used for both laboratory and in situ testing.

Multi-fan techniques: The multi-fan method may be used to infer leakage of specific in situ components.

Combined pressure testing and tracer gas analysis: Component leakage by combined pressure testing and tracer gas analysis can be applied when other methods prove to be difficult. An example includes evaluating ceiling leakage. The space above the ceiling may be too leaky for pressurisation, while joints for reductive sealing are often inaccessible. Tracer gas is applied to one of the spaces (e.g. roof space) at approximate constant concentration. If weather conditions remain constant, this should be achievable by supplying gas at constant emission and waiting for an equilibrium concentration to be reached (see Section 11.5). The occupied (main) space is depressurised to a suitable pressure (i.e. 50 Pa, The ratio between occupied zone leakage and that of the ceiling/roof void interface is given by the ratio of roof void tracer gas concentration and the concentration in the dwelling, Wouters et al (1986).

Component leakage by combined pressure testing and tracer gas analysis can be applied when other methods prove to be difficult.

Limitations

In-situ testing can be difficult because it may not be possible to reach specific components. Equipment is expensive and difficult to use.

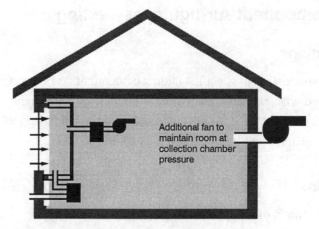

(a) Component Leakage Testing

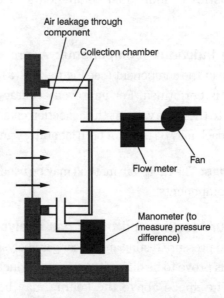

(b) Extra Fan to Control Room Pressure

Figure 11.8 Component Leakage Testing by Pressurisation

Applications are normally restricted to laboratory testing or specialist applications.

11.4 Other Measurement Methods

A variety of other measurement methods are used to measure air flow and associated parameters. These include:

Air Flow Patterns and Turbulence

Applications include:

- the measurement of flow velocity and air turbulence throughout a space,
- the evaluation of diffuser performance,
- the response to thermal parameters and flow obstruction to air flow pattern.

Methods: Methods are based on qualitative visualisation approaches and quantitative anemometric techniques.

Visualisation techniques

A qualitative assessment of air flow pattern and turbulence can be made by applying a number of visualisation techniques. These are based on developing a two dimensional sheet of bright light which is directed across a section of room. Smoke or small bubbles are used to highlight the flow pattern (see Figure 11.9). These may be photographed or recorded using a video camera. Examples are described by Gottschalk et al (1988), and Zohrabian (1989).

Anemometry (hot wire): Anemometry is used to give quantitative evaluation of spatial air velocity and turbulence distribution. Anemometers must be very sensitive and are usually based on 'hot wire' techniques. A resistance wire (the anemometer element) is heated while the current through the wire is monitored. Air speed fluctuations rapidly change the

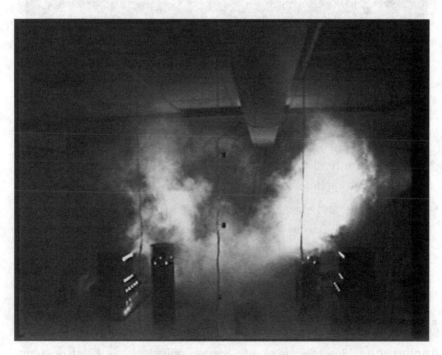

Figure 11.9 Flow Visualisation Using Smoke
(Flow induced by chilled ceiling - courtesy EA Technology, UK)

temperature and, therefore, the resistance of the wire. The resultant current change provides a measure of instantaneous air speed (turbulence). A prototype anemometer (see Figure 11.10) has been developed in which individual elements are responsive to flow in the three co-ordinate directions. This enables a three dimensional pattern of air speed and turbulence to be measured (Schädlich and Siegel, 1993). Hot wire anemometers are used in 'test' chamber studies where 'traverses' are made across sections of the chamber to build up a complete pattern of air flow.

Limitations:

- Qualitative methods are fairly easy to perform but provide only visual information.

- Quantitative (anemometric) techniques are complex and time consuming

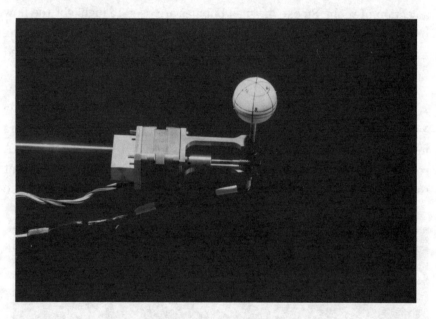

Figure 11.10 Prototype 3-Dimensional Hot wire Anemometer
(Courtesy University of Essen, Germany)

and therefore tend to be restricted to research or product (diffuser) development applications.

- Measurements and visualisation give snapshot results only. In reality, the pattern of air flow will vary depending on the location of obstructions and the balance between forced and free convection forces (see Chapter 12).

- Small changes to conditions can vastly influence air flow pattern.

Air Flow Through Ducts and Grilles

Applications: Flow measurements through individual ventilation openings are needed to ensure that the air flow rate and flow direction conforms to design requirements. They are also needed to balance ventilation systems as part of servicing or commissioning. Example applications include:

• monitoring the flow through passive ventilation stacks,

• monitoring the performance of mechanical ventilation systems,

• measuring naturally or mechanically driven air flow through air inlets and outlets.

Basic anemometry systems are straightforward to use but might not be as accurate as more complex methods.

Methods: Techniques are based on standard air flow measuring instrumentation. These include:

Orifice plates and nozzles
These are calibrated devices that are fitted in series with ductwork and have a known air flow rate Vs pressure drop relationship. The flow rate is determined by measuring the pressure drop across the device. Long straight lengths of duct are needed both upstream and downstream of the system while the constriction imposed by the orifice or nozzle can impede flow.

Pitot static traverses
Air velocity at a specific location is commonly measured using a pitot static tube. Duct air flow can be measured by inserting the tube into a prepared opening and measuring the air speed at several depths across the cross-section of the tube. The total flow rate is determined by integrating the results.

Anemometers
Several types of anemometer are used to measure the flow rate through ducts and openings; these include vane anemometers and hot wire anemometers. The vane anemometer is the most likely device for use in servicing and commissioning since it is robust and is satisfactory for measuring relatively high air flow velocities. Hot wire anemometers are delicate, precision devices for measuring very low flow rates and turbulent fluctuations.

Flow finder: Vane anemometers can disrupt or impede the flow of air through an opening thus introducing error, especially if the flow rate is low. One device specifically designed to overcome this problem and to monitor the direction and rate of air flow through an opening is the flow finder. (see Figure 11.11). Developed in conjunction with TNO (1986) in the Netherlands, it is an active device containing its own calibrated fan which is operable over a flow range of between 0 and 225 m3/h. The funnel

Vane anemometers can disrupt or impede the flow of air through an opening thus introducing error.

opening of the flow finder is placed over the opening through which the flow rate is to be measured forming an airtight seal. The internal fan speed is adjusted until there is zero pressure difference across the opening. The resultant flow rate through the device is equivalent to the undisturbed flow rate through the opening. The impact of the measurement system on the rate of flow is therefore substantially minimised.

Tracer gas injection: Sometimes tracer gas injection is used to measure air flow rate, (e.g. Riffat et al (1994)). Tracer gas is injected into the duct at a constant known rate. The flow rate of air through the duct is proportional to the tracer concentration measured in the duct.

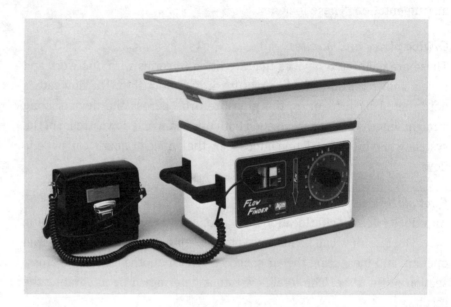

Figure 11.11 Flow Finder
(Courtesy TNO, The Netherlands)

Limitations:

• Air flow through specific openings only are measured, this is different from the total air change rate which will include air movement through air infiltration openings.

• If the structure is leaky, then only a fraction of the total air flow through the building will be measured. This could result in misleading results.

• Pitot static traverses and tracer gas methods are unlikely to be applicable to basic ventilation servicing and commissioning.

Locating Air Leaks

Applications: Simple leak locating has important applications. These include:

• identifying sources of air leakage in buildings and building components,

• air-tightness retrofit or remedial improvements to be made with relative ease.

Methods: Methods for detecting air leaks in the building structure include:

Smoke methods

Leaks may be detected by fan pressurising a building or an individual room within a building and observing the movement of smoke emitted from a smoke stick or puffer. This approach is very effective and easy to undertake. The smoke source is gently moved in the vicinity of potential sources of leaks during the course of the test. Sometimes leak locating and sealing may be undertaken while conducting a routine pressurisation test. However, air-tightness retrofit should only be undertaken in conjunction with the installation of a purpose provided (natural or mechanical) ventilation system to ensure the adequacy of ventilation. Alternatively, pressurisation may be a purely qualitative action, undertaken to develop sufficient pressure to induce a strong flow of smoke through leakage openings. Ideally, the building or room should be pressurised so that the flow of smoke, from inside to outside, can be clearly identified (see Figure 11.12).

Leaks may be detected by pressurising a building or an individual room within a building, using fan pressurisation and observing the movement of smoke emitted from a smoke stick or puffer.

Figure 11.12 Leak Detecting Using Smoke
(Courtesy Building Sciences, UK)

Thermography

Leaks may also be located by thermography. Testing may be undertaken from either the inside or outside of the building. For indoor testing, the building or room is depressurised to permit the ingress of cold outdoor air. An interior thermographic scan will indicate the location of fabric leaks. Alternatively, scanning can be undertaken externally, in which case the building is pressurised and the sources of exfiltrating hot air are located. This may be undertaken on a cold night when it is possible to locate air leaks and location of excessive fabric heat loss arising from inadequate or poorly installed insulation.

Acoustic methods

Methods involving sound sources and microphones have been used for leakage detecting.

Limitations:

• Infrared thermography is costly and experience is needed to interpret results.

• Acoustic methods are unlikely to be of value for routine investigations.

Flow Distribution - Flume Models

Applications: Flume models provide a method by which air movement, pollutant transport and temperature distribution can be predicted using scale models inserted in a water flume. They have been used to assist in the design of a variety of buildings and to predict the transient pattern of air flow through openings. (Baker et al 1992). Specific applications include:

• predicting the role and pattern of air flow and pollutant transport through defined openings,

• predicting flow patterns through a building,

• predicting flow and pollutant distribution in individual rooms.

Method: A 1:20 to 1:100 scale model of the building is constructed using transparent perspex. This model is necessarily simplified but the essential features controlling the ventilation process, including envelope openings and openings between individual rooms, are retained. This model is completely immersed in a glass sided water channel such that the pattern of flow can be observed using a video camera. Buoyancy induced flow (density stratification) is represented by sources of dense salt solution to which a tracer dye is added. The model and video camera are inverted so

(a) Water flume

(b) Flow model

Figure 11.13 The Use of a Flume Model to Visualise Ventilation
(Courtesy Paul Linden, University of Cambridge, UK)

that the salt solution appears to rise. Cooling is similarly simulated using a less dense alcohol water mixture. A typical model and flow pattern is illustrated in Figure 11.13. Quantitative measurements of flow velocities are made by measuring samples of salt solution taken from within the model. Automated image processing of the video film allow the measurement of dye intensities to give the instantaneous temperature distribution throughout the building, while flow velocities can be measured by particle tracking. Mixing and diffusion processes may also be quantified.

Limitations:

• Flume models require considerable laboratory space, thus restricting this approach to the laboratory.

• Primarily this method provides an aide to assessing the impact of stack induced air flow. The wind regime is more difficult to predict, since it is not usually possible to incorporate surrounding obstructions.

• It is not really practicable to represent infiltration or other openings resulting from construction technique or poor site practice.

Wind Pressure Distribution - Wind Tunnel Testing

Wind tunnel testing on scale models is needed when accurate information on wind pressure distribution is necessary for design purposes.

Applications: Wind tunnel testing on scale models is needed when accurate information on wind pressure distribution is necessary for design purposes. Wind tunnel methods can also be used to assess air flow patterns around buildings and air intake contaminant ingress risks.

Methods: Pressure taps, connected via plastic tubing are placed on each face of the model so that the pressure distribution can be determined (see Figure 11.14(a)). The model needs to be placed on a turn-table so that pressure can be analysed for the complete spectrum of wind direction. Wind speed is determined with respect to a specific datum height, normally corresponding to the height of the building (see also Chapter 12). Upwind roughness is normally developed using an array of cubic blocks. Smoke combined with photography is often used to provide visualisation of the flow regime.

Limitations:

• An 'environmental' wind tunnel is necessary that can accurately represent the lower levels of the Earth's turbulent boundary layer and can accommodate reasonably sized scale models of the building and surrounding environs (see Figure 11.14(b)). These are restricted to

(a) Test building showing pressure taps

(b) Wind tunnel model

Figure 11.14 Wind Tunnel Model to Measure Wind Pressure
(Courtesy CPP Inc, USA)

laboratory applications on scale models. Typical minimum scales for analysis of wind pressure distribution is 1:50. Models must also incorporate an accurate representation of the surrounding environment.

11.5 Instrumentation For Tracer Gas Detection

Tracer gas concentration is measured using a gas analyser. These can be extremely complex and costly thus adding considerably to the expense of

Tracer gas concentration is measured using a gas analyser. These can be extremely complex and costly systems which add considerably to the expense of performing a tracer gas test.

performing a tracer gas test. Various types of systems exist and it is vital that the correct detector is chosen for the gas and gas concentration used.

Infra red (IR) detection

This method makes use of the property of a gas to absorb infra red radiation of a characteristic wave length. Various IR detection methods are possible as summarised in Figure 11.15. Infra-red is commonly used to measure

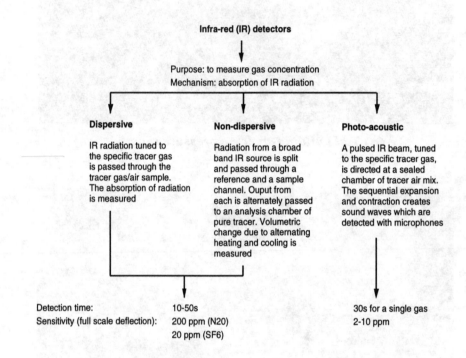

Figure 11.15 Infra-red Detection Methods

nitrous oxide and carbon dioxide. It may also be used to detect sulphur hexafluoride and other halon gases but not at the minute concentrations that are possible using other methods (see gas chromatography with electron capture). Infra red detectors are generally robust and less expensive than other types of detector.

Mass spectrometry

Mass spectrometry enables the concentrations and identity of a mix of gases to be simultaneously measured. The pressure of the sample is first reduced to approximately 10^{-5} Pa. It then enters the spectrometer where it is ionised by an electric field of variable radio frequency. The resonant frequency of ions is dependent on charge to mass ratio, this is unique to each molecule and element. Only those that are resonant to the tuned radio frequency reach a detector where they are detected by an electron

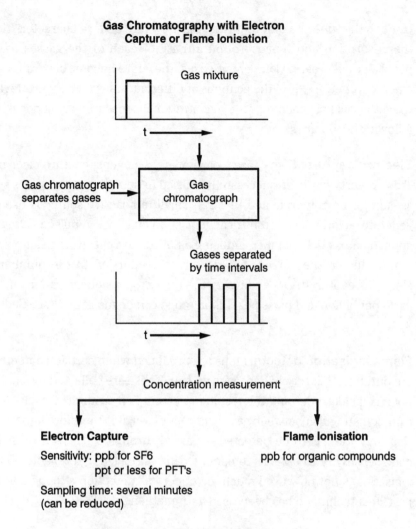

Figure 11.16 Gas Chromatography

multiplier. This produces a signal which is proportional to the number of ions that reach the detector. Up to 7 gases may be detected simultaneously in a detection period of a few milliseconds.

Gas Chromatography with Electron Capture or Flame Ionisation

Gas chromatography is used to separate gases before their concentration is measured. This is essential for multi-tracer gas testing (see Section 6) or when it is difficult for a detector system to distinguish between tracer gas and other constituents of air (e.g. sulphur hexafluoride in oxygen).

A gas chromatograph consists of a heated tube or column filled with gas adsorbing material (adsorbent). A pulse of mixed gases, such as room air with tracer gas, is injected into the column and is flushed through it with an inert carrier gas. Each of the component gases in the mix propagate

A gas chromatograph consists of a heated tube or column filled with gas adsorbing material (adsorbent).

through the tube at a different rate, this flow rate being a characteristic of the adsorption and de-adsorption affinity of each of the gasses to the particular adsorbent. Component gases, therefore become separated and emerge from the exit of the columns at different times (see Figure 11.16). Once the gas has emerged, its concentration is measured using one of the following techniques:

Electron capture: Some gases, particularly halogens, capture electrons. This property has been successfully utilised in detecting tracer gases such as sulphur hexafluoride and PFT's. A small radioactive source is used to generate a cloud of electrons in an ionisation chamber. A pulsed voltage is applied across the chamber, inducing a flow of current. As the sample gas is introduced, the current falls in direct proportion to the number of electrons captured. Depending on the type of gas, concentrations in the parts per billion and parts per trillion range can be measured (see Section 2).

Flame ionisation detector: Ions are produced when certain compounds are burnt in a mixture of hydrogen and air. These are collected by a pair of polarised electrodes and the resultant current is measured. This detector cannot distinguish between gases or types of ion, it is therefore imperative that only the gas to be detected is passed through to the sensor. It has good sensitivity to organic compounds and is rugged and reliable. Flame ionisation is not now used much for tracer gas detection although, in the past, this technique has been used with methane.

11.6 Theoretical Outline

Theory and equations: If an inert gas that is not normally present in the atmosphere is released and is perfectly mixed within a leaky enclosure, the concentration of gas at any instant in time is given by the continuity equation:

$$V \frac{dC}{dt} + QC = F$$

Term1   *Term 2*   *Term 3*

where:

V = effective volume of enclosure (m³);

C = concentration of tracer gas;

Q = air flow rate (m³/s or kg/s);

F = tracer gas injection rate (m³/s or kg/s);

t = time (s);

Hence the air flow rate, Q, may be determined if all the remaining parameters are known. Several test configurations enable Q to be evaluated; these include:

Concentration decay: If a fixed quantity of tracer gas is uniformly distributed into a space, its concentration will reach a peak level given by $C_{(o)}$. Subsequently, as the seeded air becomes diluted with incoming (unseeded) air, the concentration of tracer gas will gradually decay. Since, after distribution of the gas, the injection rate, F, becomes zero, term 3 from the continuity equation is eliminated. Integration of Terms 2 and 3 yield:

$$C_{(t)} = C_{(0)}e^{-\frac{Q}{V}t}$$

where:

$C_{(o)}$ = tracer gas concentration at start of test;

$C_{(t)}$ = tracer gas concentration at time, t, after start of test.

The air change rate, (Q/V), is given by the logarithmic gradient of the tracer gas concentration curve. This can be readily determined by plotting the tracer gas concentration decay over time on logarithmic paper.

Constant concentration: If the emission rate of tracer gas, F, is continuously adjusted such that the concentration of tracer remains constant, term 1 of the continuity equation is eliminated. The air flow rate is then given by:

$$Q = \frac{F}{C} \quad (m^3 / s \ \text{or} \ kg / s)$$

Thus the air flow rate, Q, is directly proportional to the tracer gas emission rate.

Constant emission: If tracer gas is released at a constant rate, all terms in the continuity equation remain and integration yields:

$$C_{(t)} = \frac{F}{Q} + \left(C_{(0)} - \frac{F}{Q} \right)e^{-\frac{Q}{V}t}$$

While the test is relatively easy to perform, analysis of the data can be complicated. If, however, driving forces remain constant, a steady state concentration will be reached and analysis will reduce to that of the constant concentration approach.

Long term (inverse) average: The constant emission method can further be applied to the calculation of an average inverse air change rate which has proved useful for passive tracer gas testing. Rearranging the continuity equation and averaging over time yields:

$$\left(\frac{V}{Q}\frac{dC}{dt}\right) + (C) = \left(\frac{F}{Q}\right)$$

If it is assumed that the air change time (ie. the inverse of the air change rate) is small compared to the averaging period and that the emission rate of tracer, F, is constant, then:

$$\left(\frac{V}{Q}\frac{dC}{dt}\right) \rightarrow 0 \ and \ (F) = F$$

$hence$

$$\left(\frac{1}{Q}\right) = \frac{(C)}{F}$$

From the above, the inference is often made that:

$$(Q) = \frac{F}{(C)}$$

Such an assumption is only valid if the average air change rate is constant throughout the averaging period. In practice, this averaging method provides insufficient weighting to peaks in air change rate that may result, for example, from airing by window opening or high infiltration rates induced by transient driving forces. This method, therefore, while probably being acceptable for tight buildings in which air change is dominated by controlled ventilation, may give misleading under-estimates in buildings in which air change is dominated by air infiltration or natural ventilation.

How much tracer gas?: Assuming that 1 gram molecular weight of gas occupies 22.4 litres at normal temperature and pressure, the approximate mass of gas needed to seed a space to a given starting concentration is given by:

$M = molecular\ weight * C * V / (22.4 * 10^9)\ (g)$

where:

M = mass of gas (g);

C = target concentration (ppm);

V = enclosure volume (m³).

$Example:$

25 ppm of nitrous oxide in a 200 m3 enclosure:

M = 44 * 25 * 200 / (22.4 * 1000) (g)

M = 10 (g)

References

Baker N, and Linden P, *Physical modelling of air flows - a new design tool*, Report, University of Cambridge, Dept of Architecture, 1992.

Brouns C, Waters J R, *A guide to contaminant removal effectiveness*, AIVC Technical Note 28.2,1991.

Charlesworth P S, *Air exchange rate and air-tightness measurement techniques- an applications guide*, AIVC Technical Guide 2, 1988.

Dietz R N, Goodrich R W, Cote E A, et al., *Brookhaven air infiltration measurement system (BNL/AIMS)- description and application*, Brookhaven National Laboratory, BNL 33846, United States, 1983.

Dietz R N, D'Ottavio T W, Goodrich R W, *Multi-zone infiltration measurements in homes and buildings using a passive perfluorocarbon tracer method*, ASHRAE Transactions, Vol 91, Pt 2, 1985.

Etheridge D W, *Application of the constant concentration technique for ventilation measurement to large buildings*, BSERT, Vol 6, No 3, 1985.

Furbringer J M, Roecker C, Roulet C A, *The use of a guarded zone pressurization technique to measure air flow permeabilities of a multi-zone building*, Proc AIVC 9th Conference, 1988.

Gottschalk G, Tanner P A, Suter P, *The large area quantitative visualisation method of air streams*, Proc 9th AIVC Conference, 1988.

Grieve P W, *Measuring ventilation using tracer gases*, Bruel & Kjaer, 1989.

Grot R A, Hunt C M, Harrje D T, *Automated air infiltration measurements in large buildings*, Proc. A.I.C. 1st Annual Conference *Instrumentation and measuring techniques*, 1980.

Irwin C, Edwards R E, *A comparison of different methods of calculating interzonal airflows by multiple tracer gas decay tests*, Proc 10th AIVC Conference, Vol 2, 1989.

Prior J J, Martin C J, Littler J G F, *An automatic multi-tracer-gas method for following interzonal air movement*, ASHRAE Transactions, Vol 91, Pt 2 1985.

Riffat S B, Cheong K W, *Tracer gas techniques for measuring airflow in review*, University of Nottingham, School of Architecture Report, 1994.

Roulet C-A, Vandaele L, *Air flow patterns within buildings: measurement techniques*, Air Infiltration and Ventilation Centre, Technical Note AIVC 34, (IEA Annex XX Final Report) 1991.

Sandberg M, Sundberg J, *The use of detector tubes with carbon dioxide as a tracer gas*, Air Infiltration Review, Vol.8, No.3, May 1987.

Sateri J, Jyske P, Majanen A, Seppanen O, *The performance of the passive perfluorocarbon method*, Proc. 10th AIVC Conference Vol 1, 1989.

Schadlich S, Siegel A, *Development of a thermal anemometer with a clear determination of the air flow direction*, Research Project No.8258, Department of Applied Thermodynamics and Air Conditioning, University of Essen, Germany, 1993.

Sherman M H, *A multitracer system for multi-zone ventilation measurement*, Lawrence Berkeley Laboratory Report, 1989.

Sutcliffe H, *A guide to air change efficiency*, AIVC Technical Note 28, 1990.

TNO *Flow Finder Model 153 for measurement of air flows at grilles*, ACIN, 1986.

Wouters P, L'Heureux D, Voordecker P, *The determination of leakages by simultaneous use of tracer gas and pressurisation equipment*, Air Infiltration Review, Vol 8, No.1, November 1986.

Zohrabian A S, Mokhtarzadeh-Dehghan M R, Reynolds A J, *Buoyancy-driven air flow in a closed half scale stairwell model: velocity and temperature measurements*, Proc. 10th AIVC Conference, Vol 2, 1989.

12 Calculation Methods

Applications
Generic Calculation Methods
Estimation from Building Air-tightness Data
Simplified Theoretical Models
Network (zonal) Models
Explicit Network Methods
Computational Fluid Dynamics
Ventilation and Air Flow Related Calculations
Combined Thermal and Ventilation Methods

Summary and Introduction

There are many calculation techniques available to predict ventilation and related air flow parameters in buildings. The main difficulties concern ease of use and the providing of input data. It is hoped that by following the guidelines presented in this Chapter the main pitfalls will be avoided.

Many advances are taking place, especially in the areas of user friendly access and embedded databases. As these developments continue, the ease with which calculation techniques may be applied will steadily improve. Reliable calculations are essential for good design. Ventilation and air flow calculation methods are increasingly needed to evaluate the performance of ventilation design. To some extent they are able to replace expensive and time consuming field tests and provide a comprehensive range of test conditions. Often calculation methods can lead to an improved understanding of flow behaviour and provide confidence in design. They are especially important for making preliminary evaluations of complex ventilation and air flow strategies.

Many advances are taking place, especially in the areas of user friendly front ends and embedded databases. As these developments continue, the ease with which calculation techniques may be applied will steadily improve.

In general, the designer is faced with a set of fixed conditions relating to the environment in which the building is located. These include climate, pollutant sources (e.g. from traffic and adjacent building etc.) terrain characteristics and the shielding presented by surrounding buildings. Calculation techniques form part of the process of matching design variables (e.g. building layout, approach to ventilation, etc.) with the various design constraints to achieve an optimum ventilation solution (see Figure 12.1). Reliable results are dependent on a good working knowledge of techniques and data.

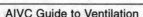

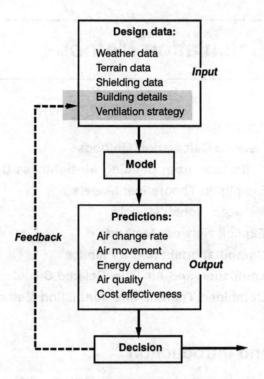

Figure 12.1 The Role of Modelling in Design

In the past, ventilation calculation methods have often been based on the most rudimentary of physical concepts, sometimes resulting in poor or inefficient design solutions. The reasons for this inadequacy are easy to understand, since techniques tend to be too complex, are not user friendly and are dependent on unreliable or difficult to apply input data. However, as designs and performance tolerances have become more demanding, it is becoming increasingly important to be able to understand and use numerical techniques. This need has resulted in the development of improved algorithms and wider availability of design data. Nowadays, a variety of quite simple methods are available to perform complex design tasks. In support of these techniques, the AIVC has developed a database covering the leakage characteristics of typical construction components and wind pressure data (Orme et al 1994). The growth of Standards covering air-tightness performance of components and buildings has also served to improve building quality and ease the difficulty of applying calculation techniques. Further stages of work on calculations for basic design are in the course of development as part of European CEN Standards activity (Dorer, 1995).

This Chapter is aimed at outlining the background and range of applicability of theoretically based calculation methods. These methods vary in complexity from air-tightness based techniques to computational fluid dynamics. Subsidiary calculations focus on the sizing of ventilation openings, the avoidance of back-draughting and the performance of ventilation heat recovery.

12.1 Applications

Typical applications for which numerical methods are needed include:

- estimating air change rate induced by air infiltration and ventilation,
- calculating the influence of parameters such as climate and building air-tightness on air change rate,
- determining the rate and direction of flow through purpose provided and air infiltration openings,
- calculating the rate of air flow between rooms,
- calculating the pattern of air flow within individual zones or rooms (ventilation efficiency parameters).

Subsidiary calculations, based on knowledge of air flow and ventilation prediction, include:

- determining the energy impact of ventilation,
- predicting pollutant concentration (indoor air quality analysis and pollutant removal effectiveness),
- estimating the transfer of pollutants between zones or between the outside and inside of a building,
- calculating room and building pressures for back-draughting or cross contamination assessment,
- the sizing of ventilation openings (to optimise ventilation performance),
- cost and energy performance analysis (e.g. to compare alternative ventilation strategies),
- thermal comfort analysis (temperature and draught risk) .

Further methods are necessary to evaluate the strength of natural driving forces. These include:

- wind pressure calculation,
- stack pressure calculation.

The steps needed and range of techniques available to undertake these various applications are described in this Chapter.

12.2 Generic Calculation Methods

The rate and pattern of air flow throughout a building is uniquely defined by:

- the distribution and air flow characteristics of all flow paths (openings) that penetrate the building envelope and that link individual rooms. These paths include constructional cracks and gaps, intentionally provided air vents, and any open windows or doors.
- the pressure difference acting across each opening. This is developed by the combined effect of naturally and mechanically induced driving forces.

Additionally, the pattern of air movement within any individual space is further influenced by:

- the locations of all sources of incoming air,
- the temperature, velocity and turbulence of incoming air at each source
- the location and flow rate of all sources of outgoing air,
- the distribution of flow obstructions (e.g. partitioning, furnishings and fittings),
- the distribution and strength of all thermal sources and sinks,
- the thermal characteristics of all surfaces.

These extra needs make the prediction of air flow patterns in enclosed spaces an extremely complex exercise.

In reality, it would be a formidable task to identify the flow characteristics, driving forces, size and location of every opening. Instead it is necessary to introduce a number of simplifying assumptions which allow the main physical concepts of air flow to be represented without compromising results.

In reality, it would be a formidable task to identify the flow characteristics, driving forces, size and location of every opening. Instead it is necessary to introduce a number of simplifying assumptions which allow the main physical concepts of air flow to be represented without compromising results. It is the degree to which the flow mechanics is simplified that identifies the type of model, the detail of data needed and the range of applicability of results. Generic forms of calculation method used for the prediction of ventilation and air flow patterns in buildings include:

- estimation from building air-tightness data,
- 'simplified' theoretical methods,
- network (zonal) models,
- computational fluid dynamics.

In addition, energy, pollutant and heat loss models may be combined with air flow and ventilation models to simulate a wide range of building environmental conditions. Each of these calculation methods are described in further detail in the following Sections.

12.3 Estimation from Building Air-tightness Data

Background: From sets of measurements, Kronvall (1978) suggested that an approximate ('rule of thumb') estimate of air infiltration rate could be inferred from building air-tightness data. This work was extended as part of an IEA project (Dubrul 1988) to account for building size and local wind and shielding conditions.

Applications:

- this approach has proved useful for energy analysis and estimating for the impact of air infiltration on ventilation performance,
- approximating average infiltration rate,
- energy analysis.

Method: The air-tightness of the building is determined at a reference pressure of 50 Pa (see also Chapter 11). This air-tightness value is divided by an empirical coefficient representing the average influence of driving forces and surrounding shielding. Conventionally a value of 20 is used although this may be varied from between 10 and 30 (Dubrul 1988, see Figure 12.2) to account for building size and the degree of shelter. Other developments based on this type of approach incorporating building size, window opening behaviour and wind regime are described by Hartmann et al (1983).

Limitations:

- air-tightness is only one of the primary parameters influencing the rate of ventilation.
- this approach largely ignores the driving forces which vary considerably over time. Time varying changes to air change are therefore ignored. This is especially relevant when a building is leaky or is ventilated by natural means, since the instantaneous rate of ventilation can differ considerably from the 'average' value. In Winter, for example, natural

> *Air-tightness approach largely ignores the driving forces which vary considerably over time.*

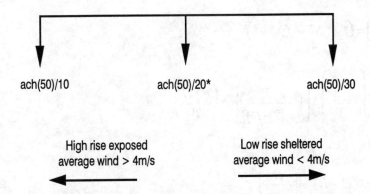

(*Only gives "average" air change, the actual value can be substantially different)

ach(50) value is measured or is sometimes specified as an airtightness requirement

Figure 12.2 Estimating Air Change from Air-tightness Data

driving forces (wind and stack pressure) can be especially high resulting in much higher air changes than predicted by this method.

12.4 'Simplified' Theoretical Models

A much improved approach which incorporates the effects of air-tightness and natural and mechanical driving forces has been developed at the Lawrence Berkeley Laboratory (Sherman et al 1980). This method is based on a theoretical analysis of ventilation which has been simplified so that direct ('non iterative') calculations can be made.

Applications: This technique may be used for:

- calculating building air change rate,
- estimating the effect of prevailing climate (wind and temperature) on ventilation rate,
- estimating the effect of air-tightness on ventilation rate.

It may further be used to predict the pollution concentration from contaminant sources within the building (see Section 8).

Method: A series of equations are used to approximate the total volume air flow rate into a space, Q_v. These are based on 'equivalent leakage area', ELA , (a measure of the leakage characteristics of the building), temperature driven flow characteristics, f_s, and wind driven flow characteristics, f_w. The resultant equations are:

$$Q_v = ELA * s[h] \quad \text{air changes / hour (ach)}$$

$$s[h] = \left(f_s^2 * \Delta T + f_w^2 * v^2 \right)^{\frac{1}{2}}$$

$$f_s = \left(\frac{1 + \dfrac{R}{2}}{3} \right) * \left(1 - \frac{X^2}{(2-R)^2} \right)^{\frac{3}{2}} * \left(\frac{g * H}{T_o} \right)^{\frac{1}{2}}$$

$$f_w = C'(1-R)^{\frac{1}{3}} A \left(\frac{H}{10m} \right)^{B}$$

$$R = \frac{ELA_{ceiling} + ELA_{floor}}{ELA} ; X = \frac{ELA_{ceiling} - ELA_{floor}}{ELA}$$

where $A, B = $ terrain parameters (See Table 12.1)

$\quad\quad C' = $ shielding parameter (See Table 12.1)

$\quad\quad v = $ 10m open site wind speed (m / s)

$\quad\quad T_0 = $ indoor air temperature (K)

$\quad ELA = $ effective leakage area (cm^2)

$\quad\quad g = $ acceleration due to gravity (9.81 m / s^2)

Effective leakage area (ELA): The *effective leakage area* is a measure of the air-tightness of the building. It is based on extrapolating the 50Pa air change rate to a reference pressure of 4 Pa. *ELA* is calculated from:

$$ELA = Q\left(\frac{\rho}{2\Delta P}\right)^{\frac{1}{2}}$$

where: $\quad Q = $ volume flow rate (m^3 / s)

$\quad\quad \rho = $ density of air (kg / m^3)

$\quad\quad \Delta P = $ pressure difference across opening ($4Pa$)

A 4 Pa. reference pressure is selected as being representative of ambient driving forces.

$ELA_{ceiling}$ is the leakage area associated with gaps and cracks at ceiling level. This may be approximated by survey or by measurement.

ELA_{floor} is the leakage area associated with floor level openings.

Terrain and shielding parameters: The terrain and shielding parameters, A, B and C' are used to evaluate the infiltration induced by local wind pressure (see Table 12.1). The values of these coefficients are based on local terrain roughness and the scale of obstructions created by surrounding objects.

Table12.1 Terrain and shielding coefficients

Shielding class	I (no shielding)	II (light)	III (moderate)	IV (heavy)	V (very heavy)
C	0.34	0.3	0.25	0.19	0.11

Shielding coefficients for LBL model

Terrain class	I (very smooth)	II (flat)	III (rural)	III (urban)	III (city centre)
A	1.30	1.00	0.85	0.67	0.47
B	0.10	0.15	0.20	0.25	0.35

Terrain coefficients for LBL model

Mechanical ventilation: The effect on air change of mechanical ventilation is determined for supply or exhaust only systems by adding the ventilation rate, Q_{mv}, to the infiltration rate, Q_{inf}, in quadrature, i.e.:

$$Q_{Total} = (Q_{inf}^2 + Q_{mv}^2)^{\frac{1}{2}}$$

Essentially, this means that at low infiltration rates, air change rate is dominated by mechanical ventilation while, at high infiltration rates it is dominated by air infiltration.

Balanced mechanical ventilation systems have very little effect on air infiltration rate. As a result air infiltration is added directly to the mechanical ventilation rate, i.e.:

$$Q_{Total} = Q_{inf} + Q_{mv}$$

In its basic form, this simplified method approximates the building by a single enclosed space. It has been shown to perform reliably (Liddament et al 1983), largely because the method takes account of both the air-tightness of the building and forces that drive the air change. A development of this technique, aimed at estimating air change rates in individual rooms within a building has also been produced (Feustel 1985).

Limitations:

• the direction of flow through openings is unknown.

• flow characteristics have been simplified.

12.5 Network (zonal) Models

Background

A network model is one in which a building is represented by a series of 'zones' or 'cells' interconnected by flow paths.

A network model is one in which a building is represented by a series of 'zones' or 'cells' interconnected by flow paths. Each 'zone' typically represents an individual room, while flow paths represent infiltration routes

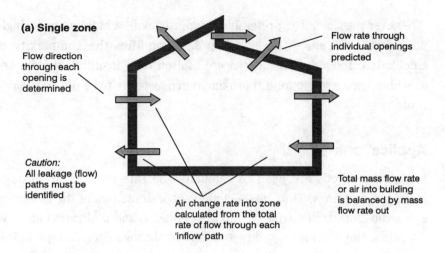

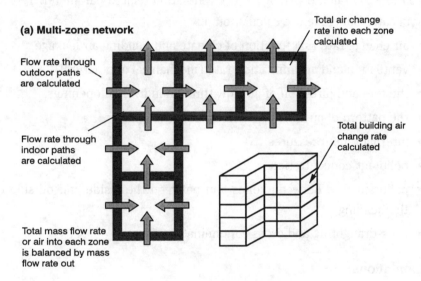

Figure 12.3 Single and Multi-zone Flow Path Networks

and purpose provided openings. Flow equations are applied that relate the pressure difference acting across each flow path to the resultant air flow through the opening. Additional equations represent air flow generated by mechanical ventilation.

In its simplest form, a network model approximates the inside of the building as a single, well mixed, enclosed space. This is known as the 'single-zone' or 'single cell' approximation (see Figure 12.3(a)). It is an acceptable approximation for open plan buildings and for small single family type buildings in which internal doors are left open or are relatively leaky. Networks in which individual rooms are separately represented are known as 'multi-zone' or 'multi-cell' (see Figure 12.3(b)). These are applicable to commercial and multi-storey type buildings in which the floor space is partitioned into separate rooms.

In its simplest form, a network model approxi-mates the inside of the building as a single, well mixed, enclosed space.

Whenever possible, it is preferable to approximate a building as a single zone structure, since this considerably simplifies the complexity of calculation. Indeed, if resources are limited or if insufficient data are available, then a single zone approximation may prove to be the only viable route.

Applications

Network methods are used to calculate the rate of air flow through individual openings. Thus this technique represents one of the closest of approximations to the true system of ventilation and infiltration air flow. By calculating the rate and direction of flow through each flow path, it is possible to evaluate virtually every ventilation related parameter. Typical applications include the calculation of:

- air change rate as a function of climate and building air leakage,
- ventilation and air infiltration rate (mechanical and natural),
- the rate and direction of air flow through individual openings,
- the pattern of air flow between zones,
- internal room pressures,
- pollutant concentration,
- pollutant flow between zones and between the inside and outside of the building,
- back-draughting and cross contamination risks.

Limitations:

- zonal models are extremely versatile,
- the need to quantify the driving forces and to account accurately for all openings in the structure of the building,
- the assumption that air and pollutant in each zone is uniformly mixed,
- this approach, as with the preceding methods, does not provide information on pollutant distribution within the individual zones.

Zonal models are extremely versatile. Performance is primarily restricted by the need to quantify the driving forces and to account accurately for all openings in the structure of the building.

Network Methods - Calculation Steps

Since network methods are so versatile, it is useful to have an understanding of the theoretical concepts and steps involved in using this type of approach. Once the background to each step of the calculation process is understood, the application of network methods become relatively straightforward. The essential steps are:

- Develop the flow equations.
- Develop a flow path network and define the pressure/air flow

characteristics of each flow path or opening.
- Determine the strength of driving forces acting across each path.
- Incorporate mechanical ventilation into the flow network.
- Solve for mass flow balance between incoming and outgoing air.

Step 1 – The Flow Equations

The rate of air flow induced through an opening is dependent upon the pressure acting across it and its dimensions and geometry. The rate of air flow through cracks and gaps is commonly approximated by a power law equation of the form:

$$Q_m = \rho C (p_{ext} - p_{int})^n \ (kg/s)$$

where: Q_m = mass flow rate through opening *(kg/s)*

ρ = density of air flowing through the opening *(kg/m³)*

p_{ext} = pressure acting on the outside of the opening *(Pa)*

p_{int} = pressure acting on the inside of the opening *(Pa)*

C = flow coefficient

n = flow exponent.

The 'flow coefficient', C, is approximately related to the size of the opening and is normally expressed in terms of m³/s (or dm³/s) for each m² of porous surface area or for each m length of crack. The flow exponent, n, characterises the type of flow and varies in value between 0.5 for fully turbulent flow to 1.0 for completely laminar flow. Many building components have values in the range of 0.6 to 0.7. Typical data are summarised by Orme et al (1994) and are tabulated in Appendix 1.

Component openings with a visible area of opening are often approximated by the orifice flow equation given by:

$$Q_m = C_d \rho A \left[\frac{2(P_{ext} - P_{int})}{\rho} \right]^{\frac{1}{2}} \ (kg/s)$$

where: C_d = discharge coefficient (0.61 for 'flat plate' orifice).

A = area of opening (m^2).

ρ = density of air (m^3/kg).

The flow coefficient, C, and flow exponent, n, are thus:

$$C = C_d A \left[\frac{2}{\rho} \right]^{\frac{1}{2}} \text{ and } n = 1/2$$

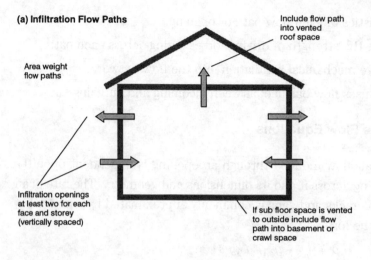

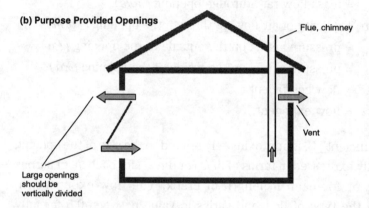

Figure 12.4 Typical Flow Paths

Step 2 – Developing a Flow Network

The flow network must represent all the openings through which air may flow. Calculated results will rapidly depart from reality if any openings are ignored.

The flow network must represent all the openings through which air may flow. Every source of penetration in the building envelope and (for multizone networks) between rooms must be identified and accurately expressed in terms of 'C' and 'n' values. Calculated results will rapidly depart from reality if any openings are ignored. This is a common error with zonal modelling. Typical air flow and leakage paths are illustrated in Figure 12.4 and include:

- purpose provided openings such as vents and chimneys,
- adventitious 'background' openings derived from the construction process (e.g. cracks, gaps, semi-porous wall surfaces and ceiling surfaces etc.),
- gaps around service penetrations,

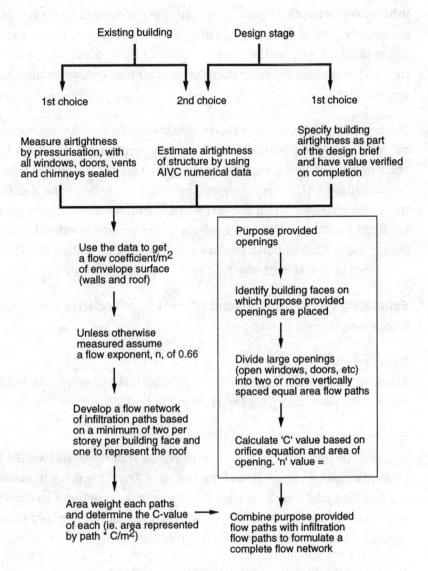

Figure 12.5 Evaluating 'C' and 'n' Values

- open windows and doors.

Fortunately, it is often possible to amalgamate several openings into a single flow path. It is recommended that the task of developing a flow network should be divided into three steps (see Figure 12.5), i.e.:

- Establish a flow network for 'infiltration' openings.

- Establish a flow network for 'purpose provided' openings.

- Combine the two networks into a single network.

Fortunately, it is often possible to amalgamate several openings into a single flow path.

Infiltration network: An infiltration network is needed to represent the natural porosity of the building fabric. By its very nature this network is rather abstract, yet, in other than the most air tight of buildings, it is often the most critical for accurate assessment of air flow behaviour throughout the building.

The most straightforward method of infiltration flow path development is by 'area weighting' in which infiltration openings are assumed to be uniformly distributed across the total exposed area of the building shell. A flow coefficient (C_t), representing the entire 'leakage characteristic' of the building is determined and divided by the total exposed envelope area to obtain a unit area leakage coefficient. The leakage coefficient of each background or infiltration flow path is determined by multiplying the unit area value by the area of envelope represented by each path.

Estimating the flow coefficient: (C_t) may be estimated by one of several techniques; these include:

Measurement
The air-tightness characteristics of an existing building may be determined by pressurisation (see Chapter 11, Section 2).

Specification
Building air-tightness is specified in the design brief and verified by pressurisation on completion of the building. Any air leakage in excess of the specified rate should be traced and rectified. Sometimes air-tightness requirements are specified by relevant regulations, standards or codes of practice, in which case these should be applied.

Estimated on the basis of existing numerical data
If measurements are not practicable and mandatory standards do not apply, then data published in the AIVC Numerical Data Guide (Orme et al, 1994) can be used to infer an air-tightness value for typical types of building construction and build quality. A summary of such data is presented in Appendix 1. Again, wherever possible, the actual air-tightness of the building should be verified once the building has been completed.

Purpose provided openings network: Individual paths should be assigned to each purpose provided opening. These include stacks, air vents and any open windows and doors. Large openings through which air flow may simultaneously take place in both directions should be represented by two or more vertically spaced equal area openings.

Other methods for dealing with bi-directional flow are considered by Allard

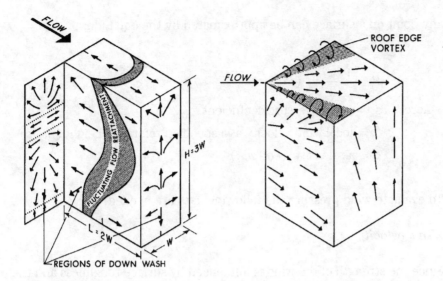

Figure 12.6 Examples of Wind Pressure Acting on a Building
(Courtesy David Wilson)

et al (1990) and Bienfait (1991). Unless otherwise known, air flow characteristics for these openings should be approximated by the area of opening, represented by each path using the orifice flow equation.

Combining infiltration and purpose provided networks: The purpose provided and infiltration networks should be combined to formulate a complete flow network in which the flow coefficients and flow exponents of each path are identified.

Step 3 – Evaluating Driving Forces (External Pressure)

The flow of air through openings is driven by pressure differences created by wind, temperature difference and mechanical ventilation. The strength of each of these forces acting at each opening must be specified.

The flow of air through openings is driven by pressure differences created by wind, temperature difference and mechanical ventilation.

Determining Wind pressure: On impinging the surface of an exposed building, a positive pressure is induced by the wind on the up-wind face. Flow separates at the sharp edges of the corners of the building inducing a negative pressure along the sides and in the wake region along the leeward face (see Figure 12.6). Pressure characteristics at roof level vary with pitch, with both faces tending to be at negative pressure (with respect to atmospheric pressure) for roof pitches below 30° whilst, above this angle, the pressure on the leading face tends to become positive.

Relative to the static pressure of the free wind, the pressure acting at any point on a surface can be approximated by the equation:

$$P_w = \frac{\rho c_p v^2}{2} \quad (Pa)$$

where: c_p = wind pressure coefficient

   v = local wind velocity at a specified reference height (m/s)

   ρ = air density (kg/m^3)

To evaluate wind pressure the following data are needed:

Wind velocity

Since the strength of the wind is influenced by surface roughness and the height above ground, a reference level for wind velocity must be specified for use in the wind pressure calculation. This is commonly taken as building height. Normally 'on-site' wind data are not available and information from a local weather station must be used. Such data must be corrected to account for any difference between measurement height and building height and to account for the influence on wind speed of intervening terrain roughness (see Figure 12.7). Since the value of wind speed is squared in the wind pressure equation, the use of raw data from a meteorological station can result in a significant calculation error. This is a common fault in the application of network methods. Ideally wind data should be obtained from a local site which shares similar topography (e.g. not separated by isolating hills). An approximate correction equation to account for heightdifference and intervening terrain is given below (BS 5925 : 1991).

$$U_z = U_m k z^a \quad (m/s)$$

where: U_z = building height wind speed (m/s)

   U_m = wind speed measured in open country at a standard height of $10m$ (m/s)

   z = building height (m)

   k, a = constants dependent on terrain (see below)

Terrain Coefficient	k	a
open, flat country	0.68	0.17
country with scattered wind breaks	0.52	0.20
urban	0.35	0.25
city	0.21	0.33

Example: Calculate the building height wind speed, U_{8m} for an 8m tall building situated in an urban location, given a weather station wind speed of 5 m/s.

$$_{8m} = 5*0.21*8^{0.33} = 2.1 \ m/s$$

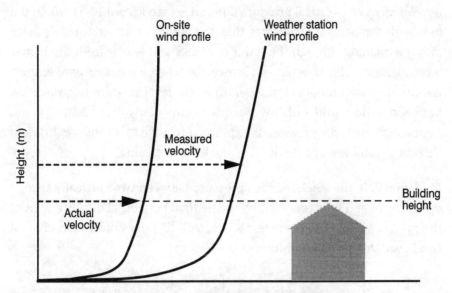

Figure 12.7 Influence of Wind Profile and Terrain Characteristics on Local Wind Speed

Pressure coefficient

The pressure coefficient, C_p, is an empirically derived parameter, largely based on the results of wind tunnel studies. It is assumed to be independent of wind speed but varies according to wind direction and spatial location on the building surface. It is significantly affected by surrounding obstructions with the result that similar buildings subjected to different surroundings may be expected to exhibit markedly different pressure coefficient values. Accurate evaluation of this parameter is one of the most difficult aspects of zonal modelling.

For low rise buildings, typically up to three storeys, pressure coefficients may be expressed as an average value for each face of the building and for each 45° or even 30° sector in wind direction. Typical design data are given in Appendix 2. For taller buildings, the spatial dependence on wind pressure takes on much greater significance, since the strength of the wind varies considerably over the height range. Example data is published by Bowen 1976. It may be necessary to undertake wind tunnel tests to obtain accurate wind pressure coefficient data (see Chapter 11, Section 4). Computational fluid dynamic techniques are also being used to predict wind induced pressures (see Section 12.7).

Determining Stack pressure

Stack pressure is generated by the difference in temperature and hence air density between the inside and outside of a building. This produces an imbalance in the vertical of pressure gradients, thus resulting in the

The pressure coefficient, C_p, is assumed to be independent of wind speed but varies according to wind direction and spatial location on the building surface.

Stack pressure is generated by the difference in temperature and hence air density between the inside and outside of a building.

development of a vertical pressure difference (see Figure 12.8). When the indoor air temperature is greater than the outdoor temperature, air flows into the building through the lower openings and leaves from the higher level openings. This flow pattern is reversed when the indoor temperature is lower than the outdoor air temperature. The level at which the transition between inflow and outflow occurs is the neutral pressure plane. Commonly, the stack pressure is expressed relative to a consistent datum such as ground level or the level of the lowest opening.

In Figure 12.8, the stack induced pressure between two vertically spaced openings, h_1 and h_2 is represented by the total horizontal displacement of the pressure curves at these levels (i.e. 'A' + 'B'). By application of Ideal Gas Laws, this pressure difference is given by:

$$P_s = -\rho_0 g 273(h_2 - h_1)\left[\frac{1}{T_{ext}} - \frac{1}{T_{int}}\right] \quad (Pa)$$

where:

$\rho_0 = $ air density at 273K (1.29 kg/m^3)

$g = $ accn due to gravity (9.81 m/s^2)

$T_{ext} = $ outdoor air temperature (K)

$T_{int} = $ indoor air temperature (K)

$h_1 = $ height of opening 1, (m)

$h_2 = $ height of opening 2, (m)

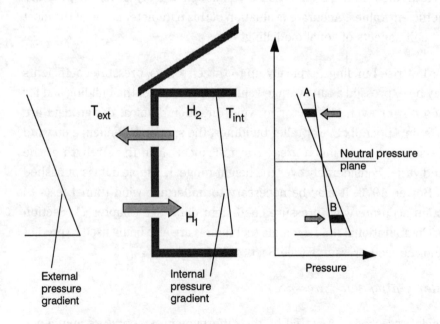

Figure 12.8 Stack Pressure Distribution Between Two Vertically Placed Openings

More detailed information on evaluating the stack pressure for multiple openings is given in the AIVC Calculation Techniques Guide (Liddament 1986).

Combining wind and stack pressure

Wind and stack pressure values are calculated for each external flow path. The total applied pressure is determined by adding these pressures together i.e.:

$$P_{total} = P_w + P_s$$

Step 4 – Mechanical Ventilation

At the most basic level, mechanical ventilation is applied as a fixed flow rate.

At the most basic level, mechanical ventilation is applied as a fixed flow rate. One way to accomplish this is to establish a path in which the flow exponent is set to zero and the flow coefficient is set to the mechanical ventilation rate. This fixed flow approach is valid provided that the pressure change in the zone can be met by the fan without any change in flow rate. In practical terms, this means that the calculated pressure difference across the fan flow path should be checked with manufacturers data to ensure that the system can supply the rated air flow at the calculated conditions.

A more precise representation of mechanical ventilation is to incorporate the system and fan pressure drop versus air flow rate relationship as if it were any other type of flow path. This requires understanding the flow characteristics of the fan and the impact of associated ductwork.

Step 5 – Solving for mass flow balance

Since the total mass flow of air into a zone must be balanced by a corresponding outflow of air, it follows that, if there are 'j' flow paths into a particular zone, the sum of these flows will equal zero

The equation of flow, the flow coefficient, flow exponent and applied pressure is applied to each flow path. Since the total mass flow of air into a zone must be balanced by a corresponding outflow of air, it follows that, if there are 'j' flow paths into a particular zone, the sum of these flows will equal zero (mass flow in equals mass flow out), i.e.:

$$\sum_{i=1}^{j} Q_{mi} = 0$$

where: Q_{mi} = mass flow rate of air through the $i'th$ flow path

j = the total number of flow paths into the zone

For the $i'th$ flow path:

$$Q_{mi} = C_i (P_i - P_{\text{int}})^{n_i} \quad \text{if } P_i > P_{\text{int}}$$

or: $\qquad Q_{mi} = -C_i (P_{\text{int}} - P_i)^{n_i} \text{ if } P_i < P_{\text{int}}$

Substituting for each flow path:

$$Q_{m1} + Q_{m2} + ... + Q_{mi} + ... + Q_{mj} = 0$$

It follows that there is a unique value of internal pressure, P_{int} for each zone at which flow balance occurs.

The objective of the calculation technique is to evaluate each internal zone pressure. It is rarely possible to evaluate this pressure by direct calculation and, instead, it is determined by 'iteration' in which an initial arbitrary pressure is first applied. The degree of deviation from flow balance is used to predict a more accurate pressure. This process is repeated until flow balance within a specified tolerance is achieved. A very simple example of a single zone model is given in Appendix 3 (Liddament 1989). Multi-zone models for which computer listings are available are published by Walton (1994 Contam93 model) and by Allard et al (1990 - the COMIS model).

Sometimes the model is simplified by calculating a volumetric, rather than mass flow rate of air through each opening. This is accomplished by dividing the mass flow by the air density. This removes instability in calculation caused by having a step difference in air density between incoming and outgoing air but ceases to become acceptable if the difference between inside and outside air temperature exceeds about 25K.

'Single sided' ventilation and turbulent fluctuations

In principle, network models can be used to predict single sided ventilation provided that air flow is being driven by a steady driving pressure and that this pressure is accurately represented by the model.

'Single sided' ventilation in which openings are provided on one side of an enclosed space only, often present calculation difficulties. In principle, network models can be used to predict single sided ventilation provided that air flow is being driven by a steady driving pressure and that this pressure is accurately represented by the model. Essentially, this means that vertically spaced openings (or single large openings) must be represented in terms of height difference so that the stack driving force is simulated. Spatial distribution in wind pressure must similarly be accommodated so that wind derived pressure differences between openings are represented.

When steady driving forces are negligible, air change is driven by random

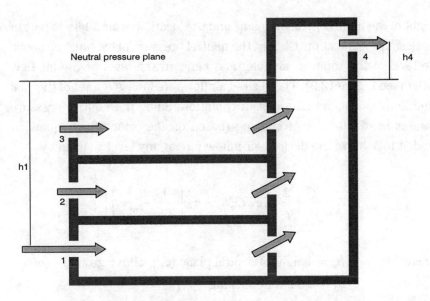

Figure 12.9 'Explicit' Calculation of Area of Opening

turbulent fluctuations. These are not simulated by network models and, hence, network methods will under predict air change. Various techniques have been proposed to account for this extra driving force (e.g. Riberon et al 1990, Rao et al 1991), although, in practice, this should represent only a negligible contribution to building air change and should not be relied upon as a normal ventilation mechanism. More often, the failure to obtain a reliable prediction of single sided ventilation is poor representation of flow in the network structure, inadequate approximation of wind pressure and a failure to incorporate infiltration or other leakage openings throughout the structure to account for cross flow air movement patterns.

12.6 Explicit Network Methods

At the early stage of design, it is often necessary to have some guidance on the sizing of openings needed to achieve a desired air flow rate. This can be accomplished by using an 'explicit' or 'inverted' formulation of the network method. Such an approach is described by Irving (1995).

The explicit method is to guide the sizing of natural ventilation openings

Applications

The primary purpose of this method is to guide the sizing of natural ventilation openings to achieve the desired flow rate into each storey of the building. It can be applied to both wind and stack driven flow.

Method

Stack driven ventilation: The zonal method is 'inverted' by fixing the height of the neutral pressure plane and the location of air inlets as part of the design specification. Clearly, the neutral pressure plane must be above the level of the topmost air inlet and beneath the level of the air flow outlet (see Figure 12.9). The desired air flow rate for a given set of thermal conditions is also set as a design condition. Since the neutral pressure plane is fixed, the size of opening (based on the orifice flow equation) needed to achieve the desired air inflow rate at any level is given by:

$$A = \frac{Q}{C_d}\left(\frac{2}{\rho}\rho_0 g 273(h_n - h_o)\left(\frac{1}{T_{ext}} - \frac{1}{T_{int}}\right)\right)^{-\frac{1}{2}} \quad m^2$$

where: h_n = height of neutral plane (e.g. above ground) (m)

h_0 = height of opening (m)

The sizing of the outflow is based on an air flow rate equal to the sum of all the inflows.

Wind driven ventilation: Openings can be similarly sized for wind driven ventilation, provided a simple configuration based on a single side for wind driven inlets and a single outlet is applied. It is also assumed that the wind pressure acting on each air inlet is identical (i.e. a uniform wind pressure distribution). Provided these assumptions apply, the internal building pressure is given by:

where: P(inlet)+P(outlet)/2

From this the size of opening necessary to provide the desired flow rate through each inlet is given by:

$$A = \frac{Q}{C_d}\left(\frac{1}{v^2 \Delta C_p}\right)^{\frac{1}{2}} \quad (m^2)$$

ΔC_p = the difference in pressure coefficient between inlet and outlet

Stack and wind driven ventilation: The same principles may be applied

to the pressures generated by both wind and stack pressure to calculate opening sizes for combined wind and temperature conditions.

Limitations

This method is limited to simple structures in which the flow network is dominated by well defined orifice type openings.

12.7 Computational Fluid Dynamics

Often, knowledge is needed about the pattern of air flow and the distribution of air temperature and pollutants within an enclosed space (see Figure 12.10). This may be especially important to check the performance of a ventilation system, to verify comfort conditions or to predict thermal transport and smoke and fire spread prediction. In the past, design has been based on scale model analysis and measurements of air flow patterns in full size buildings. More recently, the application of 'computational fluid dynamic' (CFD) mathematical models representing the flow field have become increasingly popular. These are numerical methods that approximate the enclosure by a series of 'control' volumes or elements. Air flow in each element must follow the fundamental laws of physics covering motion, energy transport and conservation of mass. The

> *CFD methods may be used to predict the distribution of air temperature and pollutants within an enclosed space.*

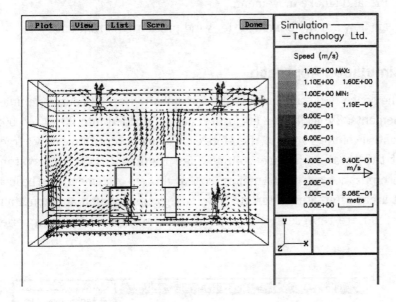

Figure 12.10 Computational Air Flow Pattern
[Courtesy Geoff Whittle, Simulation Technology Ltd (UK)]

user will almost certainly have to resort to commercial code for the application of CFD. A 2-dimensional laminar demonstration flow code is published in FORTRAN by Shih(1980). He also explains how this code may be developed to include three dimensions, turbulence, buoyancy and other flow parameters. A comprehensive three dimensional code (EXACT 3) has been published by Kurabuchi et al 1990). Both codes will operate on high specification 'PC' computers. Recent developments in this field, specifically aimed at building physics, include research within the International Energy Agency (Moser 1994) and United States ASHRAE sponsored research (Baker 1994).

Applications

Specific applications include the simulation and prediction of:

- room air flow,
- air flow in large enclosures (atria, shopping malls, airports, exhibition centres etc.),
- air change efficiency,
- pollutant removal effectiveness,
- temperature distribution,
- air velocity distribution (for comfort, draughts etc.),
- turbulence distribution,
- pressure distribution,
- fire and smoke movement,
- air flow around buildings (for wind pressure distribution).

Simulation Approach

The space to be simulated is 'discretised' into a set of control volumes or elements.

The space to be simulated is 'discretised' into a set of control volumes or elements. Typically, the enclosure may be divided into 30,000 to 50,000 control volumes or more, therefore each element represents only a fraction of the total enclosure volume (see Figure 12.11). The system of discretisation can be non uniform so that clusters of elements can be located at areas of greatest interest. Flow, energy propagation and contaminant spread are represented in each of the control volumes by a series of

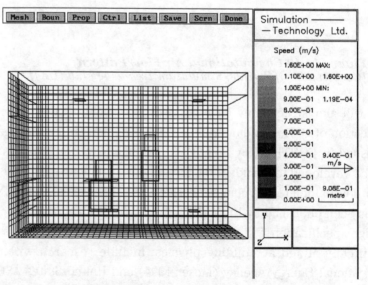

Figure 12.11 'Discretisation' of a Space
[Courtesy Geoff Whittle, Simulation Technology Ltd, (UK)]

discretised transport equations. In structure, these equations are fundamentally identical but each one represents a different physical parameter. Direct solution techniques are not available, therefore iteration is applied. All parameters are initially given arbitrary values from which the iteration can commence. These values are then adjusted until each of the transport equations balance. The process of reaching a balance is referred to as 'convergence'. Considerable computational effort is normally necessary, with the result that processing times can be lengthy, sometimes taking many hours.

To reach a flow solution considerable computational effort is normally necessary.

Key Parameters

Key parameters calculated as part of a CFD analysis include:

Pressure distribution: Air flow is driven by the pressure distribution, therefore the pressure field is fundamental to the whole flow process. Pressure is maintained by a combination of driven air or forced convection and by buoyancy forces or natural convection. Forced convection is driven by mechanical ventilation or the natural flow of air through openings. Free convection is driven by buoyancy forces created by imbalance in temperature difference.

Velocity field: Air movement is a vector having components in both speed and direction. To determine the air velocity distribution, air flow must usually be represented by three transport equations.

Temperature field: The temperature field is sustained by thermal sources and sinks distributed about the enclosure. Sources can include heat emitters, solar gain and surfaces warmed by radiation. Sinks can include chilled ceilings and cold surfaces such as windows or uninsulated walls. Buoyancy forces and free convection currents are generated by the temperature field. Temperature is a scalar quantity acting only on the vertical component of velocity field through a gravitational term.

Turbulence: Turbulence is the random fluctuation of the air stream from its mean flow direction. It contributes to the rapid mixing of air and pollutants in the space and thus has a major impact on the flow field and pollutant distribution. The representation of the turbulence of room air currently presents a challenge to the credibility of CFD techniques. Turbulence must be accurately represented but models are highly empirical. This aspect has, therefore, become an important area of research.

Boundary layer flow: Air flow close to surfaces is subjected to boundary layer effects in which the rate of flow is influenced by surface friction. This further adds to the complexity of flow modelling.

Contaminant transport: Contaminant transport is not normally assumed to influence the flow field, hence the air flow calculation is usually completed first and the resultant contaminant distribution is then calculated separately. Allowance can be made for the chemical of physical decay of a contaminant or the deposition of particulate matter.

User input – boundary conditions: The flow, turbulence, temperature and pollutant fields are unique to the prevailing 'boundary conditions'. As these alter, so will the flow fields. These boundary details must be provided by the user.

The flow, turbulence, temperature and pollutant fields are unique to the prevailing 'boundary conditions'. As these alter, so will the flow fields. These boundary details must be provided by the user.

Input data must include:

- location of openings,
- mass flow into and out of the building,
- type of flow boundary (i.e. permeable, impermeable),
- velocity (speed and direction of flow through each opening),
- level of turbulence of flow through diffusers or mixing fans,
- thermal properties of surfaces and/or surface temperatures ,
- heat sources and sinks,
- boundary obstacles,
- contaminant location, emission characteristics and properties.

Limitations

Algorithms require a substantial amount of user input and therefore a good understanding of flow physics is needed.

Computational fluid dynamic methods for buildings are still in the infancy of development. Algorithms require a substantial amount of user input and therefore a good understanding of flow physics is needed. Applications are further restricted by:

- the number of cells or control volumes that can be incorporated in the available computer space,
- a difficulty in representing the flow fields generated by natural ventilation and air infiltration ,
- difficulties in specifying heat transfer characteristics at boundaries,
- the structure of some algorithms in which there is no direct coupling between forced and free convection may prevent free convection problems from being solved.

These data requirements are very demanding and require considerable effort to represent accurately.

12.8 Ventilation and Air Flow Related Calculations

Once air flow parameters have been determined, important related calculations can be performed . Examples include:

Avoiding under-pressure – how much openable area?: The calculation of openable area is straightforward when openings are purpose provided. Using the orifice equation, the suction pressure generated by mechanical extract ventilation is given by the equation:

The calculation of openable area is straightforward when openings are purpose provided.

$$Q = C_d A \left[\frac{2\Delta P}{\rho} \right]^{0.5}$$

$Q =$ flow rate through ventilation system (m^3 / s)

$C_d =$ discharge coefficient (0.61 for 'flat plate' orifice)

$A =$ area of opening (m^2)

$\Delta P =$ inside / outside pressure (Pa)

$\rho =$ air density $(kg / m^3 \sim 1.29)$

Re - arranging:

$$A = \frac{Q}{0.61 \left[\frac{2\Delta P}{1.29} \right]^{0.5}}$$

Example: The area of make-up opening needed to avoid exceeding a 2 Pa under pressure at an extraction rate of 40 l/s (0.04 m³/s or 144 m³/h) is:

$$A = \frac{0.04}{0.61 * \left[\frac{2 * 2}{1.29} \right]^{0.5}} = 0.037 m^2 = 37,000 mm^2$$

Infiltration openings will reduce the under pressure since the net area of opening will be greater. If there are no purpose provided openings but the air leakage characteristics of the building (C and n values) are known then the under (or over) pressure generated by a mechanical system is calculated from:

$$\Delta P = \left(\frac{Q}{C} \right)^{\frac{1}{n}}$$

Pollutant Transport and Pollutant Concentration

The time it takes for the outdoor concentration to be reached is dependent on the volume of the space and the rate of ingress of outdoor air.

Pollutant emitted from a contaminant source mixes in the air within a space to give a pollutant concentration. Sources may be derived from outside or within the space. Outside pollutants are introduced by the incoming air stream resulting in a growth in indoor concentration until the outdoor value is reached. The time it takes for the outdoor concentration to be reached is dependent on the volume of the space and the rate of ingress of outdoor air. If the outdoor air is relatively free of pollutant, then incoming air will dilute indoor contaminants, resulting in a pollutant concentration that is dependent on the emission rate and the ventilation rate.

Common air quality parameters include:

- the time varying concentration of pollutant for a given ventilation rate,
- the steady state pollutant concentration,
- the ventilation rate needed to avoid a threshold pollutant concentration being exceeded,
- the decay rate of pollutant concentration after emission has ceased.

The governing dilution equations are:

(a) Time Varying Pollutant Concentration, c_t:

$$c_t = \left[\frac{Qc_e + q}{Q+q} \right] \left[1 - e^{-\left[\frac{Q+q}{V} \right] t} \right]$$

where:

c_e = outdoor contaminant concentration

q = indoor emission rate of contaminant

V = volume of ventilated space (m^3)

Q = volume flow rate of outside air (m^3 / s)

t = time from onset of contaminant emission (s)

(b) Steady State Pollutant Concentration, c_s:

$$c_s = \left\lceil \frac{Qc_e + q}{Q+q} \right\rceil$$

(c) Ventilation Rate to achieve Given Steady State Concentration, Q_s:

$$Q_s = q\left[\frac{1 - c_s}{c_s - c_e}\right] \qquad (m^3 / s)$$

(d) Decay in Pollutant Concentration, c_t:

$$c_t = c_0 e^{-\left[\frac{Q}{V}\right]t}$$

where:

c_0 = starting concentration

In each case, these equations are solved by incorporating the emission characteristics of the source and the flow rate of incoming air, as determined by calculation or measurement.

Thermal (energy) Transport

A full account of the energy needed to condition ventilation or infiltrating air to comfort levels is given by Colliver (1995). Briefly, energy must be looked at in terms of 'sensible' and 'latent' heat. (See, also, Chapter 3). These are defined as follows:

Energy must be looked at in terms of 'sensible' and 'latent' heat.

Sensible heat: This is the energy that is used to increase (i.e. heat) the energy content of dry air and the moisture vapour mixed with the dry air. Sensible heat is given by:

$$H_s = Q\rho(c_{pa} + Wc_{pw})(T_{int} - T_{out}) \qquad (Watts)$$

where:

H_s = sensible heating power   (W)

Q = air flow rate (m^3 / s)

ρ = air density (kg / m^3)

c_{pa} = specific heat of dry air $(J / kg.K)$

c_{pw} = specific heat of water vapour $(J / kg.K)$

W = change in water content of air   (kg of water / kg of dry air)

t_{int} = indoor air temperature (K)

t_{ext} = outdoor air temperature (K)

Assuming that Wc_{pw} can be neglected, the above equation reduces to:

$$H_s = Q\rho c_{pa}(T_{int} - T_{out}) \qquad \textbf{\textit{(Watts)}}$$

Latent heat: This is the energy that must be added (or withdrawn) when water is vaporised (or condensed). The latent heat transfer or energy which must be used for moisture control with humidification and dehumidification, can be determined from the amount of moisture that must be added or removed, ie:

$$H_l = L\Delta W$$

where:

$L =$ latent heat of vapourisation of water (2501.3 kJ / kg of water)

$\Delta W =$ change in water content of the air (kg / kg)

From these basic equations the energy transfer aspects of ventilation can be calculated, as shown in the following examples.

Energy impact of ventilation and air infiltration: Various methods to determine the energy impact of ventilation over given periods of time (e.g. a heating season or cooling season) are described in Chapter 3. Such methods rely on being able to approximate the enthalpy and/or temperature difference and ventilation rate over the given time period.

One example is to combine the hour by hour energy demand over the desired time period, ie:

$$E = \sum_{i=1}^{\text{total no of hours}} 3600\rho c_p Q_i (T_{int(i)} - T_{ext(i)}) \qquad (J)$$

$Q_i =$ combined air infiltration and ventilation rate at hour, i, (m^3 / s)

$T_{int(i)} =$ indoor air temperature at hour, i, (K)

$T_{ext(i)} =$ outdoor air temperature at hour, i, (K)

For very approximate calculations, air change rate may be treated as a constant, while temperature variation may be represented by degree days.

For very approximate calculations, air change rate may be treated as a constant, while temperature variation may be represented by degree days, in which case energy demand is given by:

$$E = Q * DD * 24 * 3600\rho c_p \qquad (J)$$

where: $DD =$ number of degree days

Air to Air Heat Recovery Performance: Heat recovery is only possible from the proportion of air that passes through the heat exchanger. If the efficiency of the heat recovery system, H_{eff}, is defined as the percentage of heat in the exhaust air stream that is captured by the supply air, energy input needed to heat the incoming air becomes:

Heat recovery is only possible from the proportion of air that passes through the heat exchanger.

$$H = \left(Q_{inf} + Q_{mv} \left(1 - \frac{H_{eff}}{100} \right) \right) \rho c_p \left(T_{int} - T_{ext} \right) \qquad (Watts)$$

This illustrates the significance of air infiltration in destroying any benefit from heat recovery systems. For adequate operating conditions it is essential that:

$$Q_{inf} << Q_{mv}$$

Operative Temperature

Operative temperature is used in ASHRAE Standard 55-1992 as a measure of air and mean radiant temperature combined with air speed. It is determined from:

$$T_0 = aT_a + (1-a)\overline{T}_r$$

where:

T_0 = operative temperature $(°C)$

T_a = dry bulb air temperature $(°C)$

$\overline{T}_r$ = mean radiant temperature $(°C)$

a = weighting factor dependent on wind speed (see Table below)

v (m/s)	0-0.2	0.2-0.6	0.6-1.0
a	0.5	0.6	0.7

Filtration Performance

Filtration systems are described in Chapter 9. The key equations related to filtration performance are:

Direct Filtration of Outside Air

$$c_E = \frac{eff}{100} c_e$$

where: c_E = steady state internal particulate concentration

          c_e = external particulate concentration

          eff = filtration efficiency (%)

Recirculatory Filtration of Indoor Air

$$c_E = \frac{Q_v c_e + q}{Q_v + Q_{eff} + q}$$

where:

q = internal pollution generation rate

$Q_{eff} = Q_f * eff / 100 =$ effective filtration rate

Q_f = filtration rate

Q_v = ventilation rate

(ensure continuity of units, i.e., mass flow or volume flow)

concentration of external particulates ($q = 0$)

$$c_E = \frac{Q_v c_e}{Q_v + Q_{eff}}$$

concentration for internal particulates ($c_e = 0$)

$$c_E = \frac{q}{Q_v + Q_{eff}} \quad \text{(assuming } Q_v + Q_{eff} \gg q\text{)}$$

More comprehensive examples are covered in Appendix E of ASHRAE Standard 62-1989.

12.9 Combined Thermal and Ventilation Models

Background

In addition to providing for good indoor air quality, air change and the pattern of air flow in a building play a major role in contributing to thermal comfort and energy transport.

In addition to providing for good indoor air quality, air change and the pattern of air flow in a building play a major role in contributing to thermal comfort and energy transport. The thermal performance of a building is strongly coupled to ventilation and air infiltration. A variety of thermal calculation models are available to assist in the design process. Typically these predict thermal energy transport arising from conduction, convection and radiation. Examples of current methods are summarised by (Bloomfield 1994). Despite the importance of air flow, thermal models have tended to adopt a very simplistic approach to the incorporation of ventilation and air infiltration. This can result in questionable predictions.

At the most basic level, air change is incorporated as an assumed fixed value or an assumed, time varying, 'duty cycle'. Arguably, if air change is completely dominated by the installed ventilation system, such an approach is adequate. Commonly, however, the building air change rate is influenced

(a) Sequential

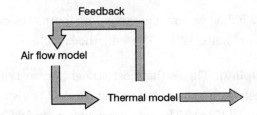

(b) 'Ping pong'

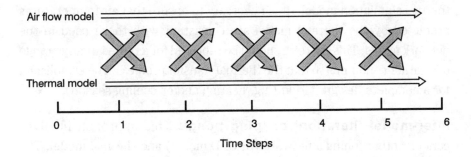

(c) Integrated

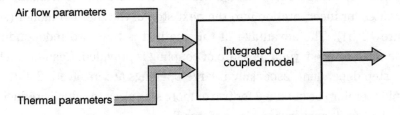

Figure 12.12 Combined Air Change and Thermal Calculation Techniques

by a broader range of mechanisms, especially when the building has infiltration openings or is naturally ventilated. Efforts have therefore been introduced to improve the air change component of thermal calculation algorithms. A summary of developments is outlined by Kendrick (1993).

Applications: Combined models are used for the following applications:

- to predict total thermal exchange from and within buildings
- to determine the impact of ventilation, heating and cooling systems on thermal comfort
- to predict the performance of, and to develop operational strategies for, building energy management systems.

Combined models are used to predict total thermal exchange from and within buildings.

Methods

Techniques for including air flow algorithms into thermal calculation models are summarised in Figure 12.12. These methods include:

Sequential coupling: This is the most straightforward of methods and involves separately running a network and thermal transport calculation model (see Figure 12.12(a)). The network model is run first, using assumed values (e.g. design values) of room air temperature. The resultant air change rate or air flow characteristics are then incorporated into the thermal simulation model. It is necessary to ensure that air temperatures predicted by the thermal model are consistent with those used in the network model. This exercise should be repeated for a representative range of weather conditions so that the thermal transfer profile can be established for a complete design period (e.g. heating and/or cooling season).

Inter-model 'iteration' or 'ping pong': This approach involves concurrently running a network (or CFD model) and thermal model. The simulation is run over a series of time steps. At each step, the thermal model calculates air temperatures which are transferred to the next time step of the network air flow model, while the network model evaluates air flow rates for incorporation into the next step of the thermal model (see Figure 12(b)). The advantage of this method is that two independent models can be used, yet a measure of coupling is provided. Results can be time step dependent, especially if large openings are involved. Solutions should therefore be obtained for two or more step sizes (gradually reducing step size) until convergence is confirmed.

Direct coupling involves solving the flow and thermal transport equations simultaneously in a directly coupled energy balance model.

Direct coupling – full integration: This involves solving the flow and thermal transport equations simultaneously in a directly coupled energy balance model (see Figure 12.12(c)). Such approaches are still under development. The nearest methods involve computational fluid dynamic strategies in which energy 'flow' equations representing conduction, convection and radiant transfer are incorporated as part of the total flow network. These concepts are described in more detail by Shih (1990).

Limitations:

• thermal calculation models are extremely complex and very dependent on the quality and interpretation of input data

• the addition of an air flow model adds considerably to the overall level of complexity and risk of error

• much more development work is needed, particularly in providing guidance on data and the use of data, before combined models can be applied to routine applications.

References

ASHRAE Standard 55 Thermal environmental conditions for human occupancy, ANSI/ASHRAE Standard 55-92, American Society of Heating Refrigeration and Air Conditioning Engineers, 1992.

Allard F, Dorer V B, Feustel H E, et al, *Fundamentals of the multi-zone air flow model – COMIS*, Technical Note 29, Air Infiltration and Ventilation Centre, 1990.

Baker A J, Williams P T, Kelso R M, *Development of a robust finite element CFD procedure for predicting indoor room air motion*, Building and Environment, Vol 29, No 3, 1994, pp 261-273.

Bienfait D, Phaff H, Vandaele L, van der Maas J, Walker R, *Single sided ventilation*, Proc 12th Conference, Air Movement and Ventilation Control within Buildings, Vol 1, 1991.

Bloomfield D P, *The work of international energy agency annex 21 on calculation of energy and environmental performance in buildings*, Proc.BEPAC Conference, Building Environmental Performance - Facing the Future, 1994

Bowen A J, *A wind tunnel investigation using simple building models to obtain mean surface wind pressure coefficients for air infiltration estimates*, report no.LTR LA 20N National Aeronautical Establishment NRCC Canada, 1976

BS5925:1991 *Code of practice for ventilation principles and designing for natural ventilation*, British Standards Institute 1991.

Colliver D, *Energy requirements for conditioning ventilation air*, AIVC Technical Note 47, Air Infiltration and Ventilation Centre,1995

Dorer V, Calculation methods for the determination of air flow rates in dwellings, CEN TC 156/WG2/AHG4/N8 (Draft) 1995

Dubrul C, *Inhabitant's behaviour with respect to ventilation*, Technical Note 23, Air Infiltration and Ventilation Centre, 1988.

Feustel H E, *Development of a simplified multi-zone infiltration model*, Proc 6th AIC Conference Ventilation Strategies and Measurement Techniques, 1985.

Feustel H E, Dieris J A, *A survey of air flow models for multi-zone structures*, Lawrence Berkeley Laboratory Report, Applied Science Division,1991.

Hartmann P, Muhlebach H, Steinemann U, *Retrofit planning tools for institutional and residential buildings with user influenced air infiltration*, Proc. 4th AIVC Conference *Air infiltration reduction in existing buildings*, 1983.

Irving S J, *An inverse solver for sizing passive ventilation openings*, Proc. AIVC 16th annual conference, 1995

Kendrick J F, *An overview of combined modelling of heat transport and air movement*, Air Infiltration and Ventilation Centre, Technical Note 40, 1993.

Kronvall J, *Testing of houses for air-leakage using a pressure method*, ASHRAE trans. vol 84 no 1 1978.

Kurabuchi T, Fang J B, Grot R A, *A numerical method for calculating indoor air flows using a turbulence model*, NIST report R89-4211, 1990.

Liddament M, Allen C, *The validation and comparison of mathematical models of air infiltration*, AIVC Technical Note 11, 1983.

Liddament M W, *Air infiltration calculation techniques guide*, AIVC 1986.

Liddament M W, *AIDA – an air infiltration development algorithm*, Air Infiltration Review, Vol 11, No 1, December 1989.

Moser A, *The IEA works on guidelines for ventilation of large enclosures*, Proc. UK, Building Research Establishment, BEPAC Conference, *Building Environmental Performance – Facing the Future* , 1994.

Orme M S, Liddament M W, Wilson A, *An analysis and data summary of the AIVC's numerical database*, Technical Note 44, Air Infiltration and Ventilation Centre, 1994.

Rao J, Haghighat F, *Wind induced fluctuating airflow in buildings*, Proc. AIVC 12th Conference, *Air Movement and Ventilation Control within Buildings*, Vol 1, 1991.

Riberon J, Bienfait D, Barnaud G, Villain J, *Effect of wind pressure fluctuations on air movements inside buildings*, Proc 11th AIVC Conference, *Ventilation System Performance*, Vol 1 1990.

Sherman M H, Grimsrud D.T., *Measurement of infiltration using fan pressurization and weather data*, Proc. A.I.C. Conference *Instrumentation and Measuring Techniques*, 1980.

Shih T M, *Numerical heat transfer*, Hemisphere Publishing Corporation, 1980.

Walton G N, *CONTAM93 User manual*, National Inst of Standards and Technology (NIST), Report NISTIR 5385, 1994.

Appendix 1

Air Leakage Characteristics of Building Components

Table A1.1 Standards, Recommendations and Legal Codes of Practice - Windows

Country/Standard Ref.	Description	Quoted Leakage Value	Leakage at 1 Pa (Flow Exponent assumed 0.66)
Belgium STS 52.0	Building Height 0-10 m	$3.00 \text{ m}^3.\text{h}^{-1}.\text{m}^{-1}$ at 100 Pa	$0.040 \text{ dm}^3.\text{s}^{-1}.\text{m}^{-1}$
	Building Height 10-18 m	$3.00 \text{ m}^3.\text{h}^{-1}.\text{m}^{-1}$ at 100 Pa	$0.040 \text{ dm}^3.\text{s}^{-1}.\text{m}^{-1}$
	Building Height >18 m	$2.00 \text{ m}^3.\text{h}^{-1}.\text{m}^{-1}$ at 100 Pa	$0.027 \text{ dm}^3.\text{s}^{-1}.\text{m}^{-1}$
Canada CAN 3-A440-M84	A1 Low Rise Buildings (<3 storeys, <600 m^2)	$2.79 \text{ m}^3.\text{h}^{-1}.\text{m}^{-1}$ at 75 Pa	$0.045 \text{ dm}^3.\text{s}^{-1}.\text{m}^{-1}$
	A2 Medium to High Rise Buildings	$1.65 \text{ m}^3.\text{h}^{-1}.\text{m}^{-1}$ at 75 Pa	$0.027 \text{ dm}^3.\text{s}^{-1}.\text{m}^{-1}$
	A3 High Performance, Institutional & Commercial	$0.55 \text{ m}^3.\text{h}^{-1}.\text{m}^{-1}$ at 75 Pa	$0.009 \text{ dm}^3.\text{s}^{-1}.\text{m}^{-1}$
	Fixed	$0.25 \text{ m}^3.\text{h}^{-1}.\text{m}^{-1}$ at 75 Pa	$0.004 \text{ dm}^3.\text{s}^{-1}.\text{m}^{-1}$
	Storm (Max)	$8.35 \text{ m}^3.\text{h}^{-1}.\text{m}^{-1}$ at 75 Pa	$0.134 \text{ dm}^3.\text{s}^{-1}.\text{m}^{-1}$
	Storm (Min)	$5.00 \text{ m}^3.\text{h}^{-1}.\text{m}^{-1}$ at 75 Pa	$0.080 \text{ dm}^3.\text{s}^{-1}.\text{m}^{-1}$
Denmark DS-418	Assumed Value (When True Value Not Known)	$0.50 \text{ dm}^3.\text{s}^{-1}.\text{m}^{-1}$ at 30 Pa	$0.053 \text{ dm}^3.\text{s}^{-1}.\text{m}^{-1}$
Finland SFS 3304	Class 1 (Max)	$0.50 \text{ m}^3.\text{h}^{-1}.\text{m}^{-2}$ at 50 Pa	$0.011 \text{ dm}^3.\text{s}^{-1}.\text{m}^{-2}$
	Class 2 (Min)	$0.50 \text{ m}^3.\text{h}^{-1}.\text{m}^{-2}$ at 50 Pa	$0.011 \text{ dm}^3.\text{s}^{-1}.\text{m}^{-2}$
	Class 2 (Max)	$2.50 \text{ m}^3.\text{h}^{-1}.\text{m}^{-2}$ at 50 Pa	$0.053 \text{ dm}^3.\text{s}^{-1}.\text{m}^{-2}$
	Class 3 (Min)	$2.50 \text{ m}^3.\text{h}^{-1}.\text{m}^{-1}$ at 50 Pa	$0.053 \text{ dm}^3.\text{s}^{-1}.\text{m}^{-1}$
France NF P20 302	A1	$20\text{-}60 \text{ m}^3.\text{h}^{-1}.\text{m}^{-2}$ at 100 Pa	$0.266\text{-}0.798 \text{ dm}^3.\text{s}^{-1}.\text{m}^{-2}$
	A2	$7\text{-}20 \text{ m}^3.\text{h}^{-1}.\text{m}^{-2}$ at 100 Pa	$0.093\text{-}0.266 \text{ dm}^3.\text{s}^{-1}.\text{m}^{-2}$
	A3	$<7 \text{ m}^3.\text{h}^{-1}.\text{m}^{-2}$ at 100 Pa	$<0.093 \text{ dm}^3.\text{s}^{-1}.\text{m}^{-2}$
Germany DIN 18055	A Building Height 0-8 m Above Grade	$6.00 \text{ m}^3.\text{h}^{-1}.\text{m}^{-1}$ at 50 Pa	$0.126 \text{ dm}^3.\text{s}^{-1}.\text{m}^{-1}$
	B-D Building Height > 8 m Above Grade	$3.00 \text{ m}^3.\text{h}^{-1}.\text{m}^{-1}$ at 50 Pa	$0.063 \text{ dm}^3.\text{s}^{-1}.\text{m}^{-1}$
Netherlands NEN 3661	Normal Exposure:		
	Building Height up to 15 m	$2.50 \text{ dm}^3.\text{s}^{-1}.\text{m}^{-1}$ at 75 Pa	$0.145 \text{ dm}^3.\text{s}^{-1}.\text{m}^{-1}$
	Building Height 15-40 m	$2.50 \text{ dm}^3.\text{s}^{-1}.\text{m}^{-1}$ at 150 Pa	$0.092 \text{ dm}^3.\text{s}^{-1}.\text{m}^{-1}$
	Building Height 40-100 m	$2.50 \text{ dm}^3.\text{s}^{-1}.\text{m}^{-1}$ at 300 Pa	$0.058 \text{ dm}^3.\text{s}^{-1}.\text{m}^{-1}$
	Coastal Exposure:		
	Building Height up to 15 m	$2.50 \text{ dm}^3.\text{s}^{-1}.\text{m}^{-1}$ at 300 Pa	$0.058 \text{ dm}^3.\text{s}^{-1}.\text{m}^{-1}$
	Building Height 15-40 m	$2.50 \text{ dm}^3.\text{s}^{-1}.\text{m}^{-1}$ at 300 Pa	$0.058 \text{ dm}^3.\text{s}^{-1}.\text{m}^{-1}$
	Building Height 40-100 m	$2.50 \text{ dm}^3.\text{s}^{-1}.\text{m}^{-1}$ at 450 Pa	$0.044 \text{ dm}^3.\text{s}^{-1}.\text{m}^{-1}$
New Zealand NZS N4211:1987	Airtight	$0.60 \text{ dm}^3.\text{s}^{-1}.\text{m}^{-1}$ at 150 Pa	$0.022 \text{ dm}^3.\text{s}^{-1}.\text{m}^{-1}$
		$2.00 \text{ dm}^3.\text{s}^{-1}.\text{m}^{-2}$ at 150 Pa	$0.073 \text{ dm}^3.\text{s}^{-1}.\text{m}^{-2}$
	Moderate Air Leakage	$2.00 \text{ dm}^3.\text{s}^{-1}.\text{m}^{-1}$ at 150 Pa	$0.073 \text{ dm}^3.\text{s}^{-1}.\text{m}^{-1}$
		$8.00 \text{ dm}^3.\text{s}^{-1}.\text{m}^{-2}$ at 150 Pa	$0.293 \text{ dm}^3.\text{s}^{-1}.\text{m}^{-2}$
	Low Air Leakage	$4.00 \text{ dm}^3.\text{s}^{-1}.\text{m}^{-1}$ at 150 Pa	$0.147 \text{ dm}^3.\text{s}^{-1}.\text{m}^{-1}$
		$17.00 \text{ dm}^3.\text{s}^{-1}.\text{m}^{-2}$ at 150 Pa	$0.623 \text{ dm}^3.\text{s}^{-1}.\text{m}^{-2}$
Sweden	All Buildings	$1.70 \text{ m}^3.\text{h}^{-1}.\text{m}^{-2}$ at 50 Pa	$0.036 \text{ dm}^3.\text{s}^{-1}.\text{m}^{-2}$
		$5.60 \text{ m}^3.\text{h}^{-1}.\text{m}^{-2}$ at 300 Pa	$0.036 \text{ dm}^3.\text{s}^{-1}.\text{m}^{-2}$
	Buildings >8 Storeys	$7.90 \text{ m}^3.\text{h}^{-1}.\text{m}^{-2}$ at 500 Pa	$0.036 \text{ dm}^3.\text{s}^{-1}.\text{m}^{-2}$
Switzerland SIA 331	Building Height 0-8 m	$5.65 \text{ m}^3.\text{h}^{-1}.\text{m}^{-1}$ at 150 Pa	$0.056 \text{ dm}^3.\text{s}^{-1}.\text{m}^{-1}$
	Building Height 8-20 m	$8.95 \text{ m}^3.\text{h}^{-1}.\text{m}^{-1}$ at 300 Pa	$0.056 \text{ dm}^3.\text{s}^{-1}.\text{m}^{-1}$
	Building Height 20-100 m	$14.25 \text{ m}^3.\text{h}^{-1}.\text{m}^{-1}$ at 600 Pa	$0.056 \text{ dm}^3.\text{s}^{-1}.\text{m}^{-1}$
United Kingdom BS6375: Part 1: 1989	Openable - Design Wind Pressure (Exposure) <1600 Pa	$6.34 \text{ m}^3.\text{h}^{-1}.\text{m}^{-1}$ at 50 Pa	$0.133 \text{ dm}^3.\text{s}^{-1}.\text{m}^{-1}$
	Openable - Design Wind Pressure (Exposure) > = 1600 Pa	$4.84 \text{ m}^3.\text{h}^{-1}.\text{m}^{-1}$ at 50 Pa	$0.102 \text{ dm}^3.\text{s}^{-1}.\text{m}^{-1}$
	Fixed - Design Wind Pressure (Exposure) <1600 Pa	$1.00 \text{ m}^3.\text{h}^{-1}.\text{m}^{-1}$ at 200 Pa	$0.008 \text{ dm}^3.\text{s}^{-1}.\text{m}^{-1}$
	Fixed - Design Wind Pressure (Exposure) > = 1600 Pa	$1.00 \text{ m}^3.\text{h}^{-1}.\text{m}^{-1}$ at 300 Pa	$0.006 \text{ dm}^3.\text{s}^{-1}.\text{m}^{-1}$
	Fixed - High Performance	$1.00 \text{ m}^3.\text{h}^{-1}.\text{m}^{-1}$ at 600 Pa	$0.004 \text{ dm}^3.\text{s}^{-1}.\text{m}^{-1}$
	Openable - High Performance	$6.60 \text{ m}^3.\text{h}^{-1}.\text{m}^{-1}$ at 600 Pa	$0.02 \text{ dm}^3.\text{s}^{-1}.\text{m}^{-1}$
USA ASHRAE 90-80	All	$0.77 \text{ dm}^3.\text{s}^{-1}.\text{m}^{-1}$ at 75 Pa	$0.045 \text{ dm}^3.\text{s}^{-1}.\text{m}^{-1}$

Table A1.2 Leakage Characteristics - Windows

Data expressed for each metre length of joint	Lower Quartile C	(n)	Median $dm^3.s^{-1}.m^{-1}.Pa^{-n}$ C	(n)	Upper Quartile C	(n)	Sample Size
Windows (Weatherstripped) Hinged	0.086	(0.6)	0.13	(0.6)	0.41	(0.6)	29
Sliding	0.079	(0.6)	0.15	(0.6)	0.21	(0.6)	19
Windows (Non-weatherstripped) Hinged	0.39	(0.6)	0.74	(0.6)	1.1	(0.6)	42
Sliding	0.18	(0.6)	0.23	(0.6)	0.37	(0.6)	36
Louvre (expressed per louvre)			0.34	(0.6)			1
Sources: BRE Unpublished, #40, #116, #320, #458, #1116, #1357, #1405, #1449.							

Table A1.3 Standards, Recommendations and Legal Codes of Practice - Doors

Country/Standard Ref.	Description	Quoted Leakage Value	Leakage at 1 Pa (Flow Exponent assumed 0.66)
Canada CGSB 82-GP-2M	Sliding Glass With Aluminium Frame	2.50 $dm^3.s^{-1}.m^{-2}$ at 75 Pa	0.145 $dm^3.s^{-1}.m^{-2}$
Denmark DS-418	Assumed Value (When True Value Not Known)	0.50 $dm^3.s^{-1}.m^{-1}$ at 50 Pa	0.038 $dm^3.s^{-1}.m^{-1}$
USA ASHRAE 90-80	Residential (Sliding Glass)	2.50 $dm^3.s^{-1}.m^{-2}$ at 75 Pa	0.145 $dm^3.s^{-1}.m^{-2}$
	Residential (Entrance - Swinging Doors)	6.35 $dm^3.s^{-1}.m^{-2}$ at 75 Pa	0.367 $dm^3.s^{-1}.m^{-2}$
	Non-Residential	17.00 $dm^3.s^{-1}.m^{-2}$ at 75 Pa	0.984 $dm^3.s^{-1}.m^{-2}$

Table A1.4 Leakage Characteristics - Doors

Data expressed for each metre length of joint	Lower Quartile C	(n)	Median $dm^3.s^{-1}.m^{-1}.Pa^{-n}$ C	(n)	Upper Quartile C	(n)	Sample Size
External Doors (Weatherstripped) Hinged	0.082	(0.6)	0.27	(0.6)	0.84	(0.6)	15
Sliding			No data				
Revolving - Laboratory test	1.0	(0.6)	1.5	(0.6)	2.0	(0.6)	4
External Doors (Non-weatherstripped) Hinged	1.1	(0.6)	1.2	(0.6)	1.4	(0.6)	17
Sliding			0.20	(0.6)			1
Roller Door per m² of surface $(dm^3.s^{-1}.m^{-2}.Pa^{-n})$ - Laboratory test	3.3	(0.6)	5.7	(0.6)	10	(0.6)	2
Internal Doors (Non-weatherstripped)	1.1	(0.6)	1.3	(0.6)	2.0	(0.6)	84
Loft Hatches (Non-Weatherstripped)	0.64	(0.6)	0.68	(0.6)	0.75	(0.6)	4
Sources: BRE Unpublished, #40, #116, #173,, #1357, #1405, #5848.							

Table A1.5 Leakage Characteristics - Wall/Window and Wall/Door Frame

Data expressed for each metre length of joint	Lower Quartile		Median $dm^3.s^{-1}.m^{-1}.Pa^{-n}$		Upper Quartile		Sample Size
	C	(n)	C	(n)	C	(n)	
Caulked joint - Laboratory and field tests	3.3×10^{-4}	(0.6)	2.5×10^{-3}	(0.6)	0.012	(0.6)	7
Uncaulked joint - Laboratory and field tests	0.053	(0.6)	0.061	(0.6)	0.067	(0.6)	5
Sources: #1357, #1414, #1514, #2964, #5378.							

Table A1.6 Standards, Recommendations and Legal Codes of Practice - Walls, Ceilings and Floors

Country/Standard Ref.	Description	Quoted Leakage Value	Leakage at 1 Pa (Flow Exponent assumed 0.66)
Netherlands Building Decree. Issued December 16, 1991	Flooring	$20 \times 10^{-6} m^3.s^{-1}.m^{-2}$ at 1 Pa	$0.020 dm^3.s^{-1}.m^{-2}$

Table A1.7 Leakage Characteristics - Walls, Ceilings and Floors

Data expressed for each m^2 of surface. Includes joints	Lower Quartile		Median $dm^3.s^{-1}.m^{-2}.Pa^{-n}$		Upper Quartile		Sample Size
	C	(n)	C	(n)	C	(n)	
Brick (bare) - Laboratory and Field Tests	0.022	(0.84)	0.043	(0.80)	0.094	(0.76)	5
Brick (plastered)	0.016	(0.86)	0.018	(0.85)	0.021	(0.84)	3
Brick (wall board panelling) - Laboratory test	0.010	(0.88)	0.042	(0.81)	0.18	(0.72)	2
Cladding (ungasketed)	0.010	(0.88)	0.032	(0.82)	0.10	(0.76)	2
Cladding (gasketed) - Laboratory test	6.9×10^{-3}	(0.90)	0.012	(0.87)	0.015	(0.86)	3
Concrete block (bare)	0.082	(0.77)	0.13	(0.74)	2.0	(0.59)	10
Concrete block (plastered, internal) - Laboratory test	0.021	(0.84)	0.021	(0.84)	0.021	(0.84)	2
Concrete panels (pre cast)	0.050	(0.80)	0.11	(0.75)	0.12	(0.74)	6
Concrete panels (pre cast, gasketed) - Laboratory test			0.026	(0.83)			1
Metal panels (walls)	0.076	(0.77)	0.090	(0.76)	0.13	(0.74)	3
Curtain walling	0.089	(0.76)	0.12	(0.74)	0.14	(0.74)	3
Plaster board (ceiling)	0.042	(0.81)	0.11	(0.75)	0.20	(0.72)	3
Fibre board (ceiling)			0.094	(0.76)			1
Timber panel (with wall board)	0.27	(0.70)	0.52	(0.67)	2.7	(0.58)	6
Timber panel (with air barrier) - Laboratory test			0.066	(0.78)			1
Timber floor (suspended)	0.11	(0.75)	0.15	(0.74)	0.45	(0.67)	15
Sources: #40, #86, #91, #142, #176, #177, #214, #311, #597, #1357, #3880, #5746, Wouters (1987), Brunelli (1969), BRE Unpublished.							

Table A1.8 Leakage Characteristics - Wall to Floor/Ceiling Joints

Data expressed for each metre length of joint		Lower Quartile		Median $dm^3.s^{-1}.m^{-2}.Pa^{-n}$		Upper Quartile		Sample Size
Wall Material	Ceiling Material	C	(n)	C	(n)	C	(n)	
Caulked: Masonry	Timber/ Fibre Board			No data				
Masonry/ Concrete	Concrete	5.0×10^{-3}	(0.6)	0.024	(0.6)	0.11	(0.6)	2
Timber	Timber/ Fibre Board	6.6×10^{-3}	(0.6)	0.011	(0.6)	0.015	(0.6)	9
- Laboratory test Timber	Concrete	0.052	(0.6)	0.083	(0.6)	0.11	(0.6)	4
Uncaulked: Masonry/ Concrete	Timber/ Fibre Board	0.45	(0.6)	0.49	(0.6)	0.53	(0.6)	2
Masonry	Concrete			No data				
Timber	Timber/ Fibre Board	0.008	(0.6)	0.023	(0.6)	0.030	(0.6)	5

Sources: #1105, #1261, #1357, #1607, #5693.

Table A1.9 Leakage Characteristics - Wall to Wall Joints

Data expressed for each metre length of joint	Lower Quartile		Median $dm^3.s^{-1}.m^{-1}.Pa^{-n}$		Upper Quartile		Sample Size
	C	(n)	C	(n)	C	(n)	
Caulked: Timber/Timber - Laboratory test	6.7×10^{-4}	(0.6)	1.6×10^{-3}	(0.6)	3.4×10^{-3}	(0.6)	40
Masonry/Timber			No data				
Uncaulked: Timber/Timber			No data				
Masonry/Timber			No data				

Sources: #1105, #5378.

Table A1.10 Leakage Characteristics - Penetrations

Data expressed for each metre length of perimeter joint	Lower Quartile		Median $dm^3.s^{-1}.m^{-2}.Pa^{-n}$		Upper Quartile		Sample Size
	C	(n)	C	(n)	C	(n)	
Discharge pipes	1.1	(0.6)	1.2	(0.6)	1.4	(0.6)	2
Sealed spiral ducts	0.027	(0.6)	0.14	(0.6)	0.78	(0.6)	2
Vent			0.80	(0.6)			1
Pipes - Laboratory Test	0.63	(0.6)	0.74	(0.6)	0.84	(0.6)	3

Sources: BRE Unpublished, #1104, #1294, #5693.

Table A1.11 Leakage Characteristics - Roofing

Data expressed for each m^2 of surface. Includes joints	Lower Quartile		Median dm^3.s^{-1}.m^{-2}.Pa^{-n}		Upper Quartile		Sample Size
	C	(n)	C	(n)	C	(n)	
Shingles (roofing)	0.60	(0.66)	0.70	(0.65)	1.1	(0.63)	3
Tiles (roofing)	2.1	(0.59)	2.3	(0.58)	4.0	(0.55)	9
Metal (roofing	0.49	(0.67)	0.63	(0.66)	0.98	(0.63)	6
Sources: #1529, #3880.							

Table A1.12 Leakage Characteristics - Chimneys

Data expressed for each m^2 of chimney flue area	Lower Quartile		Median dm^3.s^{-1}.m^{-2}.Pa^{-n}		Upper Quartile		Sample Size
	C	(n)	C	(n)	C	(n)	
Fireplace opening bare - Laboratory and field tests	670	(0.5)	750	(0.5)	790	(0.5)	3
Pegboard baffle (Sealed) - Laboratory tests			300	(0.5)			1
Pegboard baffle (Unsealed) - Laboratory tests			410	(0.5)			1
Plywood baffle (Unsealed) - Laboratory test	180	(0.5)	180	(0.5)	180	(0.5)	2
Sources: BRE Unpublished, #1259.							

Table A1.13 Leakage Characteristics (expressed by the ratio of 'closed' flow to 'open' flow) - Trickle Ventilators

	Lower Quartile	Median	Upper Quartile	Sample Size
Trickle Ventilators- Laboratory test	0.06	0.08	0.23	8
To determine the flow characteristics of a closed trickle ventilator when its 'open' flow is given by size $Q = C \Delta P^n$, multiply by value given above, to give e.g. $Q = 0.06 C \Delta P^n$, the flow equation of the trickle ventilator when the vents are closed.				
Data Source: BRE Unpublished.				

Appendix 2

Wind Pressure Coefficient Data

Table A2.1 Wind Pressure Coefficient Data

Low-rise buildings (up to 3 storeys)
Length to width ratio: 1:1
Shielding condition: Exposed

Wind speed reference level: Building height

Wind Angle

Location		Wind Angle							
		0°	45°	90°	135°	180°	225°	270°	315°
Face 1		0.7	0.35	-0.5	-0.4	-0.2	-0.4	-0.5	0.35
Face 2		-0.2	-0.4	-0.5	0.35	0.7	0.35	-0.5	-0.4
Face 3		-0.5	0.35	0.7	0.35	-0.5	-0.4	-0.2	-0.4
Face 4		-0.5	-0.4	-0.2	-0.4	-0.5	0.35	0.7	0.35
Roof (<10° pitch)	Front	-0.8	-0.7	-0.6	-0.5	-0.4	-0.5	-0.6	-0.7
	Rear	-0.4	-0.5	-0.6	-0.7	-0.8	-0.7	-0.6	-0.5
Average		-0.6	-0.6	-0.6	-0.6	-0.6	-0.6	-0.6	-0.6
Roof (11-30° pitch)	Front	-0.4	-0.5	-0.6	-0.5	-0.4	-0.5	-0.6	-0.5
	Rear	-0.4	-0.5	-0.6	-0.5	-0.4	-0.5	-0.6	-0.5
Average		-0.4	-0.5	-0.6	-0.5	-0.4	-0.5	-0.6	-0.5
Roof (>30° pitch)	Front	0.3	-0.4	-0.6	-0.4	-0.5	-0.4	-0.6	-0.4
	Rear	-0.5	-0.4	-0.6	-0.4	0.3	-0.4	-0.6	-0.4
Average		-0.1	-0.4	-0.6	-0.4	-0.1	-0.4	-0.6	-0.4

Table A2.2 Wind Pressure Coefficient Data

Low-rise buildings (up to 3 storeys)
Length to width ratio: 1:1
Shielding condition: Surrounded by obstructions
            equivalent to half the height of the building
Wind speed reference level: Building height

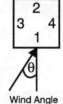

Wind Angle

Location		Wind Angle							
		0°	45°	90°	135°	180°	225°	270°	315°
Face 1		0.4	0.1	-0.3	-0.35	-0.2	-0.35	-0.3	0.1
Face 2		-0.2	-0.35	-0.3	0.1	0.4	0.1	-0.3	-0.35
Face 3		-0.3	0.1	0.4	0.1	-0.3	-0.35	-0.2	-0.35
Face 4		-0.3	-0.35	-0.2	-0.35	-0.3	0.1	0.4	0.1
Roof (<10° pitch)	Front	-0.6	-0.5	-0.4	-0.5	-0.6	-0.5	-0.4	-0.5
	Rear	-0.6	-0.5	-0.4	-0.5	-0.6	-0.5	-0.4	-0.5
Average		-0.6	-0.5	-0.4	-0.5	-0.6	-0.5	-0.4	-0.5
Roof (11-30° pitch)	Front	-0.35	-0.45	-0.55	-0.45	-0.35	-0.45	-0.55	-0.45
	Rear	-0.35	-0.45	-0.55	-0.45	-0.35	-0.45	-0.55	-0.45
Average		-0.35	-0.45	-0.55	-0.45	-0.35	-0.45	-0.55	-0.45
Roof (>30° pitch)	Front	0.3	-0.5	-0.6	-0.5	-0.5	-0.5	-0.6	-0.5
	Rear	-0.5	-0.5	-0.6	-0.5	0.3	-0.5	-0.6	-0.5
Average		-0.1	-0.5	-0.6	-0.5	-0.1	-0.5	-0.6	-0.5

Table A2.3 Wind Pressure Coefficient Data

Low-rise buildings (up to 3 storeys)
Length to width ratio: 1:1
Shielding condition: Surrounded by obstructions
equal to the height of the building
Wind speed reference level: Building height

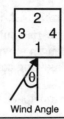

Wind Angle

Location		Wind Angle							
		0°	45°	90°	135°	180°	225°	270°	315°
Face 1		0.2	0.05	-0.25	-0.3	-0.25	-0.3	-0.25	0.05
Face 2		-0.25	-0.3	-0.25	0.05	0.2	0.05	-0.25	-0.3
Face 3		-0.25	0.05	0.2	0.05	-0.25	-0.3	-0.25	-0.3
Face 4		-0.25	-0.3	-0.25	-0.3	-0.25	0.05	0.2	0.05
Roof (<10° pitch)	Front	-0.5	-0.5	-0.4	-0.5	-0.5	-0.5	-0.4	-0.5
	Rear	-0.5	-0.5	-0.4	-0.5	-0.5	-0.5	-0.4	-0.5
Average		-0.5	-0.5	-0.4	-0.5	-0.5	-0.5	-0.4	-0.5
Roof (11-30° pitch)	Front	-0.3	-0.4	-0.5	-0.4	-0.3	-0.4	-0.5	-0.4
	Rear	-0.3	-0.4	-0.5	-0.4	-0.3	-0.4	-0.5	-0.4
Average		-0.3	-0.4	-0.5	-0.4	-0.3	-0.4	-0.5	-0.4
Roof (>30° pitch)	Front	0.25	-0.3	-0.5	-0.3	-0.4	-0.3	-0.5	-0.3
	Rear	-0.4	-0.3	-0.5	-0.3	0.25	-0.3	-0.5	-0.3
Average		-0.08	-0.3	-0.5	-0.3	-0.08	-0.3	-0.5	-0.3

Table A2.4 Wind Pressure Coefficient Data

Low-rise buildings (up to 3 storeys)
Length to width ratio: 2:1
Shielding condition: Exposed

Wind speed reference level: Building height

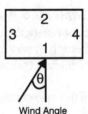

Wind Angle

Location		Wind Angle							
		0°	45°	90°	135°	180°	225°	270°	315°
Face 1		0.5	0.25	-0.5	-0.8	-0.7	-0.8	-0.5	0.25
Face 2		-0.7	-0.8	-0.5	0.25	0.5	0.25	-0.5	-0.8
Face 3		-0.9	0.2	0.6	0.2	-0.9	-0.6	-0.35	-0.6
Face 4		-0.9	-0.6	-0.35	-0.6	-0.9	0.2	0.6	0.2
Roof (<10° pitch)	Front	-0.7	-0.7	-0.8	-0.7	-0.7	-0.7	-0.8	-0.7
	Rear	-0.7	-0.7	-0.8	-0.7	-0.7	-0.7	-0.8	-0.7
Average		-0.7	-0.7	-0.8	-0.7	-0.7	-0.7	-0.8	-0.7
Roof (11-30° pitch)	Front	-0.7	-0.7	-0.7	-0.6	-0.5	-0.6	-0.7	-0.7
	Rear	-0.5	-0.6	-0.7	-0.7	-0.7	-0.7	-0.7	-0.6
Average		-0.6	-0.65	-0.7	-0.65	-0.6	-0.65	-0.7	-0.65
Roof (>30° pitch)	Front	0.25	0	-0.6	-0.9	-0.8	-0.9	-0.6	0
	Rear	-0.8	-0.9	-0.6	0	0.25	0	-0.6	-0.9
Average		-0.18	-0.45	-0.6	-0.45	-0.18	-0.45	-0.6	-0.45

Table A2.5 Wind Pressure Coefficient Data
Low-rise buildings (up to 3 storeys)
Length to width ratio: 2:1
Shielding condition: Surrounded by obstructions
equivalent to half the height of the building
Wind speed reference level: Building height

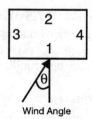

Wind Angle

Location		0°	45°	90°	135°	180°	225°	270°	315°
Face 1		0.25	0.06	-0.35	-0.6	-0.5	-0.6	-0.35	0.06
Face 2		-0.5	-0.6	-0.35	0.06	0.25	0.06	-0.35	-0.6
Face 3		-0.6	0.2	0.4	0.2	-0.6	-0.5	-0.3	-0.5
Face 4		-0.6	-0.5	-0.3	-0.5	-0.6	0.5	0.4	0.2
Roof (<10° pitch)	Front	-0.6	-0.6	-0.6	-0.6	-0.6	-0.6	-0.6	-0.6
	Rear	-0.6	-0.6	-0.6	-0.6	-0.6	-0.6	-0.6	-0.6
Average		-0.6	-0.6	-0.6	-0.6	-0.6	-0.6	-0.6	-0.6
Roof (11-30° pitch)	Front	-0.6	-0.6	-0.55	-0.55	-0.45	-0.55	-0.55	-0.6
	Rear	-0.45	-0.55	-0.55	-0.6	-0.6	-0.6	-0.55	-0.55
Average		-0.5	-0.6	-0.55	-0.6	-0.5	-0.6	-0.55	-0.6
Roof (>30° pitch)	Front	0.15	-0.08	-0.4	-0.75	-0.6	-0.75	-0.4	-0.08
	Rear	-0.6	-0.75	-0.4	-0.08	0.15	-0.08	-0.4	-0.75
Average		-0.2	-0.4	-0.4	-0.4	-0.2	-0.4	-0.4	-0.4

TableA2.6 Wind Pressure Coefficient Data
Low-rise buildings (up to 3 storeys)
Length to width ratio: 2:1
Shielding condition: Surrounded by obstructions
equal to the height of the building
Wind speed reference level: Building height

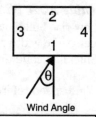

Wind Angle

Location		0°	45°	90°	135°	180°	225°	270°	315°
Face 1		0.06	-0.12	-0.2	-0.38	-0.3	-0.38	-0.2	0.12
Face 2		-0.3	-0.38	-0.2	-0.12	0.06	-0.12	-0.2	-0.38
Face 3		-0.3	0.15	0.18	0.15	-0.3	-0.32	-0.2	-0.32
Face 4		-0.3	-0.32	-0.2	-0.32	-0.3	0.15	0.18	0.15
Roof (<10° pitch	Front	-0.49	-0.46	-0.41	-0.46	-0.49	-0.46	-0.41	-0.46
	Rear	-0.49	-0.46	-0.41	-0.46	-0.49	-0.46	-0.41	-0.46
Average		-0.49	-0.46	-0.41	-0.46	-0.49	-0.46	-0.41	-0.46
Roof (11-30° pitch)	Front	-0.49	-0.46	-0.41	-0.46	-0.4	-0.46	-0.41	-0.46
	Rear	-0.4	-0.46	-0.41	-0.46	-0.49	-0.46	-0.41	-0.46
Average		-0.45	-0.46	-0.41	-0.46	-0.45	-0.46	-0.41	-0.46
Roof (>30° pitch)	Front	0.06	-0.15	-0.23	-0.6	-0.42	-0.6	-0.23	-0.15
	Rear	-0.42	-0.6	-0.23	-0.15	-0.06	-0.15	-0.23	-0.6
Average		-0.18	-0.4	-0.23	-0.4	-0.18	-0.4	-0.23	-0.4

Appendix 3

AIDA – Air Infiltration Development Algorithm

Introduction

AIDA is a basic infiltration and ventilation calculation procedure intended for the calculation of air change rates in single zone enclosures. It also resolves flow rates for up to any number of user defined openings and calculates wind and stack pressures. This program is very easy to use but, nevertheless, provides an accurate solution to the flow balance equation. As its name suggests this is a development algorithm which may be adapted to suit individual needs. This algorithm uses the concepts outlined in Chapter 12 of the AIVC Guide to Energy Efficient Ventilation.

Theoretical Outline

Solution is based on the iterative balancing of the volumetric flow balance equation given by:

$$\sum_{i=1}^{j} Q_{v_i} = 0$$

where:

Q_{v_i} = volume flow rate of air through the i'th flow path (m^3 / s)

j = the total number of flow paths into the zone

$$Q_{v_i} = C_i (P_i - P_{int})^{n_i} \qquad \text{if} \quad P_i > P_{int}$$

or:

$$Q_{v_i} = -C_i (P_{int} - P_i)^{n_i} \qquad \text{if} \quad P_i < P_{int}$$

where:

C_i = flow coefficient of i'th flow path

n_i = flow exponent of i'th flow path

P_i = external pressure of i'th flow path (Pa)

P_{int} = internal pressure of zone (Pa)

The stack pressure is given by:

$$P_s = -\rho_0 g 273 (h_2 - h_1) \left[\frac{1}{T_{ext}} - \frac{1}{T_{int}} \right] \quad (Pa)$$

where:

ρ_0 = air density at 273 K (1.29 kg/m^3)

g = acceleration due to gravity (9.81 m/s^2)

T_{ext} = outdoor air temperature (K)

T_{int} = indoor air temperature (K)

h_1 = height of opening 1 (m)

h_2 = height of opening 2 (m)

and the wind pressure is given by:

$$P_w = \frac{\rho c_P v^2}{2}$$

where:

c_P = wind pressure coefficient

v = local wind velocity at a specified reference (building height) (m/s)

ρ = air density (kg/m^3)

For each flow path, the user enters appropriate flow characteristics and wind pressure coefficients, drawing data from knowledge about the building or from the default data presented in Appendices 1 and 2.

Program Operation

AIDA is written in BASIC. A full listing of this is presented in Table 1. Initiation of the code will be machine dependent but in the BASIC environment, will normally be achieved by using the "RUN" command. Once the response "Welcome to AIDA" appears on the screen, then the "EXE" or "ENTER" key is pressed sequentially with the user responding accurately to each of the input questions identified by a "?".

Data entry is largely self explicit. The order of entry is (for each flow path):

• Building volume (m^3)
• Number of flow paths
• Height of flow path (m)
• Flow coefficient (m^3/s at 1 Pa)
• Wind pressure coefficient.

Once the flow path data is entered, climatic data are requested, these items are:

– outdoor temperature (^oC)
– internal temperature (^oC)
– wind speed at building height (m/s).

On completion of data entry, the computer responds with the message "Calculation in Progress". After iteration is completed, the infiltration rate is displayed on the screen. With this 'PC' version, the air change rate and request for further climatic data is automatically displayed, break out of the program by using "CTRL BREAK". At the completion of a session, the most recent data remains in store and can be recovered by using the "PRINT" command followed by variable name, e.g.:

PRINT Q displays infiltration rate
PRINT F(2) displays flow in path 2

All the variables used in the algorithm are listed in Table 2.

Data must be inserted with care since there is no error trapping or editing facility. If an error is made, then it is necessary to restart the program.

Clearly, since this is a demonstration algorithm, the interactive Input/ Output routine is very rudimentary. It is assumed that if wider use is made of this code, then the user will amend these routines to suit individual requirements.

Solution Technique

The flow balance equation is solved iteratively using a combination of "bi-section" and "addition". An internal pressure, known to be substantially negative with respect to the true pressure, is selected as a starting condition. For most applications a value of -100 Pa should be satisfactory and is automatically introduced at line 320. Successive iterations improve upon the internal pressure value until a flow balance within 0.0001 m^3/s is achieved. The flow balance criterion is established in line 450. An understanding of the technique may be gleaned from an analysis of lines 320 to 470 of the program. While this approach may not necessarily be the most numerically efficient, it is extremely robust and should not fail under normal circumstances over a wide range of flow conditions and leakage characteristics.

Example

Input data and results for a 3 flow path network is presented in Table 4. Although this is an arbitrary example, it has been selected to show that AIDA can handle differing flow coefficients, flow exponents, flow path heights and wind pressure coefficients within the same network.

Table 1: Program listing

```
 20 PRINT "Welcome to AIDA"
 30 PRINT "Air Infiltration Development Algorithm"
 40 PRINT "M Liddament - AIVC Guide to Ventilation 1995"
 50 DIM H(50),C(50),N(50),P(50),T(50),W(50),S(50),F(50)
 55 PRINT:PRINT:PRINT
 60 D=1.29 : REM Air Density at 0 Deg C
 70 PRINT "Enter Building Data:"
 80 INPUT "Building Volume (m3) = ";V
 85 PRINT:PRINT:PRINT
 90 PRINT "Enter Flow Path Data:"
100 INPUT "Number of Flow Paths = ";L
110 FOR J=1 TO L
115 PRINT:PRINT:PRINT
120   PRINT "Height (m)(Path";J;") = ";: INPUT H(J)
130   PRINT "Flow Coef (Path";J;") = ";: INPUT C(J)
140   PRINT "Flow Exp (Path";J;") = ";: INPUT N(J)
150   PRINT "Pres Coef (Path";J;") = ";: INPUT P(J)
160 NEXT J
165 PRINT:PRINT:PRINT
170 PRINT "Enter Climatic Data:"
175 PRINT:PRINT:PRINT
180 INPUT "Ext Temp (Deg C)   =" ;E
190 INPUT "Int Temp (Deg C)   =" ;I
200 INPUT "Wind Spd(Bldg Ht)(m/s)=" ;U
210 REM Pressure Calculation
220 FOR J=1 TO L
230   REM Wind Pressure Calculation
240   W(J)=.5*D*P(J)*U*U
250   REM Stack Pressure Calculation
260   S(J)=-3455*H(J)*(1/(E+273)-1/(I+273))
270   REM Total Pressure
280   T(J)=W(J)+S(J)
290 NEXT J
300 REM Calculate Infiltration
305 CLS:PRINT:PRINT:PRINT
310   PRINT "Calculation in Progress"
320 R=-100
330 X=50
340 Y=0
350 B=0
```

```
360 R=R+X
370 FOR J=1 TO L
380  Y=Y+1
390  O=T(J)-R
400  IF O=0 THEN F(J)=0: GOTO 430
410  F(J)=C(J)*(ABS(O)^N(J))*O/ABS(O)
420  B=B+F(J)
430 NEXT J
440 IF B<0 THEN R=R-X: X=X/2: GOTO 350
450 IF B<.0001 THEN GOTO 470
460 GOTO 350
470 Q=0
480 FOR J=1 TO L
490  IF F(J)>0 THEN Q=Q+F(J)
500 NEXT J
505 PRINT:PRINT:PRINT
520 PRINT "infiltration rate (m3/s) = ";Q
530 A=Q*3600/V
540 PRINT "air change rate (ach)  = ";A
545 PRINT:PRINT:PRINT
550 GOTO 170
```

Table 2: AIDA List of Variables

A   = Air change rate (ACH)

B   = Flow balance

C(J) = Flow coefficient (Path J)

D   = Air density (kg/m^3)

E   = External temperature (^oC)

F(J) = Calculated flow rate (Path J) (m^3/s)

H(J) = Height of flow path (Path J) (m)

I   = Internal temperature (^oC)

J   = Flow path number

L   = Total number of flow paths (Max = 10)

N(J) = Flow exponent (Path J)

O   = Pressure difference across flow path (Pa)

P(J) = Wind pressure coefficient (Path J)

Q   = Infiltration rate (m^3/s)

R   = Internal pressure (Pa)

S(J) = Stack induced pressure (Path J) (Pa)

T(J) = Total external pressure on flow path (Path J) (Pa)

U   = Wind speed at building height (m/s)

V   = Volume of building or enclosure (m^3)

W(J) = Wind induced pressure (Path J) (Pa)

X   = Iteration pressure step (Pa)

Y   = Iteration counter

Building volume	= 250 m³		
Number of flow paths = 3			
	Path 1	Path 2	Path 3
Height of path (m)	2	4	7
Flow coef (m³/s at 1 Pa)	0.03	0.06	0.02
Flow exponent	0.7	0.5	0.6
Wind pressure coefficient	0.3	-0.25	-0.4

Climatic data

	Outside temp (°C)	Inside temp (°C)	Wind speed (m/s)
Run 1	0	20	0
Run 2	5	15	2
Run 3	18	18	3

Results

Inf rate (m³/s)	Air change rate	Flow rate (m³/s) (path 1)	Flow rate (m³/s) (path 2)	Flow rate (m³/s) (path 3)
0.0437	0.63	0.0437	-0.0081	-0.0356
0.0511	0.74	0.0511	-0.0224	-0.0287
0.0615	0.8	0.0615	-0.0382	-0.0232

Table 3: Example data and results

Program Developments

Developments covering mechanical ventilation, additional flow paths, automatic wind pressure distributions and wind speed correction equations may be readily incorporated. For example, mechanical ventilation can be incorporated by expressing the ventilation rate as a 'C' value and setting the flow exponent to zero.

Index

A

Acoustic methods 186
Adjacent buildings 61
Age of air 143
Air
    age of 143
    change efficiency 141, 143
    change rate 17, 45
    change time 143
    cleaning 129
    distribution systems 155
    filters 154
    flow 182
        through ducts and grilles 182
    flow patterns 181
        anemometry (hot wire) 181
        visualisation techniques 181
    fresheners 136
    grilles 83
    infiltration 2, 8
    inlets 83, 154
    intakes 28, 83
    leakage 62
        sources of 62
    leaks 184
        locating 184
    outdoor 13
    purifiers 136
    quality 32
        perceived 32
        reservoir 72
    recirculation 2
    speed 34
    treatment plant 156
    vents 74
Air-tightness 29, 56, 62, 72, 200
    estimation 200
Allergy control 88
Anemometers 183
Apartment buildings 58
Arrestance 133
ASHRAE Standard 62 20, 144
Atria buildings 59
Average temperature difference 46

B

Bag filter 134
Blower door 175
Boundary conditions 222
Boundary layer flow 221
Brownian motion 130
Building
    integrity 62
    Regulations 53
    services 125
    structure 72
Buildings 58
    commercial 58
    office 58

C

Calculation
    methods 197
    techniques 15
Carbon
    dioxide 26
        metabolic 32
Carbon monoxide 25, 26
Centralised ducted extract 85
Chemical properties 132
Chilled ceilings 120
Clean rooms 88
Cleanability 153
Climate 11, 60, 90
    extreme 90
    mild 60
    moderate 61
    severe 61
Clothing 34
Code of Practice 54
Coefficient of air change performance 144
Coefficient of performance 100
Combined pressure testing and tracer gas analysis 179
Combined thermal and ventilation models 228
Combustion appliances 76
Comfort 30, 55
    thermal 33
Components 153
    materials 153
    siting of 153
Computational fluid dynamics 141, 219